1929

Dulac/Russel
Fleuta
ille etc

£25.0

THE QUEEN'S BOOK
OF THE
RED CROSS

THE
QUEEN'S BOOK
OF THE
RED CROSS

With a Message from
HER MAJESTY THE QUEEN
and Contributions by
FIFTY BRITISH AUTHORS AND ARTISTS

In Aid of
THE LORD MAYOR OF LONDON'S FUND
FOR THE RED CROSS AND THE ORDER
OF ST. JOHN OF JERUSALEM

HODDER AND STOUGHTON

FIRST PRINTED   •   •   •   • NOVEMBER 1939

HODDER & STOUGHTON, the publishers, are very grateful to the authors and artists whose kindness and ready co-operation in many matters of detail have alone made possible the production of The Queen's Book of the Red Cross within two months of its conception.

They also offer their thanks to the firms who have assisted in the production of this book.

The text has been printed on paper supplied through Bowater-Lloyd and W. Rowlandson & Co. Ltd. by Hazell, Watson & Viney Ltd., of London and Aylesbury, Wyman & Sons Ltd., of London, Reading and Fakenham, and Richard Clay & Co. Ltd., of London and Bungay.

The colour and photogravure illustrations have been printed by The Sun Engraving Company Ltd., of London and Watford.

The book has been bound by The Leighton-Straker Bookbinding Co. Ltd., in conjunction with Hazell, Watson & Viney Ltd., Wyman & Sons Ltd. and Richard Clay & Co. Ltd.

4

This book, which bears my name, is a tribute
to the noble work of the Red Cross, and to
the unselfish devotion of those who are carrying
it on. My feeling of gratitude and admiration
is shared, I am certain, by every other
woman in our Empire — especially by the wives
and mothers of those who are fighting to defend
its liberty.

All you who buy my book, as well as the
distinguished authors and artists who prepared it,
are helping forward the great work of mercy
on the battlefield; to all of you I would send
this Christmas message — God bless you.

Elizabeth R

THE AUTHORS
AND THEIR CONTRIBUTIONS

THE PICTURES

THE ARTISTS

WILLIAM RUSSELL FLINT, R.A., P.R.W.S., served as a Lieutenant R.N.V.R. and Captain R.A.F. in the last war. A student of the Edinburgh School of Art, he came to London nearly forty years ago. Examples of his work are to be found in over fifty permanent collections.

EDMUND DULAC is mainly known as an illustrator of books, but his activities as an artist cover a wide range, from portrait painting to stage decoration, caricatures, music, etc. He designed the King's Medal for poetry, the Coronation stamp of 1937, and the cameo portrait of His Majesty on the current postage stamps. It was his illustration of such classics as *The Arabian Nights* and *The Rubaiyat* that first brought him recognition.

FRANK BRANGWYN, R.A., LL.D., R.S.A., Institute de France, was born at Bruges. In Swansea now hang his famous panels executed for the Iveagh commission. His masterly work is as well known all over the Continent and in America as in Great Britain. He is a prolific producer of water-colour paintings and etchings in addition to his mural paintings. Most of his later work is concerned with religious subjects.

J. MORTON SALE studied at the Central School of Art. Working independently of any group or society, he has produced a number of lithographs and very many pictures in chalk and colour. He has a particular fondness for landscape painting. He also specialises in designs for book wrappers, and his book illustration is well known on both sides of the Atlantic for its ethereal and delicate quality.

EDMUND BLAMPIED, R.E., R.B.A., spent his childhood in Jersey, but came to England at the age of seventeen. His etchings and paintings hang in many galleries of Britain and America. He uses the medium of lithography, water-colour, oil, and even sculpture. He has just completed an entire series of pictures to illustrate *Peter Pan*.

LAURA KNIGHT, D.B.E., R.A., R.W.S., R.E., Hon. LL.D. St. Andrew's, first exhibited at the Royal Academy in 1903, and today is represented in permanent collections throughout the Empire and in America. She has written a book, *Oil Paint and Grease Paint*, and much of her work is concerned with theatrical and circus life.

BIP PARES studied at the Slade School in London, and has specialised in illustration and the design of book jackets, of which the total already exceeds 600. The design of the binding and jacket of this book is her work.

ARTHUR WRAGG is a North-countryman, born in Manchester and educated at Sheffield Art School. His best-known work has been accomplished in the last six years—in *Psalms for Modern Life*, *Jesus Wept*, and *Seven Words*. His work has come to be regarded as prophetic in character in its relation to our times.

AIR-COMMODORE NORMAN WILKINSON, O.B.E., P.R.I., has specialised in paintings of the sea. Previous to his present appointment, he was a Lieutenant-Commander R.N.V.R., and is Marine Painter to the Royal Yacht Squadron. He is the originator of dazzle painting for the protection of ships at sea against submarine attack.

REX WHISTLER first exhibited at the Royal Drawing Societies' Exhibition in 1911, at the age of five. He studied under Professor Henry Tonks at the Slade School and in Rome. It was while he was a Slade student in 1927 that he carried out his first mural paintings, and he has since done a succession of painted rooms in London and country houses for private patrons. His portraits and other paintings are exhibited from time to time at the leading London Galleries. He designed the stage productions of *Victoria Regina* in London and New York, and his settings for *Fidelio*, *Pride and Prejudice*, *The Rake's Progress* and many other plays are very well known.

MABEL LUCIE ATTWELL studied painting mainly in London, and has always specialised in child studies and the illustration of such books as *The Water Babies*, *Alice in Wonderland*, and *Peter Pan and Wendy*.

IVOR NOVELLO, actor, actor-manager, film artist and composer, was fifteen years old when his first song was published, and he has written some sixty in all. His best and widest public was the Army, which sang and marched to "Keep the Home Fires Burning" in the last war. He gives to THE QUEEN'S BOOK OF THE RED CROSS the manuscript of his newest song of all.

A. E. W. MASON

*Who has not read "The Four Feathers," "At the Villa Rose,"
and "No Other Tiger"?   MR. A. E. W. MASON published
his first novel no less than forty-four years ago, but he is still one
of the most active—as he is certainly one of the greatest—of the
master-craftsmen.*

THE CONJURER

I

"WILL you sit down, please?" said Otto Reimer to the square bullet-
headed man who had just marched into his shabby sitting-room in
a second-rate hotel of Mandalay.   "You are Mr. Straws of the Wolf
Dry Goods Store.   I shall make you some magic."

"Excuse," said Mr. Straws, lifting an authoritative hand.

Otto Reimer continued imperturbably.

"Across the room on an Indian tray of the best Birmingham craftmanship
rises a small pile of steamship and railway tickets, luggage labels, bar-room
vouchers, every printed thing, in fact, which connects Otto Reimer with Paul
Haussmann, passenger on the tourist ship *Dordrecht*."

"They must be burnt," said Straws.

"They will be.   At five o'clock; that is, in five minutes exactly."   Otto
Reimer was sitting at a table with his watch propped in front of him.   "The
special train will steam out of Mandalay station carrying the *Dordrecht's* tourists
back to Rangoon.   As the whistle blows, the papers on the tray will burst
into flames."

"I have no time for these fooleries," barked the aggressive Mr. Straws.

Otto Reimer sighed.   He was a slight graceful man of forty with a worn
dark face and a look of breeding.

"Well?"

Straws sat upright in a chair, his knees apart, his feet turned out.

"Otto Reimer, Captain, Austrian Artillery, wounded March 1915 on
Russian Front, transferred on recovery to General Staff and, owing to profi-
ciency in languages, sent out to do Intelligence work in India and Burma."

Straws was quoting from a paper in his hand.   "The reports of your work
were favourable."

"I thank you for those kind words," said Otto Reimer, but no irony could
penetrate the solid ivory head of Mr. Straws.   He bobbed it once and severely.

"But you were faithful to the old regime," he sneered.   "The Hapsburgs!
The fine friends!   So when the Reich marches into Vienna, you lose your
lovely valley in Carinthia, the snow on the mountains, the light shining in the
village windows——"

And Reimer broke in upon him with a command sharp and imperious: " Hold your tongue! "

Mr. Straws pushed his chair back in a hurry. He saw a strange man, who looked as if he was going to hurt him, certainly not a man he could override and bully.

" I make a little picture," he began, all smiles, and was interrupted again.

" Make them to yourself then! I was ruined—yes. I escaped to London penniless—yes. I did conjuring tricks at the Irving statue in the luncheon hour—yes. I was recognised by a man who had served under me—your chief now, Mr. Straws. I was promised that if I came out again to the East and stirred up trouble enough, I should get back my valley in Carinthia. So I came. If I wanted money, I was to get it from you. If I wanted to send a report home, I was to send it through you. My purse and my letter-box, Mr. Straws. That's what you are and that's all that you are."

Having failed to bully, it was in the natural order of things that Mr. Straws should now cringe. He said with a smirk:

" They may have to tighten their belts about their stomachs in the Father-land, but there's always money for a nice little rebellion in somebody else's country."

Straws, as he spoke, pulled a thick wallet from his pocket. At the same moment a whistle blew from an engine in the railway-station.

" That's the *Dordrecht's* special," said Otto, and an unexpected pop behind Straws's shoulder made that crestfallen man jump in his seat. He looked round towards the window and back again at Otto. Otto had not stirred from his chair. Yet amongst the papers on the brass tray in the window a flame was burning, a devouring flame which reduced them to white flakes like shreds of torn linen.

" Colossal! " exclaimed Straws.

" You want the best magic? We have it," said Otto.

It was a trick which had served to burn a munition factory or two in 1914. A small metal phial divided by a slip of glass. One compartment was filled with sulphuric acid, the other with hydrofluoric. As long as the slip of glass divided them, nothing happened. But as soon as the hydrofluoric acid ate through the glass and the acids mixed, there was a little explosion and a fire. By the thickness of the glass you could regulate the outbreak of the fire to a split second.

" I set my time-fuse for an hour," said Otto, pocketing his watch. " It's all known now, of course, but I reckon it'll serve my turn on the upper river."

He took the wallet from Straws's hand and got up. " I'm off," he said. " Bill paid, luggage gone. For all you know, Straws, I'm on the *Dordrecht's* special for Rangoon."

Mr. Straws saw his face soften and a wistful gleam in his eyes. Beyond the darkening window he was looking down a long Carinthian valley where the lights were clustering in the villages and the stars coming out above the snow on the mountain crests.

II

The shops were already lit, and he turned into a narrow, crowded street which led to the great Negyo Bazaar. He walked warily but without haste.

10

A native policeman stood idly in the road. Otto stopped before an open booth where rolls of silk were piled one upon the other, bright pink and pale green and sunset gold. But the pretty shopgirl with the gold tubes in her ears had hardly taken the big cheroot from between her lips to praise her wares when a hubbub arose at the market end of the street. The policeman sprang to attention; the idlers in the street moved; and then an Indian boy burst through the crowd like a rocket. He was running blind, thrusting, stumbling, staggering, dodging, and through all these manœuvres swift as a young stag. But his luck was against him. He ran straight into the arms of Otto Reimer and was held there in a grip of steel.

"Let me go!" the boy sobbed, and in English.

"Why?" asked Otto, and the policeman raised a shout:

"It's Nath Singh! Stop him!"

And immediately Otto loosened his grip. It might be the King of the Cannibal Islands for all he cared. It was not within his plans to be detained as a witness. The boy dived under the policeman's arm. A woman was upset; a kerosene lamp was knocked off the shelf of a booth, a stall crashed with its wares, and the policeman ran, calling loudly upon all to stop that limb of Satan, Nath Singh. Otto Reimer laughed. He had a fellow-feeling with Nath Singh—they were both of them fugitives.

He entered the shop of a tailor and came out with a package under his arm. He bought food at a café and turned into a side-street. It was ill-lit, with great patches of black shadow between a few dim lamps. Otto kept close to the wall and at the mouth of the street saw, stretched out under a clear sky of stars, the vast foreshore of the Irrawaddy; acres and acres of sandy slopes, cluttered and piled with rice bags, balks of timber, rows of barrels, and mountains of crates—the cargoes of all those double-decked, stern-wheel steamers which stretched in line with their riding-lights burning and now and then a shower of sparks bursting from their funnels. In a hollow of the sand midway between the steamers and the town Otto laid down his package and set out his meal. It was a good meal—fresh river fish, still warm from the oven, a meat pie, bread and butter were flanked by a flask of whisky and a water-bottle.

"Here goes," he said, and as he raised his first morsel to his mouth, he caught a glimpse of something white moving above a pile of logs at his back. He looked up quickly and saw beneath a white turban the face of the boy who had cannoned into him in the street. Nath Singh was watching him, round-eyed with envy.

Otto looked at his fish.

"Good?" he asked. He munched it. "Yes, very good," and he saw the boy's face crumple up as if he was in pain. Remorse seized upon Otto.

"Hungry, Nath Singh?"

"Ooooh!"

"All right! Come down! There's enough for two. But don't make a noise."

The boy slid like a seal over the logs into the hollow.

"I thank you, Sahib," he said politely, and waited, his mouth watering. Otto divided the fish and pushed one portion towards the boy. Nath Singh opened his mouth to speak, but thought twice and put the fish into it instead. Otto nodded his head gravely.

11

"You can always talk. But you can't always eat. There is a meat pie to follow."

"Meat!" Nath Singh whispered in a voice of reverence.

"You are Indian?" Otto asked, opening his jack-knife.

"Yes, Sahib."

"Let us hope for your soul's sake that it is mutton," and he divided the pie.

"My father," said Nath Singh, "had liberal ideas about meat."

"Just as well," said Otto dryly. "For this is beef. Or rather was," he added as the lad devoured it. "A drink of water?"

He poured it into the palms of Nath Singh's outstretched hands.

"Now I shall smoke."

As he took a pipe and a tobacco pouch from his pocket Nath Singh unrolled from his linen jacket a fat pale cheroot.

"So you smoke cheroots, Nath Singh?"

"This was given to me by a girl in the bazaar. She said I was to keep it until I was very, very hungry. I was going to light it, Sahib, when you were kind to me."

Otto Reimer tossed his match-box across to the boy. "Keep your head down whilst you light it," he said, and he watched him as he cupped his hands over the lighted match. Nath Singh had not whined. He had good manners besides. Otto would want an assistant.

"What were you running away from when you bounced into me?" he asked thoughtfully.

"Missionaries' Orphan School," Nath Singh answered simply.

"Very human," said Otto. "You speak English well."

"My father taught me."

"What was your father?"

Nath Singh raised his head and thrust his chin forward.

"My father was subadar retired, 60th Punjab Infantry. Last stationed at Fort Akat. Very fine soldier. I am going to join his regiment after I've seen the world."

"Here, certainly," thought Otto, "is the assistant for me."

A silence followed. But Nath Singh was thinking too, and he began respectfully to ask questions.

"Perhaps the Sahib will tell me why he too runs away."

"That's a nasty one," Otto reflected. Aloud he answered, "I'm not running away. I'm going up country to sell things."

"What things?" the boy asked gravely.

Otto was annoyed. Who was this boy that he should cross-examine him like a judge?

"I'll tell you." He flung the words out in a sudden rage against the world which forced him to his underhand work, against himself for submitting, against the boy for stinging him into the confession. "I sell riots and treason and plots and rebellions. I sell trouble for Governments. I sell fire for villages. I sell miracles. I sell wickedness. What do you think of that?"

Nath Singh stared and shifted his position. "I've lost him, like a fool!" thought Otto. But the next moment Nath Singh grinned. His face creased from ear to ear.

"My father," he said with a gurgle, "would have walloped my hide off if I had talked like that. He'd have said I was boasting."

Otto leaned back with his hands behind his head.

"Boasting? Well, perhaps I am." He sat up straight and said suddenly, "Come up the river with me and see!"

Nath hitched himself forward again, his eyes shining, his hands clasped together.

"As far as Fort Akat?"

"Beyond it. To the great forests black as night."

"Tigers?" Nath Singh whispered in a tremulous delight.

"Big stripey tigers, their jaws dripping with gore."

"Ooooh!" said Nath Singh, drawing in a great breath.

"And black panthers with eyes like jewels that stretch themselves out on branches and wait for you to pass underneath."

Again a sigh of longing to see these wondrous beasts and run these shivery perils burst from the boy.

"And great crocodiles," Otto went on, "that jump out of the water and go snap-snap at your toes just after you've snatched them away."

"Ooooh!" cried Nath Singh. "Sahib, when do we go? Now!"

Nath Singh looked behind him. At any moment a policeman might descend upon this hiding-place and drag him back to the missionaries and his lesson-books.

"We're safe enough here," said Otto.

Far away to the right and the left lights glimmered in little huts; and down by the water's edge electric flares showed coolies passing up the gangways on to the steamers with loaded backs, small as marionettes. Here there was nothing but silence and the starlit darkness.

"If the police should find us," said Otto, "I'll do some magic and we'll vanish."

"Magic!"

The boy was sitting up again, his eyes staring.

"You're a magician, Sahib?"

"The best. I read the Heavens like an open book. The monsters of the deep swallow their tails when they hear my voice."

And still Nath Singh looked at him gravely.

"My father said that magicians were the sons of the devil."

"Look here, Nath Singh," exclaimed Otto Reimer. "I agree that your father was an A.1 copper-bottomed subadar. But wasn't he a bit of a bore?"

Nath Singh's face grew set and stubborn.

"All right," continued Otto, "you go back to the missionaries' school. Better for you than stripey tigers and monkeys hanging upside down in the forest."

"Ooooh! Monkeys!" said Nath Singh.

"Nothing to do with you," Otto replied shortly; and he turned his back on Nath Singh and stretched himself out on the sand with a yawn. But Nath Singh couldn't go to sleep so easily. On the one side were the classroom and the lesson-books; on the other the forest, the burnished silver of the river, the thrilling dangers escaped by an inch with his heart in his mouth; and these things were more than any reasonable boy could bear to miss.

A small voice whispered into Otto's ear:
" Sahib, when do we go? "
Otto was not asleep. He had been waiting for just those words. He answered with a secret smile:
" In four hours. It will still be dark," and after that in the silence of sleep the stars wheeled above the heads of these two waifs.

III

Otto's bundle contained the yellow robe of a pongyi. He put it on in the dark of the morning and sank his own clothes with a weight in the river. At the first village upstream he had his head shaved, and there he was a monk, complete with acolyte and begging-bowl. He had the right of entrance into any monastery. He could stay just as long as he liked if he conformed with the simple regulations. No one could challenge him. With his dark face, a queer touch of the Mongol about his eyes, and his mastery of the native dialect, he passed quite easily as a novice.

They slipped into monasteries before their gates were closed and spread their sleeping-mats in the dark hall. Nath Singh would watch the stars for a second through the open doorway, and then knew no more until the stir of the monks and the dawning light waked him to another day.

For him morning could not come too soon nor sunset too late. There was the swim in the river with the joy of it tingling down to his toes to begin with, and then the leisurely progress along the bank with a new and adorable spectacle for every hour. Great rafts of teakwood came gliding down the stream, each with a little house built upon the planks and a high throne at the stern where a man sat and steered with a long sweep for a rudder. They rounded a bluff, and there were buffaloes knee-deep in the shallows or girls bathing in their saris amidst shouts of laughter. Bright-green fields ran down to the water's edge; and always ahead, to be dreamed of with luxurious shudders, were the dark forests, the slinky silent tigers, and the black panthers with the topaz eyes. The big river steamers would meet or overtake the travellers, lashing the water into a yellow foam and coughing and hooting as they rumbled by.

At the village of Kepal, Otto said:
" We're safe from detection now. Tomorrow we'll take the bazaar boat to Segan."

There was a note of regret in his voice. On this pilgrimage up the Irrawaddy, he had been sharing his acolyte's raptures and enthusiasms. He had become a boy himself and had recaptured a boy's delight in simple things— the breaking of the dawn, the long unspoilt day, the sense of freedom, the animal pleasure of health. But it had come to an end now.

" At Segan, Nath Singh, I shall want your help," he said.
Nath Singh's face grew grave.
" Magic, Sahib? " he asked doubtfully.
" Magic? Miracles, Nath Singh. And no more Sahib. I'm Talaban the monk, and don't you forget it! " Otto was not very pleased with the boy's steady look. " Just keep those brooding eyes and the silent tongue—yes, above all, the silent tongue." Otto bore it off boisterously enough. But he had an uneasy suspicion that the old subadar of Fort Akat was in the boy's

14

mind warning him, perhaps threatening him with wallopings. "You've got to help me, Nath Singh." He dropped to pleading, hating himself the while. "I have given you a good holiday, haven't I? You've enjoyed it—every minute of it. And that's nothing to what will be when we reach the forest!"

A mean sort of argument? Very likely. But at Segan Otto Reimer was to strike. The old Abbot of Segan, U Wisaya, a man of great fame, a preacher of discontent and rebellion, and an old friend of Reimer, had died—months ago, to be sure, but his body had been preserved in honey until the fit moment for a great funeral. The fit moment had come. There would be gathered at Segan the wild rebels of the northern villages, the dacoits, the thieves, their leaders, men with whom Reimer had intrigued and conspired in olden days. At Segan rebellion was to be launched and Reimer was to press the button and send the ship sliding down the grooves. But he must have Nath Singh as an instrument.

"You owe me a little help, Nath Singh," he insisted. No, it wasn't fair. "Of course, you can go back, if you like, to Mandalay. A steamer goes south, an hour after I go north. You can desert me if you like. I'll pay your passage."

Nath Singh was in distress. He was divided between two loyalties. Otto Reimer had talked of revolts and rebellions. Had he been boasting after all? If he had not been, why, the old subadar had bequeathed to his son a code of service and honour. On the other hand, if he had been, Nath Singh was making him an ungenerous return for his kindness, by leaving him at the moment when his help was needed. And that compunction was strong within him.

"I'll go with you to Segan," he said at length, and relief spread like a wave over Otto Reimer's face.

IV

Two days later Segan glided to them rather than they to it—an island of golden spires gleaming against a background of dark trees, like a city in a fairy tale.

Today, however, it had the look of Epsom Downs on Derby Day. A funeral is a festival, and a wide-open space was covered with the gaudy machinery of a country fair—huts with sides of matting, gambling booths, stalls where food and sweetmeats could be bought. In the front stood a truck with a great rope of jungle grass at each end. The truck held the Abbot's coffin, and the prime attraction of the Pwe would be the tug-of-war between the true friends who wanted him to pass on and the false friends who wanted him to stay. The tug-of-war would last out the three days. Anybody could join in on either side at any time and leave off when he was tired. The true friends would win in the end, and the coffin in a gaudy little temple would be run up to the top of a pagoda of pasteboard and gilt paper. Rockets would be fired at it, and in the end, after a good many casualties had been suffered, the whole glistening contraption, pagoda and temple and Abbot, would be burnt.

As soon as they had landed, Otto hired a hut, put on the dress of a layman, and leaving Nath Singh on guard went amongst the gambling booths and the stalls in search of old friends. Amongst that wild and ugly throng of hillmen

15

and fanatics Otto recognised and spoke with many, and of each he asked where was Nagein. Nagein was at Segan. Otto could learn no more, but he had little doubt that he would come face to face with him before the day was out.

He bought food and, taking it back to the hut, he ate it with Nath Singh. In a little while darkness fell and Otto lit a candle and squatted on the ground beside it opposite to the door. And in a little while, again, he saw the latch rise slowly without the tiniest click and someone was within the room.

" I am Nagein."

Otto spoke to Nath Singh:

" You shall leave my friend with me for an hour," and the boy went out. Otto patted the ground at his side.

" Sit down with me, Nagein," he said with a smile. " It is long since we talked together, you and I and Wisaya. But you expected me? "

" A message was brought to me at my village, Talaban. It is still ' Talaban '? "

Nagein sat as he was invited. The cruelty and cunning which had made his name terrible in the turbulent country to the north were stamped in the very shape of his body. He was thick and squat, and his shoulders were corded with the muscles of a bull. But his neck was topped by a narrow head ridiculously small, a thin face with a long nose, and small foxy eyes as sharp as beads. Look at his trunk, and you could imagine him in the prize-ring. Look at his face, and his proper setting was a money-lender's office in Jermyn Street with some poor spendthrift babbling for time on the carpet in front of him.

" Yes, I am Talaban," said Reimer with a smile, and he poured out his story. The giant was old and weak. Now was the time to strike—suddenly and fiercely. The villages were restless. They would storm Fort Akat first with a surprise attack. They would have arms then. The priests should give the rebels a charm against bullets. Nagein laughed. They were always ready to believe in the charm—poor fools.

" But once before, Talaban, we talked of these things," Nagein objected.

" And nothing happened. I know," Otto replied. " The war ended and there was no money. But this time there is money," and he saw Nagein's eyes light up. " You will be the King, Nagein, over all this land. You shall march down to Mandalay. . . ." Otto Reimer might be leading on this ignorant adventurer to the ruin of his country and his death. But he didn't care. He was thinking of a distant valley in Carinthia where once more he might sit at ease in his own house.

" I have some magic too. Listen, Nagein," and he lowered his voice to a whisper. " On the third day—that will give you time to warn your friends ——" And his voice sank lower still, urgent, persuasive.

Once Nagein murmured to himself, " The burning heart of Wisaya," in a voice of awe, and in a moment he took fire.

" The burning heart of Wisaya," he cried again.

" A miracle," said Otto, slapping him on the back. " More than a miracle. The flag of a great rebellion."

And meanwhile Nath Singh wandered through the crowd; and he too asked questions, even as earlier that day Otto Reimer had done. How far was it to Fort Akat, and how should a stranger find the way?

16

V

On the morning of the third day Nagein, smiling and odious, came jauntily into Otto's hut.

"Look!" he said, and he took his stand behind Otto, who was seated on his mat.

The door stood open, and between the doorposts Otto looked out upon such a scene of confusion and changing colours as no kaleidoscope could ever shake together. A blazing sun rode overhead, and below it a swarm of men shifted and gathered into groups and broke away into short rushes. Here a man preached and chanted; there some homely orator with whirling arms made passionate appeals. But not one of them could keep his audience for long. The gambling booths were doing a roaring trade, there were drunken men screaming. Hysteria was in the air.

"Look!" said Nagein.

There had been two days and two nights, excited days and sleepless nights, of carnival. The dead Abbot had brought together in this small area the turbulent spirits of his faction. All was set for riot and disorder.

"When the heart burns, Talaban! At sunset. In the presence of the burning heart—all these who run like sheep and stop and run again"—and he threw out his arm towards the rabble in its gaily coloured dress, melting and loitering and collecting again—"an army, Talaban"; and himself as frenzied as any of his followers, he ran shouting from the hut.

Otto remained seated upon his carpet. Not a spark of the excitement showed in him. He sat very still with a face which was very grave. He was entering on the most dangerous day of his life. If each step was smoothly taken, just at the exact right moment—a triumph. He could go back to his master and claim his reward. But let him make one mistake, let one little accident intervene to spoil the perfect climax of his trick, Nagein would turn on him, he would go down, stamped into the earth by the feet of a maddened crowd—and Nath Singh with him.

"Nath Singh!" he said gently.

"Sahib," the boy answered.

"I offered to send you back to Mandalay."

"Yes, Sahib."

"And you would not go."

"No."

"It is now too late, Nath Singh. You must obey me today without question. Your life and mine hang upon your obedience."

Nath Singh did not answer.

Otto showed him a rather gaudy red velvet jacket.

"I bought that as a present for you on the bazaar boat," he said. "You shall wear it this afternoon. Come to me half an hour before sunset."

Left to himself, he sewed a small sheet of tin shaped like a shallow cup into the lining of the jacket just over the heart, and in the outside of the velvet he cut a small pocket. In the afternoon, half an hour before sunset, Otto took from the tin box of his conjurer's paraphernalia a couple of small metal phials and a glass bottle of which the inside was divided by a glass slide. Into each of these partitions he poured one of his acids until it was full. Then he stopped the mouth of the bottle with a screw cap and placed it into the pocket of the jacket.

B   17

"Now, Nath Singh, it is time," and Nath Singh slipped the jacket on. As he spoke Nagein entered the hut.

"All is ready," he said.

"There will be no delay?" Otto asked anxiously. "At the exact moment of sunset the pagoda will be fired?"

"Have no fear," said Nagein.

They went out of that quiet hut. A throng of people was moving in the one direction. Otto and Nath Singh fell in amongst them. Ahead of them rose the gimcrack pagoda of gilt paper. By the ropes which were to sling the little temple and the Abbot's coffin up on to its platform, men stood ready. The tug-of-war was nearing its close. Those who would burn the Abbot were winning. Those on the other side, duly acting their parts or defeated by sheer fatigue, were staggering and sliding on the ground. Shouts rose to the Heavens:

"To the fire! To the fire!"

Otto pressed forward. Nath Singh noticed that he had wrapped himself once more in his yellow gown, but Nath Singh noticed nothing else. Nagein held his arm in a cruel grip, but the boy was thankful for it. He would have fallen and been trampled under foot but for that grip. As it was he could scarcely breathe, so close was the throng about him, so high did their heads overtop him. At the last corner of a row of shacks they were brought to a stop. They were on the edge of the strange arena, and a loud shout had risen from it which was taken up and repeated and went rolling away to the furthest rim of the crowded rabble. The spirits of light had won, the truck with the gaudy little temple was rushed towards the ropes which were to lift it into the high pagoda. In a second they saw it sidling up the guy ropes, rocking and bobbing ridiculously as it mounted.

"You too, Nath Singh," said Otto sharply in a low voice. "Up with you."

There was a stool behind him set against the corner of the shack.

"You'll see better. Up with you," and Nath Singh was lifted by the arms of Otto and Nagein on to the stool, helpless as a doll. But hardly one man at this time remarked him. A priest on a mound near to them was screaming:

"He will come back to lead us. When his heart burns, he will send us a sign, O Wisaya, Wisaya." And his voice went out in a long wail. That word too was taken up. What it meant, no one but Otto understood. But they were mad with the passion of the moment.

"When the heart burns! When the heart burns."

Nath Singh had dreamed of forests and tigers. Here they were about him and at his feet—a forest of brown arms, a jungle of tigers. He stood up high above that sea of wild faces and glistening eyes, his ears deafened by the uproar, his mind whirling in terror. The little temple reached the stage of the pagoda. A rocket was fired with a roar and a hiss and another and another. It seemed to Nath Singh that Otto had gone mad with the rest. He was stamping on the ground, his face working, his mouth muttering curses. And suddenly there was a crackle of fire. Flames ran up the dry wood and gilt paper of the temple. The pagoda itself caught fire, turned red, and blazed —and Nath Singh was aware that the priest upon the mound was pointing at him and that all those wild fierce faces tossing below him were turning in awe and wonder towards him.

"Keep still," said Otto. "This is the moment. Obey!"

18

Nath Singh obeyed. Paralysed by terror, he stood high before them all. He was conscious of a smell of burning, and then the priest cried:

"The burning heart! Wisaya lives again. The prophet of rebellion. On your knees!" And it seemed with one accord all that wild throng was upon its knees, beating the ground with its hands, shouting, "Wisaya! Wisaya!" Smoke rose into Nath Singh's eyes, and as he looked down, he saw flames bursting from his jacket above his heart.

For Otto and for Nagein too, the real hour of danger had now come. They lifted the boy down.

"Go slowly to the hut," whispered Otto. "Don't look at anyone. Don't stop for anyone. Go as if you walked in your sleep!"

A few moved as though they would rise, but the voices of the priest on the mound and of Otto rose in a high command:

"Let no one dare to stand in his way."

Many rose to their feet, following with their eyes the boy's progress through their ranks. Would the spell hold, Otto wondered? Once he was in the hut, the danger would have vanished. He and Nagein and Nagein's friend, the priest on the mound, could claim that the boy must be left until he was moved to speak.

After that Talaban would be his interpreter. The rebels would march up into the forest. At every village their numbers would swell. And in the midst of them Nath Singh, the boy Wisaya, would be carried in a litter, sitting cross-legged like a god, his face wrapt in ecstasy.

But Nath Singh walked so slowly—so dangerously slowly! Otto turned his face towards the burning pagoda. He extended his arms.

"To the Wisaya who was, peace!" he cried, and the crowd swung round with him. The pagoda was tumbling down now in burning fragments like incredibly bright strings of laburnum. And just as Nath Singh disappeared into the hut it collapsed with a roar like thunder.

"Leave the boy to me for half an hour," Otto whispered to Nagein. "In half an hour we march."

Otto's face was transformed. His trick had triumphed. He was, indeed, selling riots and rebellions. In a day he would have that wild country flaming as the pagoda had flamed. As for Nath Singh, let him disobey if he dared!

"Get them together! Marshal them," Otto cried, and Nagein, looking at his fierce and tyrannous face, wondered whether he was human or a Nat.

"You are the Lord of Magic," he cried, and whilst he turned back to the crowd, Otto slipped into the hut.

He stood for a moment shocked out of his senses. Of the clamour outside he heard not one sound. He was only aware that in the very midst of his victory, his world had crashed about him utterly like the burning pagoda of the Abbot. A single candle was alight on the floor of the hut. The red velvet jacket lay upon the floor. The sacking which made the walls of the hut was torn. Nath Singh had gone.

Otto sank down on the floor. He noticed that a piece of paper was pinned to the velvet jacket, and on it was scrawled in a boy's handwriting:

"I will wait for an hour for you on the path to the Fort at Akat."

Otto Reimer shook his head over that.

"So the old subadar has beaten me, conjuring tricks and all," he said.

In a little there was a murmur of men gathering about the door.

19

HUGH WALPOLE

From " The Wooden Horse " to " The Sea Tower," SIR HUGH WALPOLE'S books have come in a great and unbroken succession for which the English novel is immeasurably the richer. He contributes to this book a new " Herries " story—a little offshoot of the saga that has swept the whole English-speaking world and has done for Lakeland in prose something of what Wordsworth did for it in poetry.

THE CHURCH IN THE SNOW
AN INCIDENT IN THE LIFE OF ROBIN HERRIES
UNRECORDED IN *THE BRIGHT PAVILIONS*. [1]

ROBIN HERRIES, when a very young man, paid his first visit to the South of England. On a wintry day in the northern part of Glebeshire snow began to fall, to his astonishment, for he had understood that in Devonshire, Glebeshire, and Cornwall snow was a great rarity even in the extreme of winter.

It was falling now with great thickness. He dismounted from his horse and studied the drawn map that he had purchased in London. This was a rough map in red and black with dolphins sporting in the sea and a fine barque in full sail on the horizon. Nevertheless, it was excellent in its detail, and he repeated to himself with pleasure the names—Rasselas, Pelynt Cross, Treddon Cove, St. Mary Moor. Where was he now ? He looked over the bare bleak landscape, felt the snow stir coldly on his cheek, and then, brushing it from his eyes, saw most unexpectedly quite close to him a little grey church.

He looked hard at it lest it should be some hallucination, for he had been riding along a straight road for a considerable while, staring in front of him, and had seen nothing at all. There it was. There could be no question— small, sturdy, with a bell-tower, and close beside it a donkey tethered to a stone wall.

He looked again: he must be near Garth-in-Roselands—yes. And here, on the map, was the church—St. Michael and the Angels. That path to the right must lead to the village of Garth and so beyond it down to Rasselas and the sea. He would take shelter in the church for a while until this storm should be over. He walked across to it leading his horse, found the door open, and entered. Within, on one of the benches, a little table at his side, was seated a short square-set priest, and the priest was drawing on a board.

Robin had tied his horse to the wall near to the donkey, and now he walked up to the priest.

---

[1] *The Bright Pavilions : A Herries Chronicle*, to be published in the autumn of 1940.

"Forgive me for my intrusion," he said, "but it is snowing, and I thought I might shelter here until the snow was over."

The priest looked up at him, smiling. He had the merriest face, brown and wrinkled, with an ugly, humorous mouth and soft grey eyes. Catholic priests now at this time in Elizabeth's reign were rare: the most of them had been robbed, disbanded, turned out into the world for ruin and corruption.

Robin looked over the priest's shoulder and gave a little cry: "How beautiful!" he said.

Praise is pleasant from anybody, and here was an elegant gentleman, in black and silver, little more than a boy, who meant what he said. The priest was delighted.

He was certainly a master artist. The painting was for a window. The colours were broken into little squares and oblongs and were very brilliant. The scene was of a meadow in spring, thick with hawthorn blossom, and on the slope of the field a stout, elderly monk was kneeling. Near to him another monk was standing, his hand on the rough neck of a patient donkey. Robin saw at once that this monk was the little man at his side, and that the donkey was the one that he had seen near the church.

"There is to be a window," the priest explained, "in memory of our Abbot —Abbot Anastasius—who was a very good and worthy man. Our Monastery, of course, is dissolved, but some of us yet remain there, although it is in ruin. We have permission. I am the painter of this group of our Order. Yes, we are still living in our Monastery at Royle Parden, ten miles from here, by permission of the Queen, because we are Franciscans and have done no evil and are not concerned with any policies. That is Abbot Anastasius," he said, pointing to the picture, "and here am I and here is my donkey Margaret, for they wished that there should be some other figures, and why not myself, who loved the Abbot as a son loves his father."

"And you make the window in the Monastery?"

"We are famous for our stained glass. Such reds and purples and greens as ours are not to be found anywhere in the rest of England."

Robin marvelled at the painting for the brilliance of its colouring—the green of the meadow, the snowy white of the hawthorn, the blue of the sky, and, round the base, in purple lettering, the name of the Abbot and the date of his death.

He felt at once a warm kinship with the priest. Religion had been always of deep interest to him; he was unlike his big brother Nicholas, who cared for none of those things. He sat down beside the priest, who told him that his name was Brother Andrew, and, before he knew it, Robin was telling him all about himself and his life.

He was, by nature, reticent and reserved. He cared greatly for reading. He loved his home in the country, Mallory Court, where the pleached hedges were so warm, the flowers so fragrant, the splash of the fountain so musical. The three people he loved in the world were his father and mother and his brother Nicholas. His brother was a giant, the strongest man in England, the best, the bravest, the noblest-hearted.

Himself he thought that he would never marry. Nor would he be a Courtier. His friend, Philip Sidney, urged him to come to Court, but he could never be alone there. He liked better than anything else to be alone, to ride, as he had been doing during these last days, by himself through the English country. He loved England much, but there were many things wrong. He had passed groups of rioting disbanded soldiers and wandering monks. He had seen rotting corpses hanging at the cross-roads, and in many places the people had not enough to eat. Why, if God were all-powerful, did He allow such things?

A very very old question, Brother Andrew replied, and when he himself was young he had experienced a dreadful time when he had gone far from God and lived evilly with women and slept in the ditches a drunk man. Then one night, as he was sleeping in such a ditch, the Lord Christ had appeared to him in a dream and had called to him to rise and eat and drink with Him at the side of the road. He had heard a voice calling to him out of the sky, and the voice had said to him, " Andrew! Andrew! I have blessed thee and given thee the power to be thy own judge and act of thy own free will! And because I have done thee this favour when I might have made thee a slave to *My* will thou hast disgracefully used Me and thyself also. Arise and be worthy of thy own self-command." And so he had risen from the ditch and walked under the moon singing and come to his right mind.

Brother Andrew told all this as though it were as truly a fact as the picture that he was painting, so that Robin had to believe him.

It was plain that Brother Andrew, once he had started, was very ready to talk, and he continued, painting all the while, but telling Robin everything about his life. How they had, none of them, any possessions in the world. And what about your donkey? Robin asked. Brother Andrew grinned like a naughty boy caught in apple-stealing. Yes, the donkey Margaret was his and his alone. She loved him and would be obedient to no one else, but stuck her feet in the ground and showed her teeth if anyone else tried to ride her. He had prayed to God about Margaret and asked that it might not be reckoned a fault in him that he loved her so dearly. After the death of the Abbot and the dissolution of their Monastery he had been very lonely and had prayed that he might be given something or someone especial to love, and the very next following day a man had brought Margaret to the Monastery saying that he wished to sell her, and Brother Andrew had some pence for a barrel of apples that he had sold and he had bought her. The man said that in a little white circle on the under-part of her belly the letters M. M. were marked, that her name was Margaret, and that she was the most human donkey in the whole world. This she had proved to be, and that was why he would place her in the window, a thing that would be a pleasure to the Abbot, who had been a very understanding man and undoubtedly was, in Paradise, an understanding saint.

It was now approaching the middle of the day, and Andrew asked Robin Herries whether he would eat with him, which Robin said he would be very glad to do.

When they went outside the church Robin could not restrain a cry, for the snow had ceased to fall, the sun was shining, and the whole world, so far as the eye could see, was a white shining crystal, the sun bathing the field of snow as though it were a lake. Where the ground rose towards the horizon a deep purple shadow lay deep in the snow and small birds flew lazily in the blue sky. The air was so fresh that you might say that it had never been air before: it

22

seemed, in its biting, cold-warm pungency, to have the scent of the hawthorn of the picture that Brother Andrew had been painting.

Beside the wall, her rough, shaggy coat shining in the sunlight, stood patiently Margaret. You felt that she was aware of the nearness of Robin's horse, but would betray no unladylike interest. So soon as she saw Brother Andrew standing in the doorway of the church she raised her head and, with her mild patient eyes—eyes that accepted all the roughnesses of the world and turned them to unintentional charities—she stared across the sunny field at him as much as to say, " I am happy because the sun is shining and because you are here and because your painting is successful. For all these things, although I am but an ass, I thank God." She raised her head and brayed.

Brother Andrew went across the field and stroked her and tickled her behind the ear. " And now," he said, " we must eat."

In the little room that might be called the vestry of the church there was a fire burning, and on the fire an iron pot. Into the pot Andrew put many strange things: grass and hedgerow stuff, and part of a rabbit, the small bones of some birds. He stood there, his thick legs spread wide beneath his robe, stirring, and at last he poured it into two wooden bowls, adding some black bread, and first he knelt down and praised God.

It was as good and savoury as anything that Robin had ever eaten, and he wondered whether he had ever been so happy in all his life before, sitting there, dipping his bread into the soup while the sun poured in and the snow shone on the hill beyond the window, sparkling with fire and stained with grape-purple shadow.

Brother Andrew went back to his painting, and again Robin sat beside him. While he sat there he thought that he too might become a Franciscan. Would not such a life settle for him altogether his problems ? To have no possessions, to own nothing, to give up everything to God! It was true that Brother Andrew had his donkey, but that was surely a possession that would never give him any trouble.

Robin was, at this time, so young that it still seemed to him possible to solve life's problems very easily. He looked at Andrew's exquisite painting, the loving, leisured way in which he added a little stroke of purple, gave the hawthorn blossom an added touch of rose-white, painted Margaret's tail with an extra twirl of liveliness. So he, too, could write poems for the glory of God.

Idly looking through the window on his left, he saw three soldiers in armour staring in at them.

" There are three soldiers outside looking at us."

But that did not disturb Brother Andrew.

" Is one of them a stout, red-haired man with a broken lip ? "

" Yes."

" They are soldiers of Sir Warren Trenchard, whose manor is at Garth-in-Roselands. He is a merry heathen gentleman, and does not believe in God. But neither he nor his will harm us."

" They are making faces at us," Robin said indignantly.

" They tossed Brother Ignatius once in a blanket, and then tried to make him drunk, and afterwards they stripped him naked and painted him in red and black colours."

" I thought you said he never harmed you ? "

23

Brother Andrew grinned as he held his round head on one side, looking at his painting.

"We did not like Brother Ignatius. Even the Abbot disliked him."

"Oh, I see. . . . They have gone away now."

An hour later the light was failing and Andrew must set off home. He asked Robin to spend the night at the ruined Monastery, and Robin readily agreed.

They went into the field. The donkey was not there. Only Robin's horse.

Andrew gave a cry. He picked up his skirts and ran. He ran about the field, crying out, "Margaret! Margaret! Margaret!"

Robin thought that he had never seen so frantic a distress. The shadows were lying now in heavy bands across the snow and it was bitterly cold. Robin caught Andrew by the shoulder.

"Those soldiers took Margaret."

Andrew nodded his head frantically. "Yes. Yes. . . . They have teased me before about her. They have threatened at other times. . . ." His face was puckered up like a baby's. There were tears on his round cheeks.

"Even *one* possession," Robin thought, "can bring a man to misery."

He called out, "I will go to Sir Warren Trenchard's house and bring Margaret back with me."

The moment he had spoken the words he regretted them. He was young enough in any case to hate nothing so much as to make a fool of himself. His elder brother Nicholas had been always a giant of physical accomplishment, able for any feat of strength and famous through all the South of England.

But Robin had been a scholar, and not so famous a scholar either. Ladies had loved him for his straight, slender legs and his dark eyes, but he was, as yet, virgin of ladies and, in any case, loved his little cousin, Sylvia Herries.

His father, his brother, his mother, his cousins, all the friends of Mallory Court, were given to laugh at him, although in friendly fashion, for his shyness. He did not mind that *they* should laugh at him. He minded very much that others should. He was the poet, the artist, in the Herries blood, and was the more reticent because the other half-Herries was material-minded like his Uncle Henry and altogether insensitive.

So now, when he said this to Brother Andrew, he was sorry at once. To go to a house that he did not know and claim a donkey! An incredible folly. Then, when he saw in Andrew's eyes tears of relief and joy, he was ashamed of his own cowardice.

"Yes, yes! You go! You go!" Brother Andrew cried, clapping his hands and even skipping on the snow. "They will give her to you! If a cast-off monk whose Monastery has not a roof to its heads comes, they mock him for a vagabond—but an elegant London gentleman—that is quite another matter. And remember that God is on your side and that Margaret has silver bells to her ears."

So Robin rode off to the Manor house in Garth-in-Roselands. He rode swiftly, so that he might have the job finished the quicker. He imagined, to strengthen himself, how his great brother Nicholas would do. How he would ride into Sir Warren's courtyard and go forward and demand Margaret, and that his size and strength would make them render up the donkey even at sight of him.

24

Just outside the village there was a gallows with three dead men hanging and a huge black crow sitting on the head of one and pecking at it. The snow now in the twilight was grey, but, as the sun sank, the sky faded into the green of a water-meadow and a few stars, like diamond buttons on a tunic, sparkled. The hung men, their heads lazily on one side, swung slightly against the green sky.

The village street was deserted, but there was no question of the Manor House, for there were two stone gryphons on stout pillars on either side of the beautiful iron-laced gate, and beyond the gate the stone path, the box hedges. The house, shaped like the letter E, was beautiful with its many windows, divided by stone mullions and transoms into small panels and the glass in small leaded quarries. The house was built mainly of narrow, rich red brick with timber and plaster assisting. There was the music of a fountain, reminding Robin of Mallory, and suddenly the sky was filled with a multitude of stars "like angels singing," and the snow on the garden-lawns was the colour of ivory.

The hall-door was open, and Robin, walking forward, found himself in a company of people.

It was a fine hall and the fireplace was its central feature—a superb fire-place, grander than the one at Mallory, with an overmantel of wood, painted and gilt, the paintings being heraldic coats of arms. The firebacks and dogs were also grandly ornamented. On the floor there was straw-matting, which at that time was only in the houses of the rich, insanitary rushes being the usual fashion. There were three tables and a cupboard set with gilt and silver plate. All these must be mentioned, for they showed Robin that he was in the house of one of the chief persons in Glebeshire. He saw at once Sir Warren himself, a stout, broad man with a grey square beard, wearing a fur cloak over a suit of purple and silver.

Standing near the fire were several ladies and gentlemen; there were many dogs, a major-domo with a gilt-headed staff, and servants bearing drinks. Two men played on lutes and one sang. Robin stayed in the doorway until the verse was ended:

The blushing cheek speaks modest mind;
The lips, befitting words most kind.
The eye does tempt to love's desire,
And seems to say 'tis Cupid's fire.
Yet all so fair, but speak my moan,
Since nought doth say the heart of stone.

Why thus, my love, so kind bespeak
Sweet lip, sweet eye, sweet blushing cheek,
Yet not a heart to save my pain?
O Venus! take thy gifts again;
Make not so fair to cause our moan,
Or make a heart that's like our own.

The music ceased. Sir Warren, laughing, cried out something, then turned and saw Robin standing there. He cried out, rather fiercely,

25

" And—you, sir ? "

" I have come," Robin answered bravely, " to fetch a donkey wrongfully stolen by your men."

At the word " donkey " everyone burst out laughing. One very beautiful dark lady with a plumed hat did not laugh, but stared at Robin and then gently smiled.

This encouraged Robin, so he stood his ground manfully, his hand on the gold hilt of his poignard.

Sir Warren moved a pace towards him and said courteously,

" That is an accusation, sir—my men are not robbers, or only under necessity." He added, with irony, " Whose donkey ? "

" The donkey of a priest who is painting at the church on the moor."

" You witnessed its stealing ? "

" No. I did not. A space earlier I was in the church and saw your men at the window. Afterwards the donkey was gone and the priest said——"

Sir Warren, who was plainly choleric, interrupted.

" Nursery tales. You did not see the animal stolen and yet you come here——"

" I say that it was stolen, and by your men."

Sir Warren half-drew his sword.

" Your name ? "

" Robin Herries of Mallory Court in——"

" Never mind where. You must account to me for entering unasked my house and before my guests calling my men thieves——"

The beautiful lady interrupted.

" But it may be that the donkey is here. We must see. We must all judge."

And they all caught it up, delighted that there should be a game, crying, " The donkey! The donkey! The donkey! "

Trenchard, ashamed perhaps of showing anger in front of them, half-turned.

" Well—we will discover . . ."

He turned to the door, and all of them, in a troop, followed, laughing, dancing.

There were torches at the door, and as they moved out into the snowy garden they were like revellers in their gold and purple and dark jetty black, the diamonds and the gold sparkling under the torch-light, while the sky, pierced now with cold, clear stars, gave them back their illumination.

Sir Warren led them round the house-corner to the stables. There, tethered to the door of a stall, refusing the straw that a man offered her, shaking her head indignantly, and ringing her bells, was Margaret.

Robin went up to her, but she did not know him and, nervous already, poor female, at her rape, shot her ears back and showed her teeth.

" She does not know you," Trenchard said sternly.

" She is not my donkey but the priest's," Robin answered. " And her name is Margaret."

" Margaret ! Margaret ! " the crowd echoed delightedly.

Trenchard asked the man to whom the donkey belonged, and the man said, " Walter Despard."

" Call him."

Out of the dark of the stable the soldier whom Robin had seen by the church appeared.

" Is this your donkey ? " Trenchard asked him.

" Yes, Master."

" Whence had you her ? "

" Of a seaman in Southampton—last twelvemonth."

" This gentleman "—Trenchard pointed disdainfully at Robin—" swears that you stole it this very day of a priest at a church on the moor."

The soldier, seeing that his master, annoyed by the affair, was on his side, answered heartily, " By the Holy Cross this is my donkey. They will all tell you so, Master." He went on smoothly, " This gentleman is mistaken in the donkey. It is true that I was by the church this day. Will Boden was with me, and we saw a donkey tethered there. But it was not *my* donkey."

" You lie ! " Robin, feeling that all eyes were mockingly upon him, was raging at them.

" Then," Trenchard answered mockingly, " if my man lies you must prove it. He is *my* man and I take the charge on myself. You must prove it or answer to me."

But he could not prove it. That was Margaret, and he and the soldier knew it. But Margaret could not speak and the soldier would not. He saw disaster coming upon him. He had given them his name. It would be through England that he had behaved like a foolish, impertinent child. He could hear Nicholas's rebuke, see his father's mouth stiffen as he said, " You must learn wisdom, my son. You are not fit yet for the world." He saw himself fighting a dozen of them. That would be the easiest way out. He stared with a frantic, beseeching gaze at Margaret, but that poor beast could not help him.

Then, in that brief instant before his humiliating surrender, he prayed, " Oh God Who art everywhere, Who led me this day to the church and showed me in the painting and in the glittering snow how beautiful is Thy handiwork, help me now, not for my sake but for Thy eternal justice . . ."

" Well, sir," Trenchard said coldly.

Robin saw the soldier's grinning mouth, felt the stillness of their expectancy of his defeat.

The answer came. He pointed at the soldier.

" If the donkey is his, and he has had her this year past, ask him what are the initials cut under her belly. He should know if she is his."

Trenchard looked at him, then said sternly to the soldier,

" Answer him. What are the initials ? "

The soldier shifted his body from foot to foot. He looked about him. He scowled, turned to the donkey, then muttered,

" There *are* no letters. How should I tell ? "

" Certainly you must tell," Trenchard answered him. " You groom her, fasten the harness. There are *no* letters ? "

" I know of none."

Trenchard turned to Robin.

" The initials are—— ? "

" M. M."

27

Trenchard, taking a lantern from a hook, went himself to Margaret, lowered the light, and examined. Margaret, nervous and distressed, bit him in the arm.

Andrew and Robin, a happy pair, riding in the starlight to the Monastery, considered the matter.

"It proves to me one thing, Brother Andrew," Robin said, "that it is truly better in this life to have *no* possessions—not one single thing. For four hours of this day, Brother Andrew, in your distress, you have forgotten God."

"Nay," said Andrew, "not so. For during all those hours I prayed to God. It proves rather that man is intended by God to love some earthly thing, for only thus can he truly understand what God is." And he bent forward and tickled Margaret behind the ears. The silver bells tinkled crisply in the frozen air.

JOHN MASEFIELD

MR. JOHN MASEFIELD has been Poet Laureate since 1930, and was awarded the Order of Merit in 1935. His best-known poems are perhaps "The Everlasting Mercy," "The Widow in the Bye-Street," "Reynard the Fox," and "Right Royal"; his novels, such as "Sard Harker" and "Odtaa," reach the widest public; and his "Gallipoli" is one of the classics of the last war.

RED CROSS

I REMEMBER a moonless night in a blasted town,
And the cellar-steps with their army-blanket-screen,
And the stretcher-bearers, groping and stumbling down
To the Red Cross struggle with Death in the ill-lit scene.

There, entering-in, I saw, at a table near,
A surgeon tense by a man who struggled for breath.
A shell, that shattered above us, rattled the gear,
The dying one looked at me, as if I were Death.

He died, and was borne away, and the surgeon wept;
An elderly man, well-used, as one would have thought
To western war and the revels that Death then kept:
Why weep for one when a million ranked as naught?

He said, " We have buried heaps since the push began.
From now to the Peace we'll bury a thousand more.
It's silly to cry, but I could have saved that man
Had they only carried him in an hour before."

29

IAN HAY

It is no secret that " IAN HAY " is the pen-name of Major-General John Hay Beith, C.B.E., M.C., at present Director of Public Relations at the War Office. He had already a round half-dozen highly popular novels to his name when in 1915 he became the private soldier's Homer by writing "The First Hundred Thousand." The war ended, he not only enhanced his great popularity as a novelist, but became one of our favourite playwrights of comedy. For example, his recent " Housemaster " has given equal delight as novel, play, and film.

THE MAN WHO HAD SOMETHING AGAINST HIM

A MEMORY OF 1914

HE gave his name as James Sanderson and his age as thirty-eight. He was a sturdy, slow-speaking Lowland Scot, and his profession was that of a motor mechanic. The recruiting officer surveyed him curiously.

" If you live in Roxburghshire," he said, " why have you come all the way to London to enlist ? Why didn't you join up in your own town, with your own friends ? That's what you Scotsmen usually do."

James Sanderson gazed stonily at the blank wall immediately above the officer's head.

" I had something against me among my ain folk," he said, " so I came here. I'm a first-class mechanic, though, and I dinna drink."

He was accepted. Reliable transport drivers were not too easily picked up in those days.

In due course the unit went to France, and for many weeks the convoy of motor-lorries, wherein James Sanderson drove lorry No. 3, ploughed its way backwards and forwards along foundering roads, through seas of mud, feeding the mighty fighting machine that stretched, in those days, from Béthune to the North Sea. Like his comrades, James Sanderson lived in his lorry and, unlike most of them, appeared to live for it. His engine never broke down, his back-axle never seized, his brakes never failed, for the simple reason that James Sanderson never left anything to chance. However long and hard the day's work, however pitiless the weather, he never missed an opportunity to overhaul, to tinker, to lubricate. He was sober, he was honest, and he was absolutely amenable to discipline. It seemed strange that such a paragon should " have something against him among his ain folk." But he evidently had, for once, when a brigade of Scottish Lowland Territorials came and lay for a night near the parking-place of the convoy, and certain Caledonian motor-drivers made up a party to visit their compatriots and with them participate in the solemn mysteries of " New Year's," James merely shook his head, and when asked for his reasons proffered those already mentioned.

They were a happy convoy—a good type of early recruit, with an officer whom they liked and trusted. But one day trouble came. A peripatetic General descended upon them and inspected them. He was a general of the Old Regular school, and he did not entirely approve of the somewhat informal methods prevalent among some of the Kitchener units. He admitted that the condition and handling of the lorries were satisfactory, but commented adversely upon the fact that the drivers had been permitted to deface Government property with totems and mottoes of their own inception. (Most of the men had given their lorries names—humorous, sentimental, and occasionally vulgar—and had painted these upon the dashboards.) The Inspector gave orders that these were to be " expunged." Attention was also drawn to the regulation which directed that all ranks were to grow moustaches. Most of the men, chauffeurs by instinct and upbringing, were as clean-shaven as Roman legionaries.

Accordingly, that evening, Captain Markham announced that all members of his flock not already in possession of a moustache must produce one forth-with. The results by the end of a week were appalling; at the end of a fort-night not so bad. At the end of three weeks a horrid stubble had ripened into a luxurious growth, and the appearance of the convoy was almost normal. All save in one case. James Sanderson, the model and pattern of his kind, had flatly disobeyed King's Regulations. His long upper lip was still closely shaven.

After three days of semi-official recrimination with his sergeant, James Sanderson was brought up at Orderly Room, charged with refusing to obey an order—to wit, declining to grow a moustache when called upon to do so by his superior officer.

Captain Markham surveyed James Sanderson's stocky figure, close-cropped grizzled hair, and ruddy countenance thoughtfully.

" I can't understand you, Sanderson," he said. " Here you are, with an absolutely clean crime sheet, one of the best and most willing soldiers in the convoy, sticking your toes in over a simple matter like this. What's the trouble ? "

" Could I get speaking with you alone, sir ? " inquired James Sanderson.

" It's not usual," replied the Captain.

" Will I get whispering in your ear then, sir ? " asked James, reddening.

Strictly speaking, these were most irregular requests; but then the late war was a most irregular business. Captain Markham smiled.

" Sergeant," he said, " take the escort and go and stand over there by the door. Now, Sanderson."

James Sanderson leaned across the table, and announced in a low, agitated voice:

" Sirr, if I grow a moustache, I shall be for home! "

" Great Scott! Why ? "

" *Because it will be pure white !* I'm sixty-one years old. That's what I have against me among my ain folk. *They ken my age !* That's why I went to London to enlist. Dinna send me home, sirr! "

31

For a moment Captain Markham looked into the face of James Sanderson, as man to man. Then he offered his hand.

"All right," he said quietly. "Stand to attention again. Sergeant!"

"Sir."

"This case is dismissed. I have given this man special leave to shave his upper lip until further notice. Any attempt on his part to grow a moustache would be attended by—er—disastrous consequences—of—er—a subcutaneous character. You understand ? "

"Yes, sir," replied the sergeant untruthfully.

"Very good. Dismiss the accused."

And James Sanderson, with tears of gratitude in his eyes, was marched out again and turned loose in the mud and rain, free to remain there for as long as he could handle a razor.

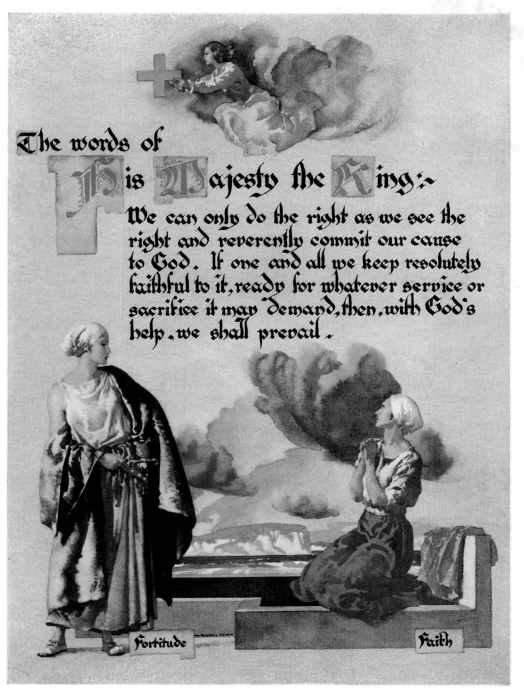

The words of His Majesty the King:

We can only do the right as we see the right and reverently commit our cause to God. If one and all we keep resolutely faithful to it, ready for whatever service or sacrifice it may demand, then, with God's help, we shall prevail.

Fortitude

Faith

THE WORDS OF HIS MAJESTY THE KING: FROM THE ORIGINAL BY W. RUSSELL FLINT

CHARLES MORGAN

MR. CHARLES MORGAN, author of "Portrait in a Mirror," "The Fountain," and other famous novels, and, more recently, a play which was an outstanding addition to modern drama, is no less famous as a dramatic critic and essayist. It is in this latter rôle that he makes his contribution here.

CREATIVE IMAGINATION

From a lecture delivered to the University of Paris in the winter of 1936. The author is content to stand by it and to allow it to represent his thought today.

Ne craignez pas que je vous inflige longtemps le tourment de m'entendre parler français. Mais permettez-moi d'user, d'abuser peut-être, de votre beau langage pour vous dire quelques mots en guise de préambule. On dit qu'il n'y a pas de plaisir comparable à l'arrêt de la douleur. Si nous souffrons ensemble maintenant, nous serons donc d'autant plus heureux lorsque ces moments d'épreuve seront terminés. Il faut souffrir pour se comprendre.

Il ne s'agit pas ici d'une visite diplomatique. Je n'ai d'ailleurs nulle autorité pour parler au nom de mes compatriotes, mais rien ne m'empêchera de dire ceci: Seules des grandes puissances de l'Europe, la France et l'Angleterre possèdent encore la chose du monde à laquelle j'attache le plus de prix: la liberté de pensée. Comme tous les peuples, nous avons nos erreurs et nos faiblesses; pourtant chez nos deux nations la suprême vilenie n'est pas accomplie. Nous sommes encore libres de penser, nos imaginations gardent encore leur indépendance, nos femmes ne sont pas pour nous des machines à faire des soldats, nous n'élevons pas nos enfants comme des loups, dans " l'imagination du sang," nous ne condamnons pas nos artistes et nos hommes de science à l'exil ou à une vivante mort. Si ce lien spirituel est méconnu ou s'il n'est pas assez puissant pour nous faire agir ensemble, nous périrons séparément, comme périssent toujours ceux qui renient les exigences profondes de leur idéal.

Je sais que les Anglais vous semblent parfois le plus irritant des peuples. Cela ne me surprend pas. J'ai du sang celte moi-même et ils produisent souvent le même effet sur moi! Nous ne sommes pas ici pour analyser les particularités de mes compatriotes, mais je voudrais cependant vous en signaler une.

Depuis les temps lointains où Shakespeare écrivait Le Marchand de Venise, *qui au point de vue logique et légal est une pièce fort irritante, nous autres Anglais avons toujours attaché plus d'importance à l'esprit de justice qu'à la lettre de la loi et nous sommes parfois surpris par votre tendance à exiger que toute alliance soit inscrite sur parchemin et scellée à la cire.*

Soyons patients les uns envers les autres. Si nous nous divisons, le monde est perdu. Je vous demande seulement de vous rappeler que toutes les signatures ne sont pas tracées à l'encre.

C

Il y a vingt-deux ans, l'Angleterre n'était tenue qu'à fournir un corps expéditionnaire de 200,000 hommes tout au plus. Aujourd'hui, sur les murs de Notre-Dame, une inscription évoque " la mémoire du million de morts de l'Empire Britannique tombés dans la grande guerre et qui, pour la plupart, reposent en France." Ces noms, ces milliers de noms ne sont pas tracés à l'encre; pourtant, si jamais l'heure sonne, nous saurons faire honneur à ces signatures-là.

I

WHAT I have to say falls naturally into three parts: first, a consideration of what creative imagination is; secondly, an attempt to apply the idea to the work of an artist, particularly to that of story-tellers and poets; and finally, an inquiry into the place of an artist in the modern world, and into the value of creative imagination as a pointer to a way of life.

Consider, first, what creative imagination is *not*.

There is a familiar saying that, if a man wants anything badly enough, he will obtain it. To some extent this is true. Nearly all our failures spring from division of mind; nearly all success from singleness and concentration. A man who wants consistently and above all else to become rich, will probably attain riches, but his power to do so is not an instance of the power of Creative Imagination. Whatever else it is, Creative Imagination is not a means by which to acquire the objects of ambition and greed.

Secondly, it is to be clearly distinguished from the theory of Creative Evolution. (I am speaking here of Shaw's application of the theory, not of Bergson's great original.) This theory is not altogether unacceptable. It is true that body and mind adapt themselves to circumstances; if I lose the use of my right hand, I become left-handed; if I lose my sight, my other senses compensate me for my loss by becoming freshly acute; if it were necessary for me and my children and grandchildren to live in trees, it is not impossible that we should develop tails that would enable us to swing from one branch to another. But when the evolutionary theory is taken to mean that, by the simple process of desiring to live long, men can not only prolong their lives but increase their wisdom, when it claims that by means of physical desire or intellectual effort we can produce spiritual change, when, in brief, an attempt is made to represent evolution as a mystical as well as a material process, the theory breaks down and is lost in clouds of rhetoric. It has done much, in recent years, to mislead the world. It is the philosophy chiefly responsible for men's willingness to accept what is called " the economic interpretation of history " and for their pathetic belief that by a series of economic or political adjustments they can banish their present discontents. It lies at the root of the hysterical materialism of totalitarian states, and to it history will trace their ultimate disillusionment. The theory of Creative Evolution is based upon the satisfaction of collective desire just as an acquisitive and ruthless man's confidence that he will succeed is based upon the satisfaction of private desire. These desires, if pursued strenuously and with a single mind, may, and often do, attain their material object, but the object, when attained, is found to be without real value. " When I get what I want, I find that I want it no longer," is the inevitable cry of all materialists. Creative Imagination does not look for specific attainments. It is a continually receding ideal.

I have said that the idea is difficult; it is difficult only in its extreme simplicity. It is this: that when we imagine with love, we create what we imagine; that what we then create has real and extending value; and that nothing else has.

You will see at once how unfamiliar the territory is into which we have come. What is the meaning of the word " imagine " ? What, in this sense, is " love " ? What is " value " ? I shall not at this stage trouble you with a formal definition of terms. Their meaning will appear if I give you instances of creative imagination.

To one instance, that of prayer, I shall refer very briefly and in the most general terms, because I do not wish to challenge religious opinion. But it is, I think, generally acknowledged by the learned of all faiths, that prayer is a means by which a man may produce spiritual change. Whether or not it produces more material results, we need not here discuss. The function of Creative Imagination is to produce spiritual change, to change the heart, the nature of a man, and only this aspect of prayer is our present concern. And prayer which produces a change of this sort conforms precisely to the two conditions which are characteristic of an act of Creative Imagination—it is ecstatic, not intellectual, and it is a mutual act between the man and his god, a receiving and an impregnation. But, in this case, man is not the giver or impregnator. His prayers, all his religious disciplines, all his great exercises, whether he be Catholic or Protestant, Buddhist or Hindu, have as their purpose to cleanse himself of spiritual impediment, to lay open his heart, to enable himself to receive his god, to permit the Supreme Spirit to enter and ravish him. Every mystical writing that I have ever seen tells, in effect, the same story—not that the man attained to God but that he was at last able to overcome his carnal and intellectual resistance to God. The medieval saints spoke continually in erotic metaphor, likening themselves to a bride that receives her bridegroom. The metaphor varies in form, but, throughout the mystical records of all peoples, there may be recognised the same account of an act of Creative Imagination by mutual action between the enraptured man and the Supreme Spirit, an acceptance and an impregnation, fierce with love.

Let us now turn back for a moment to see how far we have travelled. Creative Imagination is a means by which to produce spiritual change; love is a condition of it, for love is the essence of spiritual value. It is to be carefully distinguished from wanting something and from *willing* something; it is to be distinguished with equal care from fancy or day-dreaming; and the distinction is that all these things—wanting, willing, fancying—are single or self-regarding acts that a man may perform of himself, whereas Creative Imagination, like magnetism, requires two poles, a positive and a negative pole, before it can exist —it is not a single but a mutual act, a giving and receiving. It requires a communicating tension between giver and receiver, and one form of that tension is art.

II

This brings me to the heart of my subject. I am about to suggest to you that, in criticising art, we are all overmuch inclined to discuss it in the language of the *coteries* and to base our judgments upon the answers we give to questions which, however important they may be, are of minor importance beside the question, so seldom asked, that lies, or should lie, at the root of æsthetics. It is at the root of æsthetics because it is at the root of life. Men were accustomed to ask of a book or a picture: Is it romantic? Is it naturalistic? These were the questions that seemed vital to the contemporaries of Musset and, afterwards, to the contemporaries of Zola. If they answered yes, it was with approval; if we answered yes to the same questions today, it would probably be with disapproval. Fashion has changed. Was there not almost a riot in a French theatre about a hundred years ago because Victor Hugo seemed to have caused a revolution in art by introducing the practice of enjambment into dramatic alexandrines? We can see now that no vital artistic principle was betrayed. We do not say any longer that because Racine was an artist, therefore Hugo was not. Contemporary criticism, though reasonable and interesting in so far as it drew attention to a variation of form, is seen to have been irrelevant in so far as it affected the nature of art itself. If the critics were seeking to discover whether Hugo was or was not an artist, they were asking themselves the wrong question.

Are not we also asking ourselves the wrong questions? The fashionable challenge to a writer nowadays is: Is he modern? Is his work in accordance with the spirit of the times? Many critics go further and ask: Does he recognise that the horror of war threatens the world? Do his writings reflect that obsession? If not, he is a romantic and to be condemned. Or there is another question on which æsthetic judgment is based: Does this writer belong to my party? Is he of the Left or of the Right? I need not insist upon the evil and corruption of such a question as that, but I beg you to observe that one of these questions leads to another and that to ask whether an artist is modern is to ask in what sense he is modern, and to ask that is not far removed from asking to what party he belongs.

It is to this that the French and the English must inevitably be led if we continue to ask the wrong questions in judging a work of art. The question is not whether it is romantic or naturalistic or symbolistic, but whether it is or is not a work of creative imagination. Does it contain within it that seed which enables men to imagine creatively and will enable them to do so for generation after generation? This much is certain: no work of art is immortal of itself. Its endurance and value depend not upon what it is, judged simply by the standards of its contemporaries, but upon what it has power to become. If it is to endure, if it is to remain young, it must be continually re-created in the minds of those who receive it. It must have a new meaning for each generation of men. Racine is not valued today for the same reasons that made him valuable in the seventeenth century. The French theatre of today and French thought of today no longer desire of a dramatist that he shall report progress through messengers, and explain his characters through confidantes; in brief, the classical dramatic structure, to which Racine so rigidly conformed, is opposed to the whole spirit of modern criticism; and yet, though many attack him, Racine lives. "What," you will say, "are you holding out Racine to us as an example of the creative imagination—our Racine who, whatever the merits of his versification, is, perhaps, as bad an example as any you could have chosen of a great originating artist whose imagination lights fire in the hearts of modern men? Racine," you will say, "had many cold merits which Boileau appreciated, but why on earth have you, most ignorant Englishman, chosen Racine to illustrate your thesis?" I have chosen him because it would have been so much easier to have chosen Molière or even Corneille. I have chosen Racine because he is difficult, and if I can persuade you that *he* lives because he had in him the seed of creative imagination, then I shall have gone far towards establishing my case. And I suggest to you—and particularly to those of you who are young and, perhaps, in active rebellion against classical forms—that you cannot, if you are Frenchmen and sensitive, sit through a performance of *Phèdre* without, at some moment of the evening, being thrilled in spite of your modern resistances. Is it not true? You may argue if you will that the perfection of Racine's verses produces an effect of monotony and is, in that sense, a fault; and I, as an Englishman who loves the superb irregularities of Shakespeare, am inclined to agree with you. But I know that, imperfect though my ear is for your great language, there are lines of *Phèdre* which lift me out of myself, make me catch my breath, drive some magic through my flesh and strike new life into my own imagination. What they cause me to imagine is by no means what Racine imagined. I do not pretend that I am greatly concerned for the fate of any of the characters in his play. But he carries in his genius that vital sword which stabs me into new, independent life and compels me to imagine for myself. That is the true power and the true immortality of an artist.

May I give you another example, different in kind, and from my own language? It is a habit in England to speak of Shakespeare as a supreme dramatist and to treat his works as if the sum of human wisdom were contained in them. I do not dispute his wisdom, the range of his experience, or the depth and variety of the moral teaching that may be found in his work. These things increase his greatness, but they are not the essence of it or the reason for his immortality. The proof is that the thrill of the man, the quality in him that suddenly extends the imagination of the listener, is to be found in such a lyric as

> *O mistress mine, where are you roaming?*
> *O, stay and hear! your true love's coming,*
> > *That can sing both high and low:*
> *Trip no further, pretty sweeting;*
> *Journeys end in lovers meeting,*
> > *Every wise man's son doth know.*
>
> *What is love? 'tis not hereafter;*
> *Present mirth hath present laughter;*
> > *What's to come is still unsure:*
> *In delay there lies no plenty;*
> *Then come kiss me, sweet-and-twenty!*
> > *Youth's a stuff will not endure.*

You will observe that what Shakespeare *says* in that poem is no more than this: "You are young. Life is short. Kiss me now." Here is no original philosophy, no unique experience, no profound moral teaching. He is saying what the Elizabethans said continually because they were in perpetual terror that beauty would be ruined by small-pox and that an early death would swallow them up. But whereas many of his contemporaries wrote very tediously on this subject and are of no interest to us who have little fear of small-pox, he, with the same subject, wrote what I believe to be the greatest short poem in the English language. Though *Hamlet* may some day be forgotten, this poem will, I think, be remembered. Why? Not for what it contains but for what it communicates from outside itself. I feel when I read it as though, in the dusk of knowledge and experience, a window had been thrown open. Youth flows through; love flows through—youth itself and love itself, the reality within appearances. In this it differs from lesser poems which celebrate, however beautifully, the youth and love of one woman. Let us speak of it in this way: lesser poems illumine one face or many faces, but this lyric fills the reader himself with a divine radiance so that, while he reads, he feels himself to be, for a moment, a god, with the power, love and compassion of the gods. Dostoievsky tells of a man who, kneeling before a woman, said: "It is not to you I kneel, but to suffering humanity in your person." That is a corresponding flash of genius. No three artists could be more different than Racine, Shakespeare, and Dostoievsky, and no three artists could employ more different styles; but, in the instances I have given, they have this in common: a power to be the flash of communication between God and man, and to enable each man imaginatively to transcend his own flesh and to see God and enter into Him. I use the word "God." You are free to interpret it as you will. I am not a theologian. I know only that if the word has *no* meaning for you, art can have no meaning, creation no meaning, and imagination no range.

III

How, then, should an artist live and work? George Moore wrote, in a letter to a very young girl who was experimenting in his own art, the following words:

"If you go out and amuse yourself when you can't write, your art will waste into nothingness. An artist's life is in this like an acrobat's, he must exercise his craft daily, when inspiration is by him and when it is afar. He must not wait for inspiration, he must continue to call it down to him always and at last it will answer him. . . . If you would hear the Muse, you must prepare silent hours for her and not be disappointed if she breaks the appointment you have made with her. To receive the Muse as it is her due to be received you must have an apartment. You must dine in and alone very often."

You will observe that Moore, like Baudelaire, compares an artist's life to an acrobat's; he must continually exercise his craft as an acrobat his muscles; but I would say rather that an artist must judge his life by the lives of the saints, not only exercising his craft, which corresponds to the ritual of devotion, but preparing and, above all, submitting his spirit. Moore himself gives a hint of the same idea—"you must dine in and alone very often."

But let us first consider the exercise of an artist's craft. If craft is an end in itself, it is valueless, and there are many who, because they themselves are incapable of the same patience, profess to despise a man who will spend a month over a paragraph. Such critics declare that elaborate craftsmanship is vanity and arrogance. "Does Mr. Jones," they cry, "does Mr. Jones suppose himself to be so important that every word of his must be chosen as if the fate of the world depended on it?" There is a simple answer. Elaborate craftsmanship is an act of humility, not of arrogance. An arrogant man, immersed in the world's affairs, relies upon himself; he believes in his own wisdom and is engrossed by his own cleverness; he puts down what happens to be in his head as a politician at the street-corner improvises from his tub. An artist, on the contrary, knows that, of himself, he is nothing. He is, and feels himself to be, an instrument, and it is his duty to perfect his instrument. It is not he who will impregnate the imagination of generations yet unborn but that eternal force outside himself, whom some call God and others the Muse, which acts through him.

There is another objection to be met. It is often said that, because ordinary men and women are not themselves craftsmen of letters, style has no meaning for them and is, therefore, a waste of time. Would you say that, because most people who go to a theatre are not themselves either actors or critics, they are unaffected by style in acting? And there is a simpler answer than that. I believe that there are few Frenchmen who will not agree with me that the influence of their translation of the Bible on the language and thought of France has been, and still is, less than the influence of our Authorised Version on the language and thought of England. The reason is that the Authorised Version of our Bible is, in the matter of style, the outstanding miracle of our literature. It is said to have been composed by a committee appointed by King James I; if this is true, it is the only service to art ever done by an English committee. Its substance, its history, and its moral teaching are all contained in the French Bible, but ours is a supreme masterpiece of style, the standard of all our literature, the absolute authority for our grammar, our syntax, our choice of words, and, from generation to generation, the fire within the common speech of peasant, merchant, and aristocrat. The Bible has done more to give unity, greatness, and character to England than any other force except the sea. Why? Not only by reason of what it contains, for other translations were made from the same original, but because the artist's instrument was made perfect.

What do we mean by the perfecting of the instrument? What is a perfect style? Are not the styles of all artists different? How, then, can we lay down rules? Of course we cannot; but, if the problem be considered from the point of view of creative imagination and not as a war between naturalism, symbolism, and impressionism, certain ideas of possible value emerge from it. In an early book of mine, I used these words: "Art is news of reality not to be expressed in other terms." Now reality, the reality within appearances, is difficult to express for two reasons: not that it is itself obscure, for all mystics who claim to have had entry into it tell us that it is, above all else, simple—

Like a great ring of pure and endless light,
All calm, as it was bright—

but for reasons that spring from the limitations of our language. Language is based upon an observation of appearances, whereas reality is that which transcends appearances. Language is devoted to distinguishing between particular things, pointing out their differences or their resemblance, whereas reality transcends all differences and consists in the unity, not only of created things among themselves, but of the Creator with Creation. These are the chief limitations of language, and the purpose of style is to overcome them, so

39

using language that the reader's imagination, impregnated and bearing fruit creatively, may pass beyond the differences of appearance into the unity of truth. And if we ask further what is the style which makes it possible for a reader to receive " news of reality " through the clamour of words, the answer seems to depend upon two things: form and pressure. What form he will employ each artist must decide according to his nature; in his choice of form, his individuality consists; but his work, if it is to endure, must have form—that is to say, it must continuously, sentence by sentence, paragraph by paragraph, volume by volume, give an impression, corresponding to that given by a sonnet and by life itself, that the end is in the beginning and that what is incomplete is moving towards completion. The purpose of rhyme is to answer the preceding rhyme; the value of all forms is that by promising fulfilment of what is as yet unfulfilled they create in man that tension, that excitement of the spirit, that profound expectation and hope which is the impulse of imagination. As he may see in death the fulfilment of one expectation and in love the fulfilment of another, each opening to him a further expectation greater than that which has been satisfied, so he may discover in the form of a work of art that assurance of peace from which imagination springs. But form alone is not enough. In a great style there is pressure behind the form. As you read, you are made aware of this pressure. You feel that all the heavens of reality are pressing upon the writer's mind; you look up, you imagine, and your own heavens open before you. It is not because I value style as verbal embroidery but because I believe this form and pressure to be purges of the human spirit that I suggest an artist's elementary duty to be the perfecting of his instrument.

He has another and greater duty—to learn how to submit. " If you would hear the Muse," George Moore said, " you must prepare silent hours for her." They must be not silent only, but submissive. You must not question her or be impatient of her absence. You must not use her when she comes for your own power or vanity, but only as she herself wishes to be used. If men call you Master, it is not you but she that has taught or comforted them. If they despise and ridicule you, do not hate them or retaliate; ask of yourself only one question—whether you have betrayed her—then is their contempt justified; if it is not justified, still suffer it for her sake. Do not hit back; do not engage in personal controversy or in any controversy except in defence of the freedom of artists to be artists; do not be overmuch concerned with your contemporaries, except to discover the good that is in them. Join no faction; be at peace; be alone.

Above all, do not fear ridicule, do not fear to give yourself away. The fear of being laughed at is the curse of contemporary literature. We are told that the spirit of our time is sceptical and ironic, and that all writing must be flavoured with a grain of salt. This attitude of mind is the product of a disastrous timidity and produces in its turn a barren cleverness—poems conceived in political hatred, novels by men who are hasty to despise their characters lest we laugh because they have admired so faulty a thing as man or have loved so imperfect a thing as woman. Yet men and women, their folly, their suffering, their aspiration, the God in them, are the material of our art, and an artist must submit to them as he submits to all else. An artist is not in the world to crucify humanity but to wash its feet.

40

IV

Yet it is often said that a writer, who conducts his life in the way I have described and dedicates a great part of it to meditation and the slow improvement of his craft, exhibits a lack of sympathy with his fellow-men and is selfish in his seeming aloofness. It is asked of what value his art is in a turbulent world and what meaning it can have to men who need work, to women and children who are hungry, to the great mass of humanity that is struggling for security and peace. Of what value, it is asked, can a story be to men in fear of death, particularly a story that reflects the doctrines of no party and is not directly concerned with the contemporary struggle for existence? Those who write such stories are spoken of sometimes as being " divorced from life "; and if the reply be made that it is, then, surprising that so many people throughout the world should be eager to read them, a further charge is brought forward: that these readers must themselves be " divorced from life " or eager to " escape " from it. I remember that when last I was in Germany, I inquired carefully into the attitude of the Government towards art. That it suppressed opinion contrary to the régime I could well understand, for this is common practice in all countries that have recently undergone revolution; a government by force, still uncertain of its own position, has never been willing to face criticism. But I pressed my inquiries further, asking what the official attitude was to works of art that abstained from politics altogether—to a pure love-story, for example, such as *Romeo and Juliet,* or Turgeniev's *Torrents of Spring* or *Manon Lescaut*; and I was told that, though such a tale would not necessarily be suppressed, it would be treated with contemptuous disfavour. Why? Because it did not actively support the Government; because it did not reflect the Nazi *weltanschauung.* Those who speak of the pure artist as being " divorced from life " are Nazis without knowing it. They assume that nothing is worth writing about except their own world-outlook, their own *weltanschauung.*

Let us consider the same problem from another point of view—not that of the writer himself, but that of the common reader. It is said that the writer who does not directly concern himself with contemporary affairs and who thinks of men and women as individuals, not as units in a mass—whether that mass be a nation, a race, or an economic class—it is said that such a writer does nothing to increase the happiness or lessen the misery of mankind, or that, if he does anything, he acts only as a drug. This is not true, and, if we apply to the common reader the idea of creative imagination, we shall see that it is not true, and shall perceive also a relationship between art and life in the modern world that is not easily recognised by those who most arrogantly call themselves modern.

Distinguish clearly between happiness and pleasure. Pleasure depends upon the immediate satisfaction of desire; happiness is the feeling a man sometimes has that his life has value, that it is moving towards a great purpose, and, above all, that it is working out its own completeness; unhappiness is confusion and division of mind, a sense of being thwarted, of having lost one's way, of living haphazard in obedience to no form. An unhappy life is like a bad book —it runs hither and thither and carries within it no assurance of form. And the chief difficulty of living is the difficulty we all have in perceiving what the form of our life really is or indeed that it has a form.

Now it is characteristic of our present age—it is indeed the characteristic which most clearly sets us apart from our predecessors and gives a special meaning to the word " modern "—that where men are unhappy their unhappiness springs precisely from this division of mind, this unsatisfied longing for form and reason in life. This is a sceptical age, and great numbers of men, having put from them the faith of their ancestors, are seeking a new faith to replace it. This is a scientific age in which man's knowledge has outrun his wisdom and he is haunted by the destructive power of his own inventions, which he is unable to control. This is an age of fierce paradox, in which the distributive system is found to be so imperfect that in one part of the world food-stuffs are destroyed while elsewhere men and women are crying out for them. This is, above all, an age of questions, in which youth can find no outlet for its enthusiasm and asks continually: " Why ? Why ? Why ? What is the meaning of this life of mine ? What is its form ? What—to use Mr. Wells's phrase—is the shape of things to come ? " Where those questions find no answer, misery, rebellion, or vain discontent are often the consequence. This is the nature of modern unhappiness.

Again ask why ? If we fail to perceive the shape of things to come and are unable to distinguish, among the confusions of contemporary existence, a form that is completing itself, is not the failure a failure of imagination in ourselves ? We feel within us that there is a vital form awaiting completion—if we did not feel that, there would be small reason to live at all and none for a struggle to live well—and yet we cannot imagine the form completed. This is the value of literature to the common reader, of pictures to the spectator, of music to the listener, of art to mankind. It impregnates him with the idea of form. Far from drugging him, it spurs him to imagine those things without the imagining of which he cannot know himself or be happy or at peace. It is in this sense that art may be justly required to " hold the mirror up to nature." It is not primarily valuable as a representation of observed facts or as comment upon them. It is valuable in its power to hold up such a mirror to man as enables him to see what he has been and what he is becoming and, by a creatively imaginative act, to perceive himself as a part of nature and, perhaps, to recognise a god in himself. By form and pressure in his art, the supreme artist communicates the idea of form to mankind. An artist is not in the world for glory or for power; he is here to listen as well as to speak, that humanity may—not by him but through him—continually re-create itself.

42

D. L. MURRAY

MR. D. L. MURRAY joined the staff of "The Times" in 1920 and is now the Editor of "The Times Literary Supplement." He is a novelist in the great tradition of the English novel, and his books, which come at intervals of two or three years, are all major works, spacious in the grand style and manner.
For this occasion, he has written a short story of the Crimean War— a little pendant to that masterpiece of reconstruction "Trumpeter Sound!"

ONLY A SOJER!
A TALE OF THE SCUTARI HOSPITAL

WHEN Jem Hanson was hit in both legs by a shell from a Russian field battery while advancing with his regiment up the sunny slopes of the Alma on September 20th, 1854, he was picked up by the big-drummer, still wearing his leopard-skin, and one of the cornet-players. According to their untrained ideas of stretcher-bearing they carried him, streaming with blood, down to a farm-house by the river. Here the surgeons of the —th, in red-streaked aprons, laid him on a kitchen-table and without delay amputated his right foot, while four orderlies held him down—for he was uncommonly powerful even in his shattered condition—and a fifth did his best to stop his mouth. His other leg the surgeons bandaged in hope, and then took advantage of a lull in the arrival of cases to go outside for the solace of a cigar.

"What a brute!" said the senior. "Did you hear his language?"

"Foulest-mouthed ruffian I've met so far, even in the —th," answered his assistant. "I was surprised, sir, you didn't take action about it."

"Ah! well," the doctor shrugged his shoulders. "One must make allowances in a case like that. . . . Put it that the man was delirious and didn't know what he was saying. But it's a good answer, Williams, to those who say we ought to give these brutes that new drug, chloroform, for their operations."

"I don't quite understand, sir."

"It was the smart of the knife that saved him! The fury he got into, and the way he roused his reserves of strength to struggle and swear, were what kept him going. Render 'em unconscious, and they'll just perish of enfeeblement of the vital powers under their wounds. You see if they don't!"

Jem Hanson, meanwhile, was travelling in a requisitioned Tartar cart without springs down to a cove in the adjoining sea-shore, where on the bare timbers of a ship's boat he was taken to be piled with two or three hundred others on a transport that crossed the Black Sea to Scutari, the suburb of Constantinople. During the voyage he was the terror of the hospital orderlies

43

(ordinary soldiers detailed for this work for no special reason except that they might be convalescents themselves). He swore, he sang bawdy songs, he managed to get spirits from the sailors, and generally showed himself the toughest of what was known to be an exceptionally tough regiment, whose Colonel had written to his family when ordered to the front, " With the Russians before me and my own men behind me, I stand a poor chance of seeing England again! " Colonel —— was not on the sick transport to order Jem Hanson to be tied up to the triangle and receive another four dozen from the drummers, even if he had been in a state to have the " cat "; so, what with listening to his threats and blasphemies, and cleaning up messes on the stinking decks, and casting the many invalids who died overboard in sheets, the attendants were not sorry to take leave of Jem Hanson and his companions, and to see them carried up to the gaunt, yellow Barrack Hospital with its Oriental Towers standing amid the melancholy cypress trees of Scutari.

Jem was too weak to take notice of much during his first days in the hospital. Since the day, three years ago now, when he had enlisted in a pub near Scotland Yard, in a rage with himself and destiny, he had grown unused to comfort, consideration, and any but pipe-clay cleanliness—for most of the barracks in which he had been quartered were whitewashed sepulchres of diphtheria and typhoid. These three years, with the bullyings of the Sergeant-Major and the attentions of the drummers at the triangle, had turned a hot-tempered and ungovernable lad with no meanness in him into a sullen, sardonic brute, who would curse but never complain, and whose sole consolation was drink. The only thing that now drove Jem to the brooding verge of mutiny was that there seemed to be no means of getting spirits smuggled into the hospital. If he could have obtained rum, gin, or even beer, he would not have bothered much about the pain (which he would have been ashamed to acknowledge by as much as a wince or a sigh), or the cruel scraping of the coarse sheets, or the unappetising lumps of ration-meat, the only invalid diet, or the smell of the open cesspools under the building, or the minor, but lively, discomforts of his lot.

His deprivation did not promote equability of temper; and when one morning it was whispered along the thickly crowded wards, where the pallets were packed so closely together that a doctor or an orderly could hardly edge in between them, that in a day or two the patients might expect to have " nurses," Jem exploded in his worst style. Did they think he was a baby of such-and-such a kind ? Were they going to dress him in a bib and pinafore and give him a hymn-book and teach him to curtsey and say, " Yes, ma'am . . . no, ma'am " ? If any old woman came messing him about, he would (he intimated) suggest her proper destination.

Comrades in the ward glanced at each other askance from their hard bolsters. It was notorious in the —th that Jem Hanson was lacking in the rude chivalry towards the sex that persisted, despite all brutalisation, in most of his fellows. He seemed to have some dark rancour against them; the women of the garrison towns fled from him in the streets in terror; and once or twice he would have been knocked down by comrades who cared for the shreds of reputation the regiment still possessed, if they had had any hope of standing up to his whirling fists and belt.

" But you'll need to beyave yourse'f, cully! " expostulated a wounded

44

Hussar in the next bed to his. "These nusses are proper ladies . . . out o' the top-drawer, they are!"

"That's a good 'un!" snorted Jem. "Ladies a-comin' to look arter the likes of us! Likely, a'n't it? You know wot a sojer is—scum o' the earth. Why, they won't even let a man in uniform walk in their parks in Lunnon, and now you says they're a-goin' to come all the way out here among these cawfee-coloured Turks to nuss *us*! . . . I don't fink! . . . When I sees a lady a-comin' to smooth my downy piller with her lily-white 'and, I reckon I'll know wot to say to '*er*!"

But Jem Hanson did not seem to know exactly what to say to her when, a morning or two later, she arrived. She was a slender-looking creature, such as Jem might have broken with one blow of his fist, dressed plainly in black with a white lace cap, and had delicately chiselled features and eyes that seemed alight with a soft, steady flame. Her first words, after a polite " Good morning, Private Hanson," were, "Wouldn't you like a clean shirt? . . . Put Private Hanson down for a shirt immediately." And as the nurse who accompanied her made a note of the order, Jem found nothing to protest against. The shirt he was in had not been washed since he was picked up on the battlefield of the Alma, and the company he kept in it had been doing more to destroy his temper than any of his other sufferings, though no one before had noticed the fact, or thought it worth particular attention if they did. Meanwhile, with an " Excuse me!" the Lady had stooped down and deftly done something with his blankets that relieved the pain in his bandaged leg by about half. Then, with a smile and a little inclination of her slim neck, she went on to the next bed—and for the rest of that morning the men in the ward kept on asking Jem when he was going to tell the Lady where she ought to go.

It was probably this tactless chaffing that made Jem's temper so black by nightfall that when the little nurse who had accompanied the Lady came along the ward on some duty, he began to sing aloud the shocking song of " Sam Hall, the chimney-sweep," so that the poor girl blushed fierily and fled from the room, pursued by his hoarse laugh. Soon afterwards the other Lady came rustling in with a lamp in her hand, which she set down on a shelf while she busied herself with the task of emptying slops, which the meek little nurse had left unfinished when she fled. While the Lady was stooping under Jem's bed she said to him quietly, but with a quiver of her thin lips which he noticed in the lamp-rays, "Aren't you going to sing to *me*, Private Hanson?"; and when he glowered at her, she added, "Did you sing that song to frighten the Russians out of the Great Redoubt at the Alma?"

"The —th weren't at the Great Redoubt!" he growled; and before he knew how it had come about he was telling her briefly where he was and what he had done—it included killing six Russians in single combat, two with bullets, three with the bayonet, and one with his iron-shod boot, and it appeared to give him great satisfaction to dwell on it. Then he said abruptly, "You objecks to my singing . . . ma'am. Well, I'm only a sojer . . . and you didn't ought to be here to listen to it. You didn't ought to be doin' work like this at all. Cleanin' up arter chaps like us . . . it's no work for a lady. You've only yourse'f to thank!"

"You're quite wrong, Private Hanson," she answered. "We've all got *you* to thank. And a lady can always wait on a gentleman, especially when the gentleman wears the Queen's uniform. Now, are you going to take that arrowroot that Nurse Darcy brought you? Else I shall have to wait here till you do . . . and I'm really tired, Private Hanson."

"I'm not keepin' you," he muttered, but he obeyed noisily.

"Gentlemen wearin' the Queen's uniform!" he sneered after she had departed. "Hear that, you nawsty, common sojers!"

A few days later the surgeon in charge of the ward, after examining Jem's remaining foot, looked grim and said bluntly,

"Look here, my man; you must brace yourself to have this foot off . . . it's your only chance."

Jem braced himself instead to say, "I objecks!"

"Object!" exclaimed the scandalised doctor. "Stuff and nonsense! I never heard such a thing! Object, indeed! I'll operate this afternoon."

"I'm entitled," snarled Jem, "to say whether I'll have a limb ampytated or not, and I say I won't. . . . For why? 'Cos one wooden leg I can hop about on, and two I'm . . . blessed . . . if I can!"

"You obstinate brute!" said the doctor, gritting his teeth. "If I could only put you where you ought to be——"

The Lady interrupted with a spark in each of her normally pale cheeks. "I've seen worse wounds than this heal with careful dressing, Doctor," she said.

"You can't do it, ma'am!" said the doctor curtly.

"It must be done!" she answered with a steady look. But Jem could see that the light in her eyes had risen to a burning flame.

At the end of her round with the surgeon she came back to Jem's bedside, demurely enough, but with still a spark, he could see, flashing in her eyes. "Well, Private Hanson," she said, "you'll have to let me look after that foot of yours now I've saved it. I'll have you moved into the little ward near my room."

A reluctant smile broke over Jem's wasted face. "Got a will o' your own, haven't you?" he said. "You stood up to old Sawbones good and proper. Not so precious namby-pamby, you a'n't, neither!"

"You and I have got to obey Doctor Maclagan," she answered, pursing her mouth up primly, though her eyes were still unsubdued. "He's our superior officer, and he agrees to give your foot another chance."

"Did you obey your supeerior orf'cer, miss . . . ma'am . . . yesterday when you broke open that store with a hatchet?" he demanded, grinning.

"Who tells you these stories?" she asked him.

Jem was removed to a small room opening out of a larger ward near the Lady-in-Chief's own room, where she could attend personally to him and a couple of other cases she had her eye on. One of these got well enough to be discharged a week or so later; the other had a sudden relapse and died, so that Jem had a private room, a privilege he hardly appreciated, especially as he was left twenty-four hours with the dead man, owing to some regulation which delayed his burial. Anyhow, he made private signals with the male orderly who came in to sweep his room, and that night when the Lady came to see how he was she found him feverish and tossing on his bed. She put down her lamp to examine him in spite of his thick-voiced protests.

"Who brought you spirits?" she demanded in a low, vibrant voice. "Or, no, that can wait . . . I can guess. *Why* did you persuade that orderly to bring you spirits? Don't you know if you get a temperature like this, it may kill you? At the least, the chance of your wound healing will become almost none."

"How do you expect a sojer to live without his drink?" mumbled Jem ferociously.

She fetched him a sedative draught, and when he had taken it and spoke more clearly she sat down on a chair by the bedside and asked him, "Why can't a soldier live without his drink, Private Hanson?"

"It's a habit. What other way have we o' passing the time?"

"You have no other recreation?"

"Us? What can we do? Where can we go? Who wants us? We're only sojers—the sweepings of the gaols they call us. D'you think we gits many invitations to perlite parties and balls? . . . D'you think a man would 'list except to fergit? And what is there but the drink that can help him to fergit half so quick?"

"If you'll take my word for it, Private Hanson, you can't get out of any trouble in this life by trying to smother it. You must drag it up and look it in the face. . . . What were you before you joined the Army? A footman?"

"How the devil did you know that?—axing your pardon, ma'am."

"By the way you handled the dishes on your dinner-tray. Why did you 'list? Horse-racing . . . pilfering . . . or a young woman?"

"The last, if you want to know!" he snarled. "What is it but wimmen makes all the trouble in the world? And if you'll listen to me just a few minutes, I'll tell you a story that may make you understand why I'm not preecisely an agreeable character. Will you? I know you think I'm just a drunken sweep. . . . I'd like you to know I'm not without excuse!"

"Ah! I don't suppose Sam Hall would care *what* I thought of him."

"*I* do," said Jem gruffly. "I don't deny I was a wild young chap—too wild for livery, so the butler used to say at our house, 12A Berkeley Square— maybe you've passed it?"

"Lord Marborough's? I've called there; I know him quite well."

"I never saw you there! But, Lord above! to think as you should be willin' to sit here and talk to me! Why do you do it?"

"Never mind that now. Tell me your story. Who was she?"

"Daughter of Manby, feller wot kept a newspaper and 'baccy shop in Shepherd's Market."

"The most beautiful girl in the West End, and not like any of the others in that street, because she wasn't common."

"That's her very picture! But, Lord, ma'am, did you know Madge too?"

"No. But I think I know *you* a little, Private Hanson! Well?"

"Well, I was s'posed to be a good-lookin' chap in those days—it seems ages ago, though only three years really. And it don't matter now, as I shan't be a good-looking chap, with a wooden peg waitin' for me! Hows'ever, after a bit Madge was willin' to walk out with me. There was a feller next door, Joseph Pilkington, son of a corn-chandler, smooth-lookin', buttery, psalm-singin' chaps, both of 'em, who'd been courtin' her; but arter she met me she hadn't an eye for him. Now, I couldn't hope to make *you* understand, ma'am,

47

how I felt for Madge. I couldn't a'kept away from her—and yet I felt I was no good to her. Not that I meant her any harm; no one could look at her and dream of anything o' that sort. But I knew I was a chap without prospecks. I wasn't the sort that saves and is able to marry and settle down. I couldn't stop bettin' at the pub at the corner of the Market, and though I warn't a real drinker *then*, I used to get elewated, like, sometimes, and p'raps have a fight. The housekeeper warned me about it once, when I come on guar—on duty in the morning with a black eye."

" A black eye and powder certainly are too striking together." The Lady laughed aloud.

" That's gospel! " Jem Hanson grinned responsively. " Well, so it was. I went on walkin' out with Madge, and I could feel she was sweet on me, and yet I didn't dare to ask her to share her life with a rowdy feller like I was."

" You thought she preferred the buttery chap ? "

" Well, he was more genteel, wasn't he ? . . . Still she needn't have treated me the way she did! " His face and tone grew sombre. " I was struggling hard to break myself of these wild ways, so's to be a bit more worthy of her (as I then thought of her), and, believe me, it was a sore fight; it was pull baker, pull devil—axin' your pardon again for the word; and she *knew* all she meant to me, and all I was tryin' to do, though I never made real love to her for the reason I gave you. What happens ? I see her one fine spring evening paradin' past our house in the Square on the arm o' this Jos Pilkington —reckon she s'posed I'd be cleanin' silver or somethink down in the basement and not see her. But I warn't! " His voice grew thunderous. " I'd got an extry evenin' leave, and I was standin' at the area door in my goin'-out clothes ready to start and pop round and surprise her in the shop. I was up them steps like a lamp-lighter, catches her and her fancy boy in a side-street nearby, and I *did* surprise her, and him too! I fair battered him, and when the peelers come runnin' I was that mad I bonnets one of 'em with his own top-hat! Arter that I knew I was done for—assaultin' of the p'leece! I ran and ran and dodged 'em, and hid all that night in the Adelphi Arches; and in the morning I wentures out to get suthin' at a pub down by Scotland Yard, and that's where I meets the recruiting sergeant. I was good for nothink any longer, and so I 'listed; and they done nothink since to make me feel I was any better, by G——! However, they'll all acknowledge now I'm pretty hard; there a'n't a man in the battalion as dare fight me, not with one hand tied behind my back—and not a corporal as don't look the other way when I'm in one o' my black moods. They say it takes the Sergeant-Major *and* the Colonel to deal with me at those times! As for wimmin, the pretty-faced deceivers . . . if ever I trust another of 'em . . .! "

" Yet you have trusted me . . . haven't you . . . with your story ? "

Jem Hanson leaned back on his pillow and was silent; he looked exhausted and yet somehow relieved. " You're diff'rent," he said presently, " and I don't understand it. If I didn't wish to be respeckful to you, ma'am, I should say you was crazy . . . sittin' talkin' to a common sojer, just as if he was one o' your gentlemen! "

" You *are* one of my gentlemen, as I told you the day we met. And there are plenty more of you in the ranks."

FROM THE ORIGINAL BY EDMUND DULAC

" It is the evil things that we shall be fighting against "

" Gentlemen ? Who ever heard of a gentleman joining the Army, 'cept a few broken gamblers and swindlers ? "

" What about the officers, then ? "

" Officers ? What have we in common with them ? "

" Many things ! The risk's the same . . . the hardship's the same . . . wounds hurt as much . . . your limbs are as precious to you as theirs to them . . . death lays you side by side—and you all wear the same coat, the Queen's. That's my view of it, Private Hanson."

" Then that's why you come and nuss us pore chaps ? 'Tain't nacheral, though."

" The time is coming when it will seem natural to everyone, high and low, in our land ! "

" Bring that about, and you'll a' done something, ma'am ! "

" No. I shan't have done it. *You'll* have done it. You were helping to bring it about when you fought like six lions by the Alma, and again when you bore your amputation without a groan."

" Not without langwidge ! " He grinned.

" Yet you never used language to me ? "

" I've said, you're diff'rent. Know what I'd like ?—to be able to go back into the ranks and explain all this to the lads. I'd teach 'em what wearin' the Queen's uniform means—or bash their silly heads in ! "

A month later Private Hanson was invalided out of the Army with a small pension by a Medical Board and put under orders to return to England on the next empty transport making the voyage home. Coming out of the Board, he was astounded to receive a letter with a London post-mark. . . .

That night the Lady-in-Chief was sitting in her little room writing a long letter to her friend the Secretary at War. She had also conducted a long and acrimonious dispute with the two chief officers of the Army Medical Service, who had both left her sizzling with repressed fury; made an inventory of the hospital linen; answered by letter twelve applications from young ladies and gentlemen of breeding in England, asking to be allowed to come out and help her; settled three disputes among nurses of varying religious denominations in the branch hospitals under her jurisdiction in Constantinople and the Crimea . . . and was feeling almost tired.

Yet when a scandalised sister appeared and announced that Private Hanson asked to see her, she replied calmly, " Oh yes. Let him come in. He starts for England tomorrow."

Jem Hanson stumped in with a face, newly shaven, that shone with light. " You look fit and well, Jem," she said with her subtle smile.

" Well, arter all you done for me, ma'am ! "

" I only helped to cure that foot of yours. It was my duty as a nurse."

" Oh ? Then maybe you don't know what's in this letter ? "

" Has she written ? " The Lady's eyes lit up with real pleasure. " And said the right thing ? I thought she would ! "

" I still don't understand ! " Jem Hanson twisted the letter in his fingers. " Madge says here that you wrote to her about me—that she's been broken-hearted ever since I went for a sojer, not knowing where to find me . . . that she only went about with that chap because I wouldn't ask her to marry me, and she couldn't stand it and wanted to make me jealous. . . . Who'd a believed it ? But how could you tell, ma'am, that the little wretch had loved me all the time ? "

The Lady-in-Chief looked at him with a slightly melancholy smile. " I suppose one woman can understand another ? Your Madge acted as, I dare say, I should have done . . . in her place."

" *You* in her place, ma'am! " Jem laughed.

" Well, I wouldn't have preferred the buttery, psalm-singing fellow, and I didn't believe she could have done; that's all."

" Ah, ma'am, when the time comes for you to choose a husband of your own . . . ! "

She interrupted, " Jem, do you see all these letters I must answer before I go to bed ? "

" I understand. I'm encroaching. It's a shame to waste your time like this."

" Oh! you don't waste my time, Jem. But do you suppose I am ever likely to have time . . . for what you just suggested, with so many silly fellows like you who have to be stood on their feet, because they can't help themselves ? Here's General Brown writes to me that I ' spoil the brutes! ' and shan't get any thanks for it."

" A man can be truly grateful, ma'am, though he is only a sojer! "

" I thought we'd agreed, Jem, never to use that phrase again," said Florence Nightingale.

T. S. ELIOT

*The publication of MR. T. S. ELIOT'S "The Waste Land"
had as startling and decisive effect on English poetry as had the
"Lyrical Ballads." His more recent play, "Murder in the
Cathedral," had a similar impact upon the theatre. Quite lately
he has confounded and delighted us with a collection of poems
about cats. It is in such light-hearted vein that he is represented
in these present verses.*

THE MARCHING SONG OF THE POLLICLE DOGS

THERE are dogs out of every nation,
  The Irish, the Welsh and the Dane;
  The Russian, the Dutch, the Dalmatian,
And even from China and Spain;
The Poodle, the Pom, the Alsatian
  And the mastiff who walks on a chain.
And to those that are frisky and frollical
  Let my meaning be perfectly plain:
That my name it is Little Tom Pollicle—
  And you'd better not do it again.

There are dogs that are sniffy and curious,
  There are dogs that are drowsy and dumb;
There are dogs that are sleeky and spurious,
  There are dogs that are mimsy and mum.
There are dogs that are frantic and furious—
  And I say of such: let 'em all come.
And to those that are rowdy and rollical
  Let my meaning be perfectly plain:
That my name it is Little Tom Pollicle—
  And you'd better not do it again.

51

There are dogs that are frowsy and frumpious,
　　There are dogs that are freaky and frail;
There are dogs that are growly and grumpious,
　　There are dogs that are puny and pale.
But I say, if you're surly and scrumpious,
　　Just you tread on the tip of my tail!
For my meaning is not amphibolical
　　And I'd like it to be very plain
That my name it is Little Tom Pollicle—
　　And you'd better not do it again.

For our motto is still *cave canem*—
　　That's the cry of the Pollicle Clan,
And our words we'll not stop to explain 'em,
　　But bark 'em as loud as we can.
For the way to show how you disdain 'em
　　Is to bark at dog, devil and man.
And be ye the most diabolical
　　Of what diabolic may be—
Yet my name it is Little Tom Pollicle,
　　And WHA MAUN MEDDLE WI' ME ?

T. S. ELIOT

BILLY M'CAW: THE REMARKABLE PARROT

OH, how well I remember the old Bull and Bush,
   Where we used to go down of a Sattaday night—
     Where, when anythink happened, it come with a rush,
   For the boss, Mr. Clark, he was very polite;
And what with the Station it being so near,
And what with the water got into the beer
   (There was two kinds of beer, the thick and the clear)
A very nice House it was.   Oh dear !
I'll never forget it.   From basement to garret
A very nice House.   Ah, but it was the parret—
The parret, the parret named Billy M'Caw,
   That brought all those folk to the bar.
   Ah! he was the Life of the bar.
Of a Sattaday night, we was all feeling bright,
And Lily La Rose—the Barmaid that was—
She'd say: " Billy!
             Billy M'Caw!
Come give us a dance on the bar! "
   And Billy would dance on the bar.

Lily, she was a girl what had brains in her head;
She wouldn't have nothink, no not that much said.
If it come to an argument, or a dispute,
She'd settle it offhand with the toe of her boot
   Or as likely as not put her fist through your eye.
But when we was thirsty, and just a bit sad,
Or when we was happy, and just a bit dry,
She would rap on the bar with that corkscrew she had
And say: " Billy!
             Billy M'Caw!
Come give us a tune on your pastoral flute! "
   And Billy'd strike up on his pastoral flute.

And then we'd feel balmy, in each eye a tear,
And emotion would make us all order more beer—
For the way that Bird played, with his Robin Adairs,
And his All in the Downs, and his Wapping Old Stairs,
Would bring tears to the eyes of a donkey, it would.
There was no use of saying that Bird wasn't good.
And when we was feeling exceedingly tearful,
Then Lily would say: " Now, let's have something cheerful!
Billy!
     Billy M'Caw!
Come give us a tune on your moley guitar! "
 And Billy'd strike up on his moley guitar.

Oh, how well I remember the old Bull and Bush
 Where the folk came from near and from far.
A very nice House. From basement to garret
A very nice House. Ah but it was the parret,
 The parret, the parret named Billy M'Caw,
Who brought all those folk to the bar.
 Ah, he was the Life of the bar.

H. M. TOMLINSON

MR. H. M. TOMLINSON has expressed for us in his stories, in a way that everyone can understand, the poetry of ships and of the sea. Perhaps his most widely read books of all are " Gallions Reach " and " London River," but there are many who think that his finest achievement is " All Our Yesterdays."

PORTS OF CALL

ON a November evening, by the patchy glare of spotlights aloft, the steamer *Kezia* was finishing her lading in a Glasgow dock. She was the only ship in a spacious basin, and she looked smaller than her tonnage.

Robin, as he neared her, was surprised. So this was to be his home for a spell! He was not used to the sort of sea-carrier which bears the bulk of commerce between nations, and so had expected a more important ship. He was also pleased. There was no pretension whatever about this little steamer. It was cheering, her confident activity in the midst of a wide world threatening with the latest powers of ingenious and aggressive mankind. She was indifferent to all adverse chances, and kept on with the job. This looked like life near the bone.

He paused to appreciate her. To make his first voyage to the Levant and the Black Sea in this little thing was something like a venture. He knew great liners, but the *Kezia's* plain iron body, her deck nearly at the level of the quay, was novel. She could not be called gracious, especially in a wintry drizzle, but she pleased him, for he was impatient of gloss and ornament to life. It was false. He pushed away deceitful romance even in art and books, as this generation does, which grew up amid the ruin by gunfire of tradition and accepted good. He watched the last items of the cargo going inboard— gas-pipes, galvanised-iron buckets in long nests, and kegs of paint and grease— as if he saw the stark truth, and accepted it. The rough men at work, handling unconcerned the unaccommodating bulges and angles of cargo, careless of the weather and of outsiders who got in their way, were as cheering as a bracer. No masquerade about them. No politeness.

Mr. Cary, his elder and companion, and the only other passenger, paused because Robin had stopped to look on, and not because he, too, enjoyed the sight of a parcel of iron pails hoisted aloft over a ship's hatchway under a livid sky. He nodded without conviction when Robin exclaimed that there was the stuff for artists to paint, and poets to sing.

Perhaps it is, thought Mr. Cary. Very likely it is. Daffodils which take the winds of March with beauty have joined crinolines and warming-pans,

55

since men have turned from the slow rhythm of the seasons to be wholly absorbed in the fascinating speed of engines. And he was used to this sort of scene. He was not elated. He had noticed, and more than once, that when he was about to put to sea it was winter, rough goods were going into the holds, and the glass falling. It was falling tonight. He had crossed the Bay in freighters before, and the prospect of doing it again in that ship had not much fun in it. Still, there was something to be said for Robin's view of it all. A lot to be said for it. It did exemplify this age. It was gaunt and hard, and its artificial glare and shadows were pitiless in their extremes. The confession must be made. This picture was a clear representation of things as they are.

But there was something else in the scene, and young friend Robin, sensitive artist though he was, had not noticed it. It was there only for an elder traveller. This smell on the quayside of wooden packages, raw and damp, and of the litter of wet straw, and of whiffs of warm steam from loudly intermittent winches, was memorable. It was consoling, in a queer way. It was home-like. It came from the past as much as from the moment. It smelled of other voyages. It peopled the twilight for him with messmates, whose voyaging was over now, over long ago, when he was as young as Robin, and outward bound, and the outlook as inclement as this.

Weren't they the better days? He thought they were. That was sentimentality, of course—and how quick Robin would be to point it out!—but Mr. Cary was sure they were better. Anyhow, whatever the barometer said then, and however strange a new ship, in those days you did not put to sea under a vague threat that wilted the spirit—there were no mutterings of never-ending war hanging about in the offing. You never had to think of that. Nor of passports. There were no formalities with officials. You just went, if you felt like it, and no questions asked.

Yes, no doubt about it, they were the days. Nobody cared then whether you were bound for Huelva or Zion. That was your affair. What had happened to this blessed planet since those years? That shadow of a seaman at the bulwarks of the *Kezia*, directing the hoisting of an awkward piece, and the smells, and the rain, and the undertone of a gutter discharging into the dock, when it was not silenced by another shattering roar from a winch, were like a phase of the long ago returned. It was lucky for young Robin he knew nothing of what he could not hear and see; no nostalgia for him; no useless regrets; no romance through the association of past and present; no mockery, by things as they are, of old and long-cherished illusions. . . .

Illusions? Was that all they were, dreams? But if the dream of fellowship is deceptive; if reverie, with its faith in the loveliness of innocence, and in values not to be expressed except by the mind at its best; if such are only moods of deceptive self-indulgence, then of what help was the transient reality of rough cargo going into a tramp steamer under electric flares on a wet night? Robin was right enough in his insistence on facts, and no nonsense about them. Yet what good is art, if it does not give with the thrill of appearance the impression of continuity in time without end?

"I wish," exclaimed Robin, "I could render that light on those dim shapes!"

"Keep at it," said Cary. "Never give up. Light is the stuff to throw on indefinite shapes."

56

Robin smiled, but kept it to himself. He understood. Trust these old 'uns, who lost all their dreams in that war, to hold on to just one tiny feather of mysticism, as a souvenir! Old Cary would stick to his last bit of Plato if the heavens fell. It was all he had now. One ought not to smile at it; anyhow, not noticeably.

But Cary was well aware of Robin's reservation. Naturally, he was an old dodderer. He knew that. Young people regard their elders with the silent contempt they deserve. Not always silent, either. What else was to be expected? It was the mistakes of their teachers and leaders that had at last presented youngsters with an anarchic world in which they must build anew, and with no principles to go upon that they had not learned to distrust; all that was left to them for guidance was self and its interest—just as it was in the beginning, when everybody lived in caves! No common bond for them anywhere now, except in some preposterous uniform or another. So how could reconciliation ever come about? Yet it would have to be found, if things were to go on and growth to be made. It would have to be. Until Robin and he agreed about first things, then anarchy must reign.

That night in his bunk Cary, while waiting for sleep, was assured that the sea at least was keeping to its old ways. No change there. The sea was in a rough temper. He did not disapprove. He felt the *Kezia* sinking head-first into a trough, felt her heart beating wildly as the up-ended screw raced. Now she was going to catch it! Then a sea crashed on the bulkhead of his cabin, which looked forward. He could hear the cataracts about the gear outside. But he relished it. By her buoyancy and rhythm he knew she was all right. She was used to it, this little thing. Here was the simple life again, just as Robin admired it, and with no frills. But how was Robin enjoying the traditional old sea? Yet at once Cary saw a difficulty there. Though the two of them were in the same ship, they would make different voyages. Though they shared the same daylight, they would see different things. The thing seen is never the same for two people. There is a grave disparity between old and young these days. And even the ancient sea, which never changes, could not bring reconciliation.

That was plain enough next morning, in their first easy encounters with the men of the ship. They accepted Robin at once, on level terms, as though he were one of themselves; and it gratified Cary to notice it. They knew their own kind. They were more distant with the older man; he was not of their era. Robin merged with the ship's company before there had been time enough to learn properly his way about the ship. There on the bridge was Robin already, in happy converse with the chief officer, whose soiled working jacket bore a war decoration, which Cary had noticed the night before, a decoration never given to a sailor unless he has earned it in a signal way. It was comforting to know there was such a seaman aboard, but it was long odds that Robin had not so much as remarked that decoration. The pair of them, nevertheless, were happy up there on the windward side of the bridge, no doubt over one of the world's more recent jokes.

Robin said he was enjoying it. It was a brave new world to him. He hung on to the dodger, facing the brilliance and boisterousness ahead. The light was bright and hard. It reflected from the oilskins of the men, from the polish of the tarpaulins covering the hatches, for her head was soaring like a balloon over the seas, and flights of spray raked her, as radiant as sheets of fire in the level morning light. Just the aspect of things to accord with the fighting spirit of a rebellious young heart.

" This is a promising start," he called cheerfully to Cary.

" The same old game," said Cary.

" Old? Why, this was born only ten minutes ago. That's the right idea, isn't it? "

" Quite. New each morning, yet older than Asia."

They crouched low to a burst of water. Robin laughed. " Have it your own way. I think it looks like the first morning of all. Things not settled down yet. We've got to go through it. Look at that! "

They looked. A mile to port was a schooner. She had been veiled and dim. But in tacking she caught a ray invisible to them. She became more glorious than a ship ever is. As she heeled, her very body flashed gold.

" She's Argo," said Cary. He was laughing now.

" What an idea! " cried Robin.

" But don't try to present it," he was advised.

" Why not ? "

" Because who would believe it? "

" There she is. We see her."

" We don't. We see the old, old story. Hardly anyone ever believes the shining image which shows when the hour is right, when we are above all doubts."

Robin did not answer. It was a puzzle. Still, it was worth making a voyage to see just that. That schooner out there was certainly a rum aspect of reality, as if for a moment an impossible light discovered her, and she was transfigured; became the image of the original ship in a wild ocean men were daring for the first time. And that, of course, was plumb silly. To represent that ship as he saw her then, as if she were a burst of splendid music, would be a lie, after all. Her own men would not recognise her. He admitted that aloud, regretfully.

" Only the heroes would know her," suggested Cary.

Robin made a gesture of impatience.

Cary was soon to see that Robin's impatience was justified. They were then across the Bay. There to port was Finisterre. The air was mild. The sunset had amber clouds. The shapes of distant ships were black on a clear horizon, with a lucent western wall behind them. Spain was a high tumbled mass of purple. The famous cape was a purple whale, with a diamond flashing in its head. Cary was sitting on a bunker hatch, cutting cake tobacco. He was satisfied to be at sea again. Not much was changed in sunrise and sunset. One could escape at sea into an earlier period of the earth.

Robin came along. He stopped by the hatch, gazing at Finisterre. Cary thought of reminding his friend that Corunna was round that corner over there. The Tagus was a little further south, from which Philip's Armada sailed. That Iberian coast, for the English, was occult with momentous events that are past. They would pass Cape St. Vincent tomorrow, and see Trafalgar. But Cary said nothing about it, on second thoughts. Young people are weary of that sort of history, and with good reason. Let the dead past bury its dead.

" Japan is threatening us," said Robin at last.

58

"What's that?"

"I said Tokyo is breathing fire and slaughter."

"What do you mean—who said so?"

"Don't know his name—news just through—the wireless."

So that was it. Cary had forgotten that every cabin in a ship may now have an ear open to all the talk of the round globe.

Robin went on. He amplified his information. Germany was still cutting up rough. Rome was severe. There had been floods in the Midlands; and the men of the *Kezia* were now sharing the football pool—the results of today's matches had just arrived.

Cary made no comment. He went on slicing tobacco under the light of a full moon. Robin strolled off, showing no surprise whatever in a modern marvel which allows a ship at sea to get all the gossip that is going about. One used to go to sea for solitude, mused Cary. But now look at it! Our cleverness has abolished it even from mid-ocean. You hear the gibbering wherever you are. Once, when you took your departure from the Lizard Light, there was no more news except what was made in the ship, till you arrived out. You had a lucky chance to hear from yourself for once. He had wondered, like a fool, why the eager talk at the mess-table had resembled the headlines in a sensational newspaper; now he knew.

Well, the sea was no different, and there was the same old moon the Phœnicians saw when they boldly ventured this way; but the *Kezia* was not only in another age, she was in another world. And here he was, making only his first voyage in it, with all to learn. He was a beginner again. So was it surprising that Robin paid little attention to old values and virtues? Were they applicable, in this latest phase of the liveliness of men? It might be possible that those values were really quite useless. The only good today is the successful use of power to gain more power.

Their first port of call was Casablanca. It was Robin's first view of a coast of Africa. They both watched the tawny slopes with white cubes of houses dotted about, and sniffed the smell of herbs on an off-shore wind. For a space, it must have looked the same to them as it did to Elizabethan seamen. The port appeared, and they were soon ashore. Then they might have been in France; and the French are such subduing engineers. The harbour and its works of concrete and steel was daunting in its extent and efficiency. Robin was a little puzzled by this geometrical appearance of Africa. They sat at a metal table in the thin shade of a mimosa, outside a brand-new café, viewing the modern flats opposite. Those flats might have been anywhere, from the Marylebone Road to Montevideo. Robin expressed faint surprise. Call this Africa!

"It used to be," said Cary. "It was when I first voyaged this way."

"What, this place?"

"This place. It was only a mosque and an Arab village. It had nothing but goats, agriculture, ophthalmia, and the Koran."

"It has a lot more now. It must surprise the Arabs."

"It surprises us."

"Anyhow, ophthalmia has been civilised out of it."

"Has it? We'll go into the old quarters, presently, and you shall see for yourself, if you think you can face it."

59

Cary refrained, as the day was so good and the wine so pleasant, from pointing out to Robin that it is misleading to confuse change with progress, especially as change is reducing the coasts in all seas to a uniform likeness, from San Francisco to Suez.

Next day the *Kezia* was in the Mediterranean. At sunset there was an unusual cloud to the north, which Robin stood to admire. That cloud saw the sun long after the sea was night. Cary did not discuss it, though he also admired. It was useless to talk of that cloud, after the concrete of Casablanca, for it was only light on the snows of the Sierra Nevada. The Alhambra was there. Better leave romance in abeyance. The Alhambra might have ceased to exist, as business in Spain continued to be so remarkably brisk.

Land was out of sight in the morning, till Algeria was sighted. The *Kezia* was alone. Robin and Cary stood on the forecastle head, both in agreement about one thing. It was a place cluttered up, the eyes of the ship, with rusty and greasy gear. The seams of the wooden deck oozed blobs of tar, for the day was bright and the sun direct. Their standing-room had the smell of the flotsam on a hot strand, and the ship's head was buoyant over swells that would have been invisible, except that the turquoise plain before them had purple shadows.

"There is nothing much the matter with the earth as God made it," admitted Robin, looking to Algeria, which was only tinctured gossamer to the south-east. "There's a turtle—look, you can just see his nose!"

The turtle sensed the wash from the ship's stem, and dived. It removed its trifling imperfection from the polish of the sea. Nothing had appeared that day to remind them that other men were near, except an aeroplane, which hung about them a little too long, and a ship of war in the distance, when the anxious officer of the watch sent for the captain, because one never knows, these days. But their dubiety soon vanished, like the turtle.

Cary noted the destroyer fade, like a ghost, become merely a smear of vapour. There was, he agreed then, not a lot to complain of in the earth, the way it was made. As to its unpleasant surprises, we had added most of them. Our additions to the look of the earth all originated in this sea, too, he told Robin. Here was the beginning of copper and iron weapons, which resulted in the foundation of the State, as we know it.

"But of art, too," added Robin. "Don't forget that. Don't forget Greece, because we're going there. I suppose you know Athens?"

"No, I've always dodged it."

"What? Cut out the Parthenon? Don't say you did that!"

"Yes, I always have. I didn't want to be disappointed."

"Well, aren't you a nice one! And to be always reminding me of the tradition, too!"

"Well, let us own up to it! You know as well as I do that keeping faith these years is about as easy as keeping a candle alight in a gale. I've been watching things longer than you. That is why I dodged Athens. I wanted to keep the illusion, if I could. But I shall see it this voyage, as you happen to be with me, in support."

Before Greece could be reached a sirocco met the *Kezia*, to show them what the Mediterranean could do when it tried. Sea and sky became one grey welter, in which nothing was sighted except an Italian transport rolling gunwales under with a deck-load of aeroplanes. Robin watched nervously the labouring Italian, for she came unpleasantly close, with her up-to-date freight.

"This is not the prelude to Helicon that I expected," he confessed, in his shaking tarpaulins.

"Then read tonight the twenty-seventh chapter of the Acts of the Apostles. It will give you a better understanding of St. Paul. I'll lend you the book, if you haven't got it, and I don't suppose you have."

Yet morning came still and fair, as if the sea were all innocence. It was lustrous. The Ionian might have been trying to accord with the best words of its poets, when the *Kezia* had Kephalonia in sight, and Robin fondly hoped that he could make out Ithaca. Cary, too, hoped so. He said it was a conjuration. If afterwards they met with disappointment, there at that instant stood Hellas. It was no legend. They had seen it. While they still were conning it, the ship's Cockney steward came to stand with them. He leaned on the bulwarks, looking to the home of Odysseus. Then he began to tell them a tale or two of Greece, for he had often landed there, and what he said would have surprised Homer. He freely explained things that scholars would have been astonished to learn. The day remained fair, and there was Ithaca before them, like an impression, faintly remembered, of what was lovely but is far. The steward, having related some facts, briskly left them.

"I wish," muttered Robin, "he had not said that."

"He told us the truth, I suppose," said Cary, "as well as he knows it. There's your realist for you."

Their steamer put into the shore of Achaia, opposite the Bay of Lepanto. She was soon out again, and continued along the Gulf of Corinth. The *Kezia* was trivial beneath a high coast close to either beam, and the chart for navigating in those waters was alive with names such as Delphi, Helicon, Eleusis, Salamis. What is there to say about that? There is no more to be said about it. The two travellers were silent. The superb shores easily maintained the tradition. It was morning again when their ship rounded the isle of Salamis, and docked at Piræus.

Cary and Robin landed on the threshold of Athens, which was of concrete. Overside began to hurtle, without wasting time, the gas-pipes, drums of oil and paint, from England. Piræus was cabarets and boarding-houses for sea-men, the stalls of money-changers, and cheap shops, all looking across a tangle of tram-lines and mooring-ropes to a fishing fleet. It did not detain them. It was a musky and vivacious scene, but no different from what may be found all round the Mediterranean.

They boarded a slick electric train for Athens. They did not expect much. They began to expect less as they passed through a wide aridity: stucco houses, goats tethered to dust heaps, and shabby palms without end. Probably, Cary imagined, it was too late in life, or too late in history, to see Athens. He was resigned. He was trying to decipher a Greek advertisement when Robin startled him with a cry of wonder. Robin was staring out of the win-dow and up. Above the stucco and the factory stacks, the speed of the train allowed Cary a glimpse, only that—he hardly believed it—of the phantom of a temple in the very blue of the sky, as though it were a celestial sign. Did he see it? It surely was there?

61

Neither spoke. They desired to know more now. They were impatient for the next stop, where they alighted. And there was Athens about them, yet no sign of that temple anywhere. Not a trace. Quite otherwise. It seemed that their ship's steward, with his modern fables, was about right. Nothing but streets with sidewalks from which most of the paving was missing. The shops of the butchers evidently put most of their faith in offal. Dealers in furniture displayed wares that would have been refused at home by the keepers of seaside lodgings. Athens markets betrayed the fact that life there had receded to a low ebb. Pericles, evidently, was dead.

They hailed a taxi. They judged they had better get this over, and then away back to the ship. "This is what I was always afraid of," Cary was saying, when the cab stopped at the foot of some ruins, to which a neatly railed path ascended. Up they climbed, till they stood on the Acropolis.

It had also begun to rain. The high surrounding hills were dark and unpromising. Robin surveyed slowly the elevated scene, with its ruins and tumbled stones. "I'm glad of this drizzle," he said. He really looked pleased. "It gives us the place to ourselves."

That was true. Nobody else was about. They wandered off exploring, and separately. The rain, which was warm and gentle, might have been only the precipitation of silence. Against the slaty sky the massive colonnades of the Parthenon strangely glowed, as if ancient fire was inextinguishable in the heart of their marble. Those columns dilated with their original fervour. The temple pavements were shining, as though the one to whom the abandoned courts were dedicated had left in them the virtue of her original light. She went long ago, but it had not yet failed.

Cary, at length, looked round for Robin. Where was he? There was much to be said, but no way of saying it. Words can spoil everything. An important experience transcends expression. It is a confirmation, which must remain a secret. Where was Robin? Ah! There he came. And how happy he looked! Better not ask him anything. He might know little and care less of the glory that was Greece, but to see those courts, though in the rain, was to see mind in a manifestation beyond all the scholars could tell us. Once, man did this. He had this in him. So the place was for everybody. It was for the meek at heart as well as for the wise and important. It was majesty itself, on a high throne, silent and assured of lasting power, admonishing the spread of a modern and amorphous city.

Robin came and stood beside Cary, but had nothing to say. The rain had ceased now. The sun, for a minute, before it sank below the western hills, peered over the ramparts, through a break in the nimbus. The sun and the temple looked across at each other, from above the world, familiars in a place apart. The courts were fired. A pair of tortoiseshell butterflies sported through the glowing colonnades. A raven stood at the base of a honey-coloured column, unnaturally black and salient.

The two travellers descended from the temple, and turned, to see it for the last time. A falcon floated from its cornice, swooped and soared, as aerial as the masonry. Robin did not move. He stared. Cary had to touch him to bring him round. Then he flung out an arm, in a gesture that was the same as Cary's secret thought.

A. A. MILNE

MR. A. A. MILNE: Wherever there is a nursery there is a well-thumbed copy of " When We Were Very Young," and " Winnie-the-Pooh " has his corner. Theatre-goers know Mr. Milne equally well as the author of " Mr. Pim Passes By," " The Dover Road," " Michael and Mary," and many other successful plays.

THE GENERAL TAKES OFF HIS HELMET
(A NOTE FROM AN EARLIER WAR)

SCENE: *The tent of* HANNIBAL *outside Saguntum.*
It is the 237th day of the siege.
HANNIBAL, *who has been reviewing some of his army, strides into the tent, followed by* MALCHUS, *his A.D.C. As soon as he is in, he begins to pull off his helmet—a magnificent affair of gold and feathers.*

HANNIBAL: I *hate* these helmets! Ye gods, how I *hate* these helmets! (*It comes off.*)

MALCHUS (*soothingly*): It's a hot day for helmets, anyhow, sir. (*He takes off his own, and puts them both down.*)

HANNIBAL: *You've* nothing to complain of. Look at the size of your helmet compared with mine. (*He takes off his sword-belt.*)

MALCHUS: True, O Hannibal, but then look at the size of your brain compared with mine.

HANNIBAL: If that's meant for flattery, I don't want it, and if it's meant for irony, I won't have it.

MALCHUS: It was meant for the truth, sir.

HANNIBAL: In that case it was a gross under-statement. My helmet is only about twice the size of yours. (*He has sunk on to a divan. Drinks are on a low table close to his hand. He drinks.*)

MALCHUS (*keeping his temper*): Quite so, sir.

HANNIBAL: Those fellows in the little leather caps—I envied *them*, Malchus, I envied *them*.

MALCHUS: The sanitary squads, sir?

63

HANNIBAL: Oh, were those the sanitary squads?

MALCHUS: Yes, sir.

HANNIBAL: H'm. . . . How would it be if in future they all wore helmets like mine, and the Commander-in-Chief wore a little leather cap like theirs?

MALCHUS: With what object, sir?

HANNIBAL: Damn it, with the object that they'd get headaches and I shouldn't.

MALCHUS: Quite so, sir. Is it an order?

HANNIBAL: I don't know. I'll tell you later. . . . After all, I suppose all these feathers and things *are* more dignified.

MALCHUS: If *you* wore the leather cap, sir, then in a little while the leather cap would be more dignified.

HANNIBAL: Obviously one would hope that such would be the case, but in actual fact it wouldn't.

MALCHUS: No, sir.

HANNIBAL: On the other hand, it *would* be cooler.

MALCHUS: Yes, sir. (*There is a little silence.*)

HANNIBAL: Malchus, tell me just for interest: I've often wanted to know. If I make it an order, what exactly happens?

MALCHUS (*surprised*): The order is obeyed.

HANNIBAL (*thoughtfully*): You know, sometimes you give the impression of being quite intelligent, and sometimes you give the impression of being completely the reverse. Is there a reason, or is it just chance?

MALCHUS (*bewildered and annoyed*): I am afraid I don't——

HANNIBAL: There are men who rose from the ranks to be Commanders. I didn't. I was born to it. That puts me at a disadvantage. There are things which I don't know. (*He drinks.*) What I want to know now is what happens to this order as soon as I have given it to *you*?

MALCHUS: Oh, I see, sir. I write it out, and when your Excellency has signed it, I hand it to your Chief of Staff.

HANNIBAL: Never mind the signature. *I* tell *you*; *you* tell the Chief of Staff. Whom does *he* tell?

MALCHUS: The generals commanding divisions.

HANNIBAL: And they?

MALCHUS: The captains commanding companies.

HANNIBAL: And they?

MALCHUS: The officers commanding the company's sanitary squads.

HANNIBAL: Ah! And they?

64

FROM THE ORIGINAL BY FRANK BRANGWYN

" I will not leave you comfortless, I will come to you "

MALCHUS: They would then make out a requisition for the number of helmets they wanted—and, I suppose, the sizes—and that would go back to the captains commanding the companies, and they——

HANNIBAL (*holding up a hand*): Don't tell me. They would pass it back to the generals commanding divisions——

MALCHUS: Exactly, sir. And they would pass it back to the Chief of Staff.

HANNIBAL: Good. You will be glad to hear that so far I have followed you with ease. You will also have observed that so far nobody has done anything at all, except tell somebody else to do it. But there must be a horrifying moment when somebody actually has to set to and *make* a helmet, simply because there is nobody else he can get to do it for him. Who is that unlucky man?

MALCHUS: Well, sir, I suppose the order eventually comes to the master-armourer——

HANNIBAL: Ah!

MALCHUS: And *he* tells the armourer-sergeants——

HANNIBAL: I was hasty. I beg your pardon.

MALCHUS: Who tell the armourers to—er—make the helmets.

HANNIBAL: And they make them?

MALCHUS: Yes, sir.

HANNIBAL: How?

MALCHUS: I beg your pardon, sir?

HANNIBAL: I said—how?

MALCHUS (*not knowing*): Well—er——

HANNIBAL: Imagine yourself to be an armourer. The armourer-sergeant has just told you to make a hundred and forty-nine helmets. Damn it, Malchus, you can't *do* it!

MALCHUS (*stiffly*): I am not an armourer.

HANNIBAL: You start with a wodge of gold, say, and you beat it into a thin plate. Well, that's all right. Then you sort of (*he makes motions with his hands*) bend it—or don't you?

MALCHUS (*shocked*): You wouldn't have *gold* helmets for the sanitary squads?

HANNIBAL (*very solemnly*): If even my elephants have ivory tusks, are my sanitary squads to be grudged gold helmets?

MALCHUS: Quite so, sir.

HANNIBAL: What I want you to observe is how very much easier it is to be a Commander-in-Chief than it is to be an armourer. All *I* do is to say, "Let the sanitary squads wear gold helmets," and in a week from now——

MALCHUS: Better say a fortnight to be on the safe side.

HANNIBAL (*firmly*): In three days from now——

MALCHUS (*quickly*): Three days, sir.

HANNIBAL: In three days the sanitary squads are wearing gold helmets. Marvellous! Incredible! And what have *I* done towards it? Nothing that demands the exercise of the intelligence or the operation of manual skill. Any fool can give orders, Malchus, but it takes a clever man to execute them.

MALCHUS: It takes a genius to give the right orders, sir.

HANNIBAL (*boiling up*): And who the Hades is to know if they *are* right? Do *you* set yourself up as a judge?

MALCHUS: The gods forbid, sir!

HANNIBAL: Then who?

MALCHUS: Nobody in the army would dare to, sir.

HANNIBAL: Exactly. I give the order to besiege Saguntum (*his voice rises— almost to a shout*), and for two hundred and thirty-seven days we've been besieging the blasted town (*his voice drops and he says, almost to himself*)—and who knows whether I'm right or wrong?

MALCHUS: I always understood, sir, that it was meant to be a declaration of war against Rome, Saguntum being under Roman protection.

HANNIBAL (*mildly*): What other commander has ever taken two hundred and thirty-seven days to declare war? Why not march straight on Rome?

MALCHUS: Well, sir, you can't leave a fortified town in your rear to cut off your line of retreat.

HANNIBAL (*coldly*): My line of *what*?

MALCHUS (*hastily*): I mean, sir, you can't have a fortified town like Saguntum harassing your rear——

HANNIBAL: My dear Malchus, use words in some relation to their meaning. How can a fortified town harass the rear of a rapidly departing army? It can't run after us. . . . Or take elephants.

MALCHUS: Take what, sir?

HANNIBAL: Elephants. Am I right to burden myself with all these elephants? Who knows?

MALCHUS: Surely, sir, they will strike terror into the hearts of the Romans.

HANNIBAL: If they ever get within trumpeting distance of a Roman. At present it looks as if some of the young ones may just see the siege of Saguntum out. How long do elephants live?

MALCHUS: Eighty years.

HANNIBAL: Some of the *very* young ones. . . . Suppose I send them back to Carthage—somebody takes them?

MALCHUS: Yes, sir.

HANNIBAL: *I* shouldn't know how to take thirty-seven elephants back to Carthage—would you?

MALCHUS (*annoyed*): I don't happen to be an authority on elephants.

HANNIBAL: You aren't an authority on elephants, you can't make a helmet. (*With interest*) What *can* you do?

MALCHUS (*exploding*): If it comes to that, Hannibal, what can *you* do?

HANNIBAL (*sighing*): This is one of your bad days. For the last ten minutes I have been confessing my complete inability to do *anything*; and now you ask me, insolently, and with the air of making a point, what I can do.

MALCHUS: Oh, I was insolent, was I?

HANNIBAL: You were. You still are. It's a hot day, of course.

MALCHUS (*his temper quite gone*): I'm insolent, am I? All right, then, crucify me. "Discipline must be maintained"—you've said it often enough. Go on! Crucify me!

HANNIBAL: There you go again. You're making a ridiculously unwarranted demand on my powers. I simply don't know how to *begin* crucifying anybody. (*Thoughtfully*) One starts by making a cross, I suppose. Well, but where do I get the wood from? And then it's got to be shaped—and nailed together in some way. The more I think about it, the more complicated it seems.

MALCHUS: You've only got to look outside, there are plenty of old crosses ready for you. "Discipline must be maintained."

HANNIBAL: That's twice you've said that, and in the same unnatural voice. Is it supposed to be an imitation of me?

MALCHUS: It is.

HANNIBAL (*interested*): Is my voice really like that?

MALCHUS: Yes. I'm sick of the sound of it.

HANNIBAL: Just let's try, if you don't mind. I want to get this established. I'll go first. "Discipline must be maintained." Now *you* say it.

MALCHUS (*sulkily*): Discipline must be maintained.

HANNIBAL: It's not very good, is it? Apparently you add to your inability to make helmets, or conduct elephants across country, an inability to give recognisable imitations.

MALCHUS (*bowing*): Inabilities I have the honour of sharing with my lord Hannibal.

HANNIBAL: True. And in addition *I* can't wear a helmet without getting a headache, *I* can't take Saguntum, and *I* can't even keep the respect of a very ordinary young man with red ears.

MALCHUS (*stricken with remorse*): Hannibal! (*He draws his sword*) I am not worthy to live! Say the word and I will fall on it!

HANNIBAL: You'd probably miss it.

MALCHUS (*holding it to his heart*): Say the word and I will plunge it in my heart!

HANNIBAL (*jumping up*): Ah, there's something we both *could* do! We've found it at last. No orders to give to others. No wondering afterwards if we were right or wrong. A decision, private in application, personal in execution, which we can never regret. My sword!

MALCHUS (*aghast*): Hannibal!

HANNIBAL (*surprised*): At least my orders are obeyed.

MALCHUS: I would rather obey any other than that.

HANNIBAL: Curious! It is the most humane order I have ever given. My sword, Malchus.

> MALCHUS *comes forward with the sword-belt. As* HANNIBAL *puts out his hand, there is a commotion outside the tent.* AN OFFICER *bursts in.*

OFFICER: Surrender, my lord! An embassy of surrender from Saguntum!

HANNIBAL (*calmly, after a moment's effort to control his feelings*): Ah! . . . You have my sword there, Malchus?

> MALCHUS *gives him the sword-belt, which he fastens on.*

They are being conducted here?

OFFICER: Yes, my lord.

HANNIBAL: My helmet, Malchus.

> *He takes it from* MALCHUS *and begins to put it on his head. As it touches his forehead, he flinches slightly. Then, with great dignity:*

No! They are brave men, and have fought bravely. In respect for their valour I shall receive them bare-headed.

> TWO GUARDS *come in and stand one each side of the entrance.* HANNIBAL *takes up a commanding position.*

Bare-headed! (*He catches the eye of* MALCHUS *and winks.*)

CECIL ROBERTS

*MR. CECIL ROBERTS graduated to the ranks of the very
popular novelists by the way of the War Correspondent and the
Newspaper Editor. A versatile writer and an admirable public
speaker, he is most widely known as author of " Victoria Four-
Thirty," " Pilgrim Cottage," and " They Wanted to Live."
Just before sailing on his present American lecture-tour he
completed a new book, " And So To Bath," which is to be
published in the New Year. Here is what he found down Ferry
Lane at Brentford.*

DOWN FERRY LANE

FEW of the millions who rush along the Brentford High Street can be
aware of the odd sights that lie down the narrow alleys leading to the
Thames. Curious, I stopped my car by the fire station, and, resisting
the appeal of the Goat Wharf, plunged down Ferry Lane. The name seemed
to promise a ferry at least. In the first hundred yards the scene became
nautical. Two men in fishing jerseys came out of an inn called The Waterman's
Arms. They were not old salts but one wore sea-boots and smoked clay pipes.
My curiosity grew. The lane became only a passage-way. Presently a
Georgian house, built of dark grey bricks, revealed a rural past. It had once
stood in a large garden. An outdoor clock with gilt numerals still kept the
time on one of the walls. The old house was now the offices of a timber
merchant. The alley narrowed to a few feet. Then suddenly I came to the
River Thames.

It was low tide, a pebbly beach below me was reached by a flight of steps.
Across the river lay the green, tree-bordered expanse of Kew Gardens. On
the broad silver stream a rowing club " eight " went swiftly by. What a
transformation of scene a few yards had effected! A hoarding provoked my
curiosity. Beyond a high wall I could see a mountain of coal slack. It was
on a wharf where coal barges unloaded, hidden from view. I peered over the
barricade on the edge of the stone jetty and my heart jumped. A massive
wall had cracked under the pressure of the coal slack, bringing down the coping
stone and some masonry. A granite column standing in a triangular space
was already in peril of being overthrown. The purpose of the wooden
barricade was now clear—to keep the public away from the collapsing wall.
Why the heap of coal slack was not removed I do not know, and when I saw
what it threatened to overturn I marvelled still more.

There were inscriptions on this round pillar of granite, about ten feet high,
and to read them, at peril of my life, I went over the barricade. This is
what I found.

69

54 B.C. At this ancient fortified ford the British tribesmen under Cassivelaunus bravely opposed Julius Caesar on his march to Verulamium.

I paused in my reading and took a deep breath. So here, in the very shadow of this heap of coal slack cracking the boundary wall, the great Caesar had crossed the Thames, driving before him the wild natives. Local patriotism had erected this granite memorial, local industry seemed likely to push it down.

The first excitement subsiding, I read on:

A.D. 780-1. Near by Offa, King of Mercia, with his Queen, the Bishops and principal officers held a council of the Church.

A.D. 1016. Here Edmund Ironside, King of England, drove Cnut and his defeated Danes across the Thames.

A.D. 1642. Close by was fought the Battle of Brentford between the forces of King Charles I and the Parliament.

I was absorbed in my discovery, oblivious of the menacing coal slack, when a voice fell on my startled ears.

" Hey, you! What are you doing in there? " it cried, threateningly.

I looked up quickly to find a policeman's helmet and face visible over the hoarding.

" I am raising the ghosts of Julius Caesar, the King of Mercia, King Canute, and Charles I," I replied, solemnly.

" And what if that wall cracks over you," demanded the Law, young and fresh-complexioned.

" I shall feel I have perished in noble company," I retorted. " Don't you feel ashamed? "

" Ashamed? Me? " asked Robert, now really astonished by my madness.

" Mussolini would raise a temple here. We raise a coal heap. King Canute tried to push back the sea, can't Brentford try to push back a coal heap? I'm ashamed of you! " I said, severely.

" You'd better come out of there," said Robert, but this time with a note of entreaty.

" Have you read what is on this pillar? "

" I can't say as I have, sir."

" Then I will read it to you. You should feel proud that your beat leads down Ferry Lane."

" It doesn't—I'm looking for a lost kid."

Resisting the temptation to tell him to go to Goat Wharf, I read out one of the inscriptions while he listened, solemnly.

" Well, it does surprise me. Nobody around here ever told me that," said Robert. " It's a pity that wall's knocking it over."

" Perhaps you'll report the matter," I said, climbing over the barricade. " I feel it's just as important as a lost kid."

" More! " said the policeman, feelingly. " Kids are lost every day, their mothers don't bother about 'em until bedtime, but a thing like this you can't find every day. And nowhere else but in Brentford, I'll warrant! "

The fellow was visibly swelling with local pride. " And where will you find a lovely picture like this, sir? " he asked, turning to survey the Thames, now reflecting the crimson upper sky.

I agreed that it was lovely. There was beauty before us—and horror behind. Together we walked back up Ferry Lane in the friendliest fashion. Robert began to be very indignant about the column threatened by the coal. I paused by The Waterman's Arms and looked at him.

" Thank you very much, sir, but I'm on duty."

" Oh, of course. Well, I hope you find the kid."

" He'll turn up all right," said Robert. " Well, good evening, sir. Something ought to be done about that column."

" You might report that wall—for disorderly conduct."

He grinned and we parted.

One day I shall go back and see what happened to the column. Like Robert I feel no curiosity about the kid.

But I was not to leave Ferry Lane without a further adventure.

The door of The Waterman's Arms swung open to reveal a jolly waterman. He was a curly-headed young " tough " in a blue sweater, blue trousers, and sea-boots. Not more than twenty-two, his snub-nosed face beamed with rosy goodwill.

" —evening! " he said, grinning.

" —evening! " I replied, grinning, and added: " Do you mind telling me what you are doing in those sea-boots? Are you a bit of local colour for The Waterman's Arms, or are you the real thing? "

He considered this for a moment and looked at me with his clear blue eyes, suspicious of " leg-pulling." " I'm the captain of that boat," he answered at length, nodding his head in the direction of the high wall.

I turned and saw the mast-head of a boat, with a pennant fluttering there, above the high wall hiding the timber wharf.

" The captain! " I exclaimed, duly impressed. " But you're very young for such a position."

" Twenty—but I've worked my way up," he answered. " And now I'm sailing that boat all over England," he said, proudly.

I expressed my interest, and showed that I was deeply impressed by the contact with a captain. On my invitation we adjourned to The Waterman's Arms.

The phrase " all over England " had puzzled me a little, but it transpired he was captain of a sailing barge. There was not a canal in any part of England he had not sailed on. He had just come from Colchester with a cargo. He was picking up another and taking it to Bristol. He never knew where he would be sent. Sometimes he left the inland canals and went coastwise.

" In your barge? " I asked, astonished, and saw I had made a bad slip.

" It ain't a barge—it's a sailing boat. Barges get pulled or pushed. We sail," he declared, proudly. " Would you like to see her? "

I accepted the invitation at once. We finished our drinks and went out. The captain led the way through a small door in the opposite wall. Alongside the wharf lay the ship, with its great russet sail furled. The bow was brightly painted with green and blue bands. Her name was *Annie Laurie*. A terrier jumped up on to the hatch and barked at us. There was no one visible.

" The crew's ashore? " I asked, as we picked our way towards her.

71

"No—he's there, cooking supper," answered the captain.

I smothered my surprise. We clambered on board, and the captain, looking down the hatchway, from which emerged a strong smell of kippers, bellowed, "Bert!"

The crew emerged, a freckled, red-haired imp wearing nothing but a pair of khaki shorts. His eyebrows rose at the outer corners, giving him a clownish smirk. He was a lad of fifteen or so, with a shock of red hair and a sturdy body tanned with the sun.

"This is Bert," said the captain.

The crew grinned at me.

"Supper ready?" asked the captain.

"In 'alf a mo'" replied Bert, and disappeared again.

"Ain't she fine?" asked the captain, surveying his ship with pride. "You know, some blokes ask me if I ain't lonely, allus on the move. Why, it's grand! I've been all over England, and I've allus got me 'ome with me. How many fellows can say that—and I'm me own boss in a way."

"And you sail this—just you and the boy?"

"Yes—me and the kid. He's not on the log really," added the captain, "the Company won't pay him anything—so I keep him."

"But surely, if the boy's working——"

"Well, you see—he's a what-do-you-call-it?" said the captain, picking up the terrier and pulling its ears.

I looked puzzled, and then the word came to me.

"A stowaway?" I asked.

"That's it—'im and this dog. I came on board one night—been to the pictures at Grantham—and there he was, with the dog, both of 'em asleep in a crate of straw. I yanked them out of it. They both looked pinched to death, so I gave 'em a meal. They been here ever since, that's over a year ago."

"But his people—they know he's here?" I asked.

"His folk—says he ain't got none. And I'm asking no questions. He's a good kid," said the captain.

He sniffed the kippery odour whirling up out of the cabin, and then his blue eyes twinkled.

"Funny, you know," he said, pushing up the mongrel's head, "he gets a shilling a week, and he——" nodding in the direction of the cabin—"gets nowt! You see the dog's on the rating as a rat-killer and the kid don't exist; he's my pigeon. But he'll get a boat one day—he's a spry kid," added the captain, proudly.

"And good with the frying-pan?"

"He can cook, work, sew, paint—and find a rabbit or a bird now and then, when it don't really matter," said the captain, grinning.

It was time to go. I thanked the captain. I left him, spitting over the bow of the *Annie Laurie*, a reek of kippers filling the evening air, and after this singular and pleasant interlude regained my car and the road to Bath.

E. M. DELAFIELD

E. M. DELAFIELD is a pen-name that spells wit, brilliance, and versatility. Of all the memorable characters in her novels and plays, none has yet eclipsed the fame of the irrepressible Provincial Lady, whose first Diary was published in 1931. It is an enlivening thought that she is sharing many of our present experiences and that " Provincial Lady in War-time " will soon be issued by Messrs. Macmillan. In the meantime, here is a foretaste of it.

PROVINCIAL LADY IN WAR-TIME

OCTOBER 1ST. Serena undertakes to introduce me to Commandant of neighbouring A.R.P. Organisation. It is possible, she says, that she may allow me to do some voluntary work there. Can hardly believe this in view of discouraging reception of all advances made to other Organisations, but am grateful for Serena's good intentions.

Am at last introduced by Serena to Commandant. She is dark, rather good-looking young woman wearing out-size in slacks and leather jacket, using immensely long black cigarette-holder, and writing at wooden trestle-table piled with papers.

Serena—voice sunk to quite unnaturally timid murmur—explains that I am very anxious to make myself of use in any way whatever while waiting to be summoned by Ministry of Information.

The Commandant—who has evidently heard this kind of thing before—utters short incredulous ejaculation, in which I very nearly join, knowing even better than she does herself how thoroughly well justified it is.

Serena—voice meeker than ever—whispers that I can drive a car, if necessary, and have passed my First Aid examination—(hope she isn't going to mention date of this achievement, which would take us a long way back indeed)—and am also well used to Home Nursing. Moreover, I can write shorthand and use a typewriter.

Commandant goes on writing rapidly and utters without looking up for a moment—which I think highly offensive. Utterance is to the effect that there are no paid jobs going.

Oh, says Serena, sounding shocked, we never thought of anything like *that*. This is to be voluntary work, and anything in the world, and at any hour.

Commandant—still writing—strikes a bell sharply.

It has been said that the Canteen wants an extra hand, suggests Serena, now almost inaudible. She knows that I should be perfectly willing to work all through the night, or perhaps all day on Sundays, so as to relieve others.

And, naturally, voluntary work. To this Commandant—gaze glued to her rapidly moving pen—mutters something to the effect that voluntary work is all very well——

Have seldom met more unendearing personality.

Bell is answered by charming-looking elderly lady wearing overall and armlet-badge inscribed *Messenger*, which seems to me unsuitable.

Commandant—tone very peremptory indeed—orders her to Bring the Canteen Time-Sheet. Grey-haired messenger flies away like the wind. Cannot possibly have gone more than five yards from the door before the bell is again struck, and on her reappearance Commandant says sharply that she has just asked for Canteen Time-Sheet. Why hasn't it come?

Obvious reply is that it hasn't come because only a pair of wings could have brought it in the time—but no one says this, and Messenger again departs and can be heard covering the ground at race-track speed.

Commandant continues to write—says Damn once, under her breath, as though attacked by sudden doubt whether war will stop exactly as and when she has ordained—and drops cigarette ash all over the table.

Serena looks at me and profanely winks enormous eye.

Bell is once more banged—am prepared to wager it will be broken before week is out—at this rate. It is this time answered by smart-looking person in blue trousers and singlet and admirable make-up. Looks about twenty-five, but has prematurely grey hair, and am conscious that this gives me distinct satisfaction.

(Not very commendable reaction.)

Am overcome with astonishment when she enquires of Commandant, in brusque, official tones: Isn't it time you had some lunch, darling?

Commandant for the first time raises her eyes and answers No, darling, she can't possibly bother with lunch, but she wants a Staff Car instantly, to go out to Wimbledon for her. It's urgent.

Serena looks hopeful but remains modestly silent while Commandant and Darling rustle through quantities of lists and swear vigorously, saying that it's a most extraordinary thing, the Time-Sheets ought to be always available at a second's notice, and they never *are*.

Darling eventually turns to Serena, just as previous—and infinitely preferable—Messenger returns breathless, and asks curtly Who is on the Staff Car? Serena indicates that she herself is scheduled for it, is asked why she didn't say so, and commanded to get car out instantly and dash to Wimbledon.

Am deeply impressed by this call to action, but disappointed when Commandant instructs her to go *straight* to No. 478 Mottisfont Road Wimbledon and ask for clean handkerchief, which Commandant forgot to bring this morning.

She is to come *straight* back, as quickly as possible, *with* the handkerchief. Has she, adds Commandant suspiciously, quite understood?

Serena replies that she has. Tell myself that in her place I should reply No, it's all too complicated for me to grasp—but judging from life-long experience, this is a complete fallacy and should in reality say nothing of the kind but merely wish, long afterwards, that I had.

Departure of Serena, in search, no doubt, of tin helmet and gas mask, and am left, together with Elderly Messenger, to be ignored by Commandant

74

whilst she and Darling embark on earnest argument concerning Commandant's next meal, which turns out to be lunch, although time now five o'clock in the afternoon.

She must, says Darling, absolutely *must* have something. She has been here since nine o'clock and during that time what has she had? One cup of coffee and a tomato. It isn't enough on which to do a heavy day's work.

Commandant—writing again resumed and eyes again on paper—asserts that it's all she wants. She hasn't time for more. Does Darling realise that there's a *war* on, and not a minute to spare?

Yes, argues Darling, but she could eat something without leaving her desk for a second. Will she try some soup?

No.

Then a cup of tea and some buns?

No, no, no. *Nothing.*

She *must* take some black coffee. Absolutely and definitely must.

Oh, very well, cries Commandant—at the same time striking table quite violently with her hand, which produces confusion among the papers. (Can foresee fresh trouble with mislaid Time-Sheets in immediate future.) Very well—black coffee, and she'll have it here. Instantly.

Darling dashes from the room throwing murderous look at elderly Messenger who has temporarily obstructed the dash.

Commandant writes more frenziedly than ever and snaps out single word *What,* which sounds like a bark, and is evidently addressed to Messenger, who respectfully lays Canteen Time-Sheet on table. This not a success, as Commandant snatches it up again and cries *Not* on the table, my God, *not* on the table! and scans it at red-hot speed.

She then writes again, as though nothing had happened.

Decide that if I am to be here indefinitely I may as well sit down, and do so.

Elderly Messenger gives me terrified, but I think admiring, look. Evidently this display of initiative quite unusual, and am, in fact, rather struck by it myself.

Darling reappears, with a tray. Black coffee has materialised and is flanked by large plate of scrambled eggs on toast, two rock-buns, and a banana.

All are placed at Commandant's elbow and she wields a fork with one hand and continues to write with the other.

Have sudden impulse to quote to her historical anecdote of British Sovereign remarking to celebrated historian: Scribble, scribble, scribble, Mr. Gibbon.

Do not, naturally, give way to it.

Darling asks me coldly if I want anything, and on my replying that I have offered my services to Canteen tells me to go *at once* to Mrs. Peacock. Decide to assume that this means I am to be permitted to serve my country, if only with coffee and eggs, so depart, and elderly Messenger creeps out with me.

I ask if she will be kind enough to take me to Mrs. Peacock and she says Of course, and we proceed quietly—no rushing or dashing. *Query:* Will not this dilatory spirit lose us the war? *Answer,* undoubtedly, Nonsense! Make note not to let myself be affected by aura of agitation surrounding Commandant and friend.

Messenger takes me past cars, ambulances, Rest Room, from which unholy din of feminine voices proceeds, and gives me information.

75

A Society deb. is working in the canteen. She is the only one in the whole place. A reporter came to interview her once and she was photographed kneeling on one knee beside an ambulance wheel, holding tools and things. Photograph published in several papers and underneath it was printed: Débutante Jennifer Jamfather Stands By on Home Front.

Reach Mrs. Peacock, who is behind Canteen counter sitting on a box, and looks kind but harassed.

She has a bad leg. Not a permanent bad leg, but it gets in her way, and she will be glad of extra help.

Feel much encouraged by this. Nobody else has made faintest suggestion of being glad of extra help—on the contrary.

Raise my voice so as to be audible above gramophone—(Little Sir Echo) and wireless—(. . . And so, bairns, we bid Goodbye to Bonnie Scotland)—roarings and bellowings of Darts Finals being played in a corner, and clatter of dishes from the kitchen—and announce that I am Come to Help—which I think sounds as if I were one of the Ministering Children Forty Years After.

Mrs. Peacock, evidently too dejected even to summon up customary formula that there is nothing for me to do except Stand By as she is turning helpers away by the hundred every hour, smiles rather wanly and says I am very kind.

What, I enquire, can I do?

At the moment, nothing. (Can this be a recrudescence of Stand By theme?)

The five o'clock rush is over, and the seven o'clock rush hasn't begun. Mrs. Peacock is taking the opportunity of sitting for a moment. She heroically makes rather half-hearted attempt at offering me half packing-case, which I at once decline, and ask about her leg.

Mrs. P. displays it, swathed in bandages beneath her stocking, and tells me how her husband had two boxes of sand, shovel, and bucket prepared for emergency-use—(this evidently euphemism for incendiary bombs)—and gave full instructions to household as to use of them, demonstrating in back garden. Mrs. P. herself took part in this, she adds impressively. I say Yes, yes, to encourage her, and she goes on. Telephone call then obliged her to leave the scene—interpolation here about nature of the call involving explanation as to young married niece—husband a sailor, dear little baby with beautiful big blue eyes—from whom call emanated.

Ninth pip-pip-pip compelled Mrs. P. to ring off and, on retracing her steps, she crossed first-floor landing on which husband, without a word of warning, had meanwhile caused box of sand, shovel, and bucket to be ranged, with a view to permanent instalment there. Mrs. P.—not expecting any of them—unfortunately caught her foot in the shovel, crashed into the sand-box, and was cut to the bone by edge of the bucket.

She concludes by telling me that it really was a lesson. Am not clear of what nature, or to whom, but sympathise very much and say I shall hope to save her as much as possible.

Hope this proceeds from unmixed benevolence, but am inclined to think it is largely actuated by desire to establish myself definitely as Canteen-worker—in which it meets with success.

Return to my flat in Buckingham Street coincides with exit of landlord who at once enquires whether I have ascertained whereabouts of nearest air-raid shelter.

Well, yes, I have in a way. That is to say, the A.R.P. establishment in Adelphi is within three minutes' walk, and I could go there. Owner returns severely that that is Not Good Enough. He must beg of me to take this question seriously, and pace the distance between bedroom and shelter and find out how long it would take to cover in the event of an emergency. More-over, he declares there is a shelter nearer than the Adelphi, and proceeds to indicate it.

Undertake, reluctantly, to conduct a brief rehearsal of my own exodus under stimulus of air-raid alarm, and subsequently do so.

This takes the form of rather interesting little experiment in which I lay out warm clothes, heavy coat, *Our Mutual Friend*—Shakespeare much more impressive but cannot rise to it—small bottle of boiled sweets—sugar said to increase energy and restore impaired *morale*—and electric torch. Undress and get into bed, then sound imaginary tocsin, look at my watch, and leap up.

Dressing is accomplished without mishap and proceed downstairs and into street with *Our Mutual Friend*, boiled sweets, and electric torch. Am shocked to find myself strongly inclined to run like a lamplighter, in spite of repeated instructions issued to the contrary. If this is the case when no raid at all is taking place, ask myself what it would be like with bombers overhead—and do not care to contemplate reply.

Street seems very dark, and am twice in collision with other pedestrians. Reaction to this is merry laughter on both sides. (Effect of blackout on national hilarity quite excellent.)

Turn briskly down side-street and up to entrance of air-raid shelter, which turns out to be locked. Masculine voice enquires where I think I am going, and I say Is it the police? No, it is the Air-raid Warden. Explain entire situation, he commends my forethought and says that on the first sound of siren-alarm He Will be There. Assure him in return that in that case we shall meet, as I shall also Be There, with equal celerity, and we part—cannot say whether temporarily or for ever.

Wrist-watch, in pocket of coat, reveals that entire performance has occupied four and a half minutes only.

Am much impressed, and walk back reflecting on my own efficiency and wondering how best to ensure that it shall be appreciated by Robert, to whom I propose to write spirited account.

Return to flat reveals that I have left all the electric lights burning—though behind blue shades—and forgotten gas-mask, still lying in readiness on table.

Decide to put off writing account to Robert.

Undress and get into bed again, leaving clothes, and other properties, ready as before—gas-mask in prominent position on shoes—but realise that if I have to go through whole performance all over again tonight, shall be very angry indeed.

October 2nd. No alarm takes place. Wake at two o'clock and hear something which I think may be a warbling note from a siren—which we have been told to expect—but if so, warbler very poor and indeterminate performer, and come to the conclusion that it is not worth my attention and go to sleep again.

Post—now very late every day—does not arrive until after breakfast.

Short note from Robert informs me that all is well, he does not care about the way the Russians are behaving—(he never has)—his A.R.P. office has more volunteers than he knows what to do with—and young Cramp from the garage, who offered to learn method of dealing with unexploded bombs, has withdrawn after ten minutes' instruction on the grounds that he thinks it seems rather dangerous.

Robert hopes I am enjoying the blackout—which I think is satirical—and has not forwarded joint letter received from Robin as there is nothing much in it. (Could willingly strangle him for this.)

Vicky's letter, addressed to me, makes some amends, as she writes ecstatic-ally about heavenly new dormitory, divine concert, and utterly twee air-raid shelter newly constructed (towards which parents will no doubt be asked to contribute). Vicky's only complaint is to the effect that no air-raid has yet occurred, which is very dull.

Also receive immensely long and chatty letter from aunt Blanche, keeping house at home in my stead. Evacuee children Marigold and Margery are well, their attendant and Cook have failed to reach identity of views regarding question of the children's supper, but this has now been adjusted by aunt Blanche and I am not to worry, and Robert seems quite all right, though not saying much.

Our Vicar's Wife has been to tea—worn to a thread and looking like death—but has declared that she is getting on splendidly and the evacuees are settling down, and a nephew of a friend of hers, in the Militia, has told his mother, who has written it to his aunt, who has passed it on to Our Vicar's Wife, that all Berlin is seething with discontent, and a revolution in Germany is scheduled for the first Monday in January.

Is this, asks aunt Blanche rhetorically, what the Press calls Wishful Think-ing?

She concludes with affectionate enquiries as to my well-being, begs me to go and see old uncle A when I have time, and is longing to hear what post I have been offered by the Ministry of Information. P.S. What about the Sweep? Cook has been asking.

Have never yet either left home, or got back to it, without being told that Cook is asking about the Sweep.

Large proportion of mail consists of letters, full of eloquence, from trades-people who say that they are now faced with a difficult situation which will, however, be improved on receipt of my esteemed cheque.

Irresistible conviction comes over me that my situation is even more difficult than theirs, and moreover, no cheques are in the least likely to come and improve it.

Turn, in hopes of consolation, to remainder of mail and am confronted with Felicity Fairmead's writing—very spidery—on envelope, and typewritten letter within, which she has forgotten to sign. Tells me that she is using type-writer with a view to training for war-work, and adds candidly that she can't help hoping war may be over before she finds it. This, says Felicity, is awful, she knows very well, but she can't help it. She is deeply ashamed of her utter uselessness, as she is doing nothing whatever except staying as Paying Guest in the country with delicate friend whose husband is in France, and who has three small children, also delicate, and one maid who isn't any use, so that Felicity

78

and friend make the beds, look after the children, do most of the cooking, and keep the garden in order. Both feel how wrong it is not to be doing real work for the country, and this has driven Felicity to the typewriter and friend to the knitting of socks and Balaclava helmets.

Felicity concludes with wistful supposition that *I* am doing something splendid.

Should be very sorry to enlighten her on this point, and shall feel constrained to leave letter unanswered until reality of my position corresponds rather more to Felicity's ideas.

Meanwhile, have serious thoughts of sending copies of her letter to numerous domestic helpers of my acquaintance who have seen fit to leave their posts at a moment's notice in order to seek more spectacular jobs elsewhere.

Remaining item in the post is letter-card—which I have customary difficulty in tearing open and only succeed at the expense of one corner—and proves to be from Barbara Carruthers *née* Blenkinsop, now living in Midlands. She informs me that this war is upsetting her very much : it really is dreadful for *her*, she says, because *she* has children, and situation may get very difficult later on and they may have to do without things and she has always taken so much trouble to see that they have *everything*. They are at present in Westmoreland, but this is a considerable expense and moreover petrol regulations make it impossible to go and see them and train-service—about which Barbara is indignant and says it is *very* hard on her—most unsatisfactory. How long do I think war is going on ? She had arranged for her elder boys to go to excellent Preparatory School near London this autumn, but school has moved to Wales, which isn't at all the same thing and Barbara does feel it's rather too bad. And what do I think about food-shortage ? It is *most* unfair if her children are to be rationed, and she would even be prepared to pay extra for them to have additional supplies. She concludes by sending me her love and enquiring casually whether Robin has been sent to France yet, or is he just too young ?

Am so disgusted at Barbara's whole attitude that I dramatically tear up letter into fragments and cast it from me, but realise later that it should have been kept, in order that I might send suitable reply.

Draft this in my own mind several times in course of the day, until positively vitriolic indictment is evolved which will undoubtedly never see the light of day, and would probably land me in the Old Bailey on a charge of defamatory libel if it did.

Purchase overall for use in Canteen, debate the question of trousers and decide that I must be strong-minded enough to remain in customary clothing which is perfectly adequate to work behind the counter. Find myself almost immediately afterwards trying on very nice pair of navy-blue slacks, thinking that I look well in them and buying them.

Am prepared to take any bet that I shall wear them every time I go on duty.

As this is not to happen till nine o'clock tonight, determine to look up the Weatherbys, who might possibly be able to suggest whole-time National Service job—and old uncle A about whom aunt Blanche evidently feels anxious.

Ring up uncle A—his housekeeper says he will be delighted to see me at tea-time—and also Mrs. Weatherby, living in Chelsea, who invites me to lunch and says her husband, distinguished Civil Servant, will be in and would much like to meet me. Imagination instantly suggests that he has heard of me (in what connection, cannot possibly conceive) and, on learning that he is to be privileged to see me at his table, will at once realise that Civil Service would be the better for my assistance in some highly authoritative capacity.

Spend hours wondering what clothes would make me look most efficient, but am quite clear *not* slacks for the Civil Service. Finally decide on black coat and skirt, white blouse with frill of austere, *not* frilly, type, and cone-shaped black hat. Find that I look like inferior witch in third-rate pantomime in the latter, and take it off again. Only alternative is powder-blue with rain-bow-like swathings, quite out of the question. Feel myself obliged to go out and buy small black hat, with brim like a jockey-cap and red edging. Have no idea whether this is in accordance with Civil Service tastes or not, but feel that I look nice in it.

Walk to Chelsea, and on looking into a small mirror in handbag, realise that I don't, after all. Can do nothing about it, and simply ask hall-porter for Mrs. Weatherby, and am taken up in lift to sixth-floor flat, very modern and austere, colouring entirely neutral, and statuette—to me wholly revolting—of misshapen green cat occupying top of book case, dominating whole of the room.

Hostess comes in—cannot remember if we are on Christian-name terms or not, but inclined to think not, and do not risk it—greets me very kindly and again repeats that her husband wishes to meet me.

(Civil Service appointment definitely in sight, and decide to offer Serena job as my private secretary.)

Discuss view of the river from window—Mrs. Weatherby says block of flats would be an excellent target from the air, at which we both laugh agreeably—extraordinary behaviour of the Ministry of Information, and delightful autumnal colouring in neighbourhood of Bovey Tracy, which Mrs. Weatherby says she knows well.

Entrance of Mr. Weatherby puts an end to this interchange, and we are introduced. Mr. W. very tall and cadaverous, and has a beard, which makes me think of Agrippa.

He says that he has been wishing to meet me, but does not add why. Produces sherry and we talk about blackout, President Roosevelt—I say that his behaviour throughout entire crisis has been magnificent and moves me beyond measure—Mrs. Weatherby agrees, but Agrippa seems surprised and I feel would like to contradict me but politeness forbids—and we pass on to cocker-spaniels, do not know how or why.

Admirable parlour-maid—uniform, demeanour, and manner all equally superior to those of Winnie, or even departed May—announces that Luncheon is served, madam, and just as I prepare to swallow remainder of sherry rapidly, pallid elderly gentleman crawls in, leaning on stick and awakening in me instant conviction that he is not long for this world.

Impression turns out to be not without foundation as it transpires that he is Agrippa's uncle, and has recently undergone major operation at London Nursing Home but was desired to leave it at five minutes' notice in order that bed should be available if and when required. Uncle asserts that he met this —as well he might—with protests but was unfortunately too feeble to enforce

FROM THE ORIGINAL BY J. MORTON SALE

The Red Cross of Comfort

them and accordingly found himself, so he declares, on the pavement while still unable to stand. From this fearful plight he has been retrieved by Agrippa, and given hospitality of which he cannot speak gratefully enough.

Story concludes with examples of other, similar cases, of which we all seem to know several, and Mrs. Weatherby's solemn assurance that all the beds of all the Hospitals and Nursing Homes in England are standing empty, and that no civilian person is to be allowed to be ill until the war is over.

Agrippa's uncle shakes his head, and looks worse than ever, and soon after he has pecked at chicken soufflé, waved away sweet omelette and turned his head from the sight of Camembert cheese, he is compelled by united efforts of the Weatherbys to drink a glass of excellent port and retire from the room.

They tell me how very ill he has been—can well believe it—and that there was another patient even more ill, in room next to his at Nursing Home, who was likewise desired to leave. She, however, defeated the authorities by dying before they had time to get her packing done.

Find myself exclaiming Well done! in enthusiastic tone before I have time to stop myself, and am shocked. So, I think, are the Weatherbys—rightly.

Agrippa changes the conversation and asks my opinion about the value of the natural resources of Moravia. Fortunately answers his own question, at considerable length.

Cannot see that any of this, however interesting, is leading in the direction of war-work for me.

On returning to drawing-room and superb coffee which recalls Cook's efforts at home rather sadly to my mind—I myself turn conversation forcibly into desired channel.

What an extraordinary thing it is, I say, that so many intelligent and experienced people are not, so far as one can tell, being utilised by the Government in any way!

Mrs. Weatherby replies that she thinks most people who are *really* trained for anything worth while have found no difficulty whatever in getting jobs, and Agrippa declares that it is largely a question of Standing By, and will continue to be so for many months to come.

Does he, then, think that this will be a long war?

Agrippa, assuming expression of preternatural discretion, replies that he must not, naturally, commit himself. Government officials, nowadays, have to be exceedingly careful in what they say as I shall, he has no doubt, readily understand.

Mrs. Weatherby strikes in, to the effect that it is difficult to see how the war can be a very *short* one, and yet it seems unlikely to be a very *long* one.

I enquire whether she thinks it is going to be a middling one, and then feel I have spoken flippantly and that both disapprove of me.

Should like to leave at once, but custom and decency alike forbid as have only this moment finished coffee.

Ask whether anything has been heard of Pamela Pringle, known to all three of us, at which Agrippa's face lights up in the most extraordinary way and he exclaims that she is, poor dear, quite an invalid but as charming as ever.

Mrs. Weatherby—face not lighting up at all but on the contrary resembling a thunder-cloud—explains that Pamela, since war started, has developed unspecified form of Heart and retired to large house near the New Forest where she lies on the sofa, in *eau-de-nil* velvet wrapper, and has all her friends down to stay in turns.

Her husband has a job with the Army and is said to be in Morocco, and she has despatched the children to relations in America, saying that this is a terrible sacrifice, but done for their own sakes.

Can only reply, although I hope indulgently, that it all sounds to me exactly like dear Pamela. This comment more of a success with Mrs. W. than with Agrippa, who stands up—looks as if he might touch the ceiling—and says that he must get back to work.

Have abandoned all serious hope of his offering me a post of national importance, or even of no importance at all, but put out timid feeler to the effect that he must be very busy just now.

Yes, yes, he is. He won't get back before eight o'clock tonight, if then. At one time it was eleven o'clock, but things are for the moment a little easier, though no doubt this is only temporary.

(*Query:* Why is it that all those occupied in serving the country are completely overwhelmed by pressure of work but do not apparently dream of utilising assistance pressed upon them by hundreds of willing helpers? *Answer* comes there none.)

Agrippa and I exchange unenthusiastic farewells, but he sticks to his guns to the last and says that he has always wanted to meet me. Does not, naturally, add whether the achievement of this ambition has proved disappointing or the reverse.

Linger on for a few moments in frail and unworthy hope that Mrs. Weatherby may say something more, preferably scandalous, about Pamela Pringle, but she only refers, rather bleakly, to Agrippa's uncle and his low state of health, and asserts that she does not know what the British Medical Association can be thinking about.

Agree that I don't either—which is true not only now but at all times—and take my leave. Tell her how much I have liked seeing them both, and am conscious of departing from spirit of truth in saying so, but cannot, obviously, inform her that the only parts of the entertainment I have really enjoyed are her excellent lunch and hearing about Pamela.

Go out in search of 'bus—all very few and far between now—and contemplate visit to hairdresser's, but conscience officiously points out that visits to hairdresser constitute an unnecessary expense and could very well be replaced by ordinary shampoo in bedroom basin at flat. Inner prompting—probably the Devil—urges that Trade must be Kept Going and that it is my duty to help on the commercial life of the nation.

Debate this earnestly, find that 'bus has passed the spot at which I intended to get out, make undecided effort to stop it, then change my mind and sit down again and am urged by conductor to Make up My Mind. I shall have to move a lot faster than that, he jocosely remarks, when them aeroplanes are overhead. Much amusement is occasioned to passengers in general, and we all part in high spirits.

Am much too early for uncle A, and walk about the streets—admire balloons which look perfectly entrancing—think about income-tax, so rightly described as crushing, and decide not to be crushed at all but readjust ideas about what constitutes reasonable standard of living, and learn to cook for self and family—and look at innumerable posters announcing contents of evening papers.

Lowest level seems to me to be reached by one which features *exposé*, doubtless apocryphal, of Hitler's sex-life—but am not pleased with another which enquires—idiotically—Why Not Send Eden to Russia?

Could suggest hundreds of reasons why not, and none in favour.

Remaining posters all display ingenious statements, implying that tremendous advance has been made somewhere by Allies, none of whom have suffered any casualties at all, with enormous losses to enemy.

Evolve magnificent piece of rhetoric, designed to make clear once and for all what does, and what does not, constitute good propaganda, and this takes me to Mansions in Kensington at the very top of which dwell uncle A and housekeeper, whose peculiar name is Mrs. Mouse.

Sensation quite distinctly resembling small trickle of ice-cold water running down spine assails me, at the thought that rhetoric on propaganda will all be wasted, since no Government Department wishes for my assistance—but must banish this discouraging reflection and remind myself that at least I am to be allowed a few hours' work in Canteen.

Hall-porter—old friend—is unfortunately inspired to greet me with expressions of surprise and disappointment that I am not in uniform. Most ladies are, nowadays, he says. His circle of acquaintances evidently more fortunate than mine. Reply that I have been trying to join something—but can see he doesn't believe it.

We go up very slowly and jerkily in aged Victorian lift—pitch dark and smells of horsehair—and porter informs me that nearly all the flats are empty, but he doubts whether 'Itler himself could move the old gentleman. Adds conversationally that, in his view, it is a *funny* war. Very funny indeed. He supposes we might say that it hasn't hardly begun yet, has it? Agree, though reluctantly, that we might.

Still, says the hall-porter, as lift comes to an abrupt stop, we couldn't very well have allowed '*im* to carry on as he was doing, could we, and will I please mind the step.

I do mind the step—which is about three feet higher than the landing—and ring uncle A's bell.

Can distinctly see Mrs. Mouse applying one eye to ground-glass panel at top of door before she opens it and welcomes my arrival. In reply to enquiry she tells me that uncle A is remarkably well and has been all along, and that you'd never give him seventy, let alone eighty-one. She adds philosophically that nothing isn't going to make him stir, and she supposes, with hearty laughter, that he'll never be satisfied until he's had the both of them smothered in poison-gas, set fire to, blown sky-high, and buried under the whole of the buildings.

Point out that this is surely excessive and enquire whether they have a shelter in the basement. Oh yes, replies Mrs. M., but she had the work of the world to get him down there when the early-morning alarm was given, at the very beginning of the war, as he refused to move until fully dressed and with his teeth in. The only thing that has disturbed him at all, she adds, is the thought that he is taking no active part in the war.

She then conducts me down familiar narrow passage carpeted in red, with chocolate-and-gilt wall-paper, and into rather musty but agreeable drawing-room crammed with large pieces of furniture, potted palm, family portraits in gilt frames, glass-fronted cupboards, china, books, hundreds of newspapers and old copies of *Blackwood's Magazine*, and grand piano on which nobody has played for about twenty-seven years.

Uncle A rises alertly from mahogany knee-hole writing-table—very upright and distinguished-looking, typical Diplomatic Service—(quite misleading, uncle A retired stockbroker)—and receives me most affectionately.

He tells me that I look tired—so I probably do, compared with uncle A himself—commands Mrs. M. to bring tea, and wheels up an armchair for me in front of magnificent old-fashioned coal-fire. Can only accept it gratefully and gaze in admiration at uncle A's slim figure, abundant white hair, and general appearance of jauntiness.

He enquires after Robert, the children, and his sister—whom he refers to as poor dear old Blanche—(about fifteen years his junior)—and tells me that he has offered his services to the War Office and has had a very civil letter in acknowledgment, but they have not as yet actually found a niche for him. No doubt, however, of their doing so in time.

The Government is, in uncle A's opinion, underrating the German strength, and as he himself knew Germany well in his student days at Heidelberg, he is writing a letter to *The Times* in order to make the position better understood.

He asks about evacuees—has heard all about them from Blanche—and tells me about his great-niece in Shropshire. She is sitting in her manor-house waiting for seven evacuated children whom she has been told to expect, beds are already made, everything waiting, but children haven't turned up. I suggest that this is reminiscent of Snow White and seven little dwarfs, only no little dwarfs.

Uncle A appears to be immeasurably amused and repeats at intervals : Snow White and no little dwarfs. Capital, capital!

Tea is brought in by Mrs. M. and uncle A declines my offer of pouring out and does it himself, and plies me with hot scones, apricot jam, and home-made gingerbread. All is the work of Mrs. M. and I tell uncle A that she is a treasure, at which he looks rather surprised and says she's a good gel enough and does what she's told.

Can only remember, in awe-stricken silence, that Mrs. M. has been in uncle A's service for the past forty-six years.

Take my leave very soon afterwards and make a point of stating that I have presently to go on duty at A.R.P. Canteen, to which uncle A replies solicitously that I mustn't go overdoing it.

He then escorts me to the lift, commands the hall-porter to look after me and call a cab should I require one, and remains waving a hand while lift, in a series of irregular leaps, bears me downstairs.

No cab is required—hall-porter does not so much as refer to it—and take a 'bus back to the Strand.

Bathroom has notice pinned on door—" Occupied "—which I assume to be Serena, especially on finding large bunch of pink gladioli in sitting-room, one empty sherry-glass, and several biscuit-crumbs on rug. Moreover, blackout has been achieved and customary sheets of paper pinned up, and also customary number of drawing-pins strewn over the floor.

Serena emerges from bathroom, very pink, and says she hopes it's All Right, and I say it is, and thank her for gladioli to which she replies candidly that flowers are so cheap nowadays, they're being practically *given* away.

She asks what I have been doing, and I relate my experiences—Serena carries sympathy so far as to declare that Mr. Weatherby ought to be taken out and shot and that Mrs. W. doesn't sound much of a one either, but uncle A too adorable for words.

She then reveals that she came round on purpose to suggest we should have supper at Canteen together before going on duty.

Am delighted to agree, and change into trousers and overall. Greatly relieved when Serena ecstatically admires both.

1.30 a.m. Return from Canteen after evening of activity which has given me agreeable illusion that I am now wholly indispensable to the Allies in the conduct of the war.

Responsibilities, so far as I am concerned, involve much skipping about with orders, memorising prices of different brands of cigarettes—which mostly have tiresome half-penny tacked on to round sum, making calculation difficult —and fetching of fried eggs, rashers, sausages-and-mashed, and Welsh rarebits from kitchen.

Am much struck by continuous pandemonium of noise in Canteen, but become more accustomed to it every moment, and feel that air-raid warning, by comparison, would pass over my head quite unnoticed.

CEDRIC HARDWICKE

For most theatre-goers, SIR CEDRIC HARDWICKE made his name as Churdles Ash in "The Farmer's Wife." This one man has indeed played many parts—King Magnus in "The Apple Cart," Mr. Barrett in "The Barretts of Wimpole Street," Dr. Haggett in "The Late Christopher Bean," and leads in the Malvern Festivals, not to speak of leading rôles in such films as "Dreyfus" and "Stanley and Livingstone."

ONE MAN IN HIS TIME PLAYS MANY PARTS

"FOR the second time in the lives of most of us we are at war." Such were the words spoken by His Majesty in the course of his historic broadcast to the peoples of the British Commonwealth of Nations on September 3rd.

Hearing or reading that sentence, all of us old enough to remember 1914 must, I feel sure, have found our thoughts travelling back twenty-five years to memories of where we were and what we were doing on the outbreak of what we came to call the "Great War." It was natural that we should thus hark back. In my own case it was almost inevitable, for, by an odd chance, the outbreak of the present struggle, as of the former, found me out of England.

In the autumn of 1913 I had sailed for South Africa as a member of the Benson Shakespearean Company. Not a prominent one: far from it. Indeed, I had had little professional experience. I had "walked on " in the Melville Brothers' highly successful piece *The Monk and the Woman*. I had played a lift boy in one of Arthur Bourchier's productions. That was about all, if we except my appearance in the rôle of Sir Harry Bumper in *The School for Scandal*. And the exception may well be made, since the producer decided, rightly no doubt, that I must at all costs be prevented from singing " Here's to the Maiden of Bashful Fifteen," with the result that my part, at no time a heavy one, was reduced to the modest limits of two words, in the form of a question: " Maria who? " Moreover, even with this inconsiderable share in the dialogue, I did not escape censure, for the dramatic critic of the local paper tempered his glowing tribute to the company as a whole with the remark that " Harry Bumper overdid his part the least little bit." Perhaps if I had had only one word to say, I might have come off unscathed!

From Cape Town we went to Johannesburg, where a general strike forced us to close down. Thence we proceeded to Pietermaritzburg, where the heat was terrific, and, by way of Durban and East London, returned to the Cape. There the tour was due to end. But some of us fell in with Henry Herbert's suggestion that we should set out again and play in small " dorps " where no company from England had previously penetrated, and whose inhabitants had never seen a Shakespearean play. It was an odd business and, save that we travelled in a large railway-coach hitched on to any local or goods train that deigned to take us with it, quite as makeshift an enterprise as any rural barn-storming of the old days. We could arrange no detailed schedule. We merely lived, ate, and slept (or endeavoured to) in the coach and, getting out when the train reached whatever its destination might be, walked four or five miles, with our scenery and portable stage borne by ox wagon, to the school, hotel dining-room, or local town hall which served as our theatre.

We were largely cut off from the outside world. Even when we arrived at Bulawayo we knew little of what was passing in Europe. But we found W. H. Patterson, the theatrical magnate of those parts, decidedly worried because the natives had told him that they had seen " a vision in the sky of a lion assailed by a bull," which their witch-doctors interpreted as meaning that England was being attacked by a powerful enemy. The date was August 4th. But not for four days did news reach us from a more orthodox source of the outbreak of war. Once convinced of the truth, we made our difficult way to the coast and eventually got back to England.

Heaven forbid that I should indulge in long-winded reminiscences of my military career! Suffice it to say that the war was for me a topsy-turvy affair. Wearying of route marches in full kit, I applied to be transferred to the artillery, but found myself instead at the horse transport depot of the Royal Army Service Corps, with which body I went to France in 1915. Three years later I was transferred again, this time to the Northumberland Fusiliers and, though I was mixed up in the March retreat, I found existence in the infantry far less hectic than in the reputedly more secure and tranquil R.A.S.C. It happened, too, that while I had been out of England when the war began, I was in it at the close, for the last day of my leave coincided with the Armistice. To complete the unexpectedness of things, though I was at home when the fighting ceased, I subsequently returned to France and remained there long after almost everybody else had come back. For a time I was at various base depots and for some months a member of a kind of travelling court martial. It was not altogether pleasant work. But, at St. Pol, I had the solemn and unforgettable experience of mounting guard with others over the body of the Unknown Warrior. It fell out, too, that, officially at least, I was the last British officer to leave the war zone. My final duty was to haul down the Union Jack fluttering over G.H.Q., and that flag has remained ever since in my old theatre basket.

Such was the part I chanced to play in that larger theatre in which so many thousands of others enacted rôles far more distinguished than mine. Some months ago I had, in the film character of David Livingstone, to say these words: " When will men learn that war only sows the seeds of another, that no people can gain lasting security by imposing their will on the weaker or less fortunate? "

Well, they have not yet learned. Once again, therefore, men, and women also, in many walks of life have undertaken to play those parts, different in detail, but essentially the same in the qualities they demand, which they themselves or their parents discharged without ostentation, but with such unrivalled determination, a quarter of a century ago. Now, as then, they will not fail.

What my own rôle may be this time I have, as yet, no means of knowing. It is possible that I may be allowed to put on a uniform and do what I can, for my name is still on the Reserve List. Forty-six is not a vast age, though I am painfully aware that I am credited with being well advanced in senility. Save for the rôle of King Magnus in *The Apple Cart*, I have nearly always appeared since the days of *The Farmer's Wife* as a character stricken in years or, at all events, decidedly mature. Indeed, an American producer was so convinced of my decrepitude that the contract he offered me was not for a year, but for life! In any case, whatever my ostensible age, I have always been heavily disguised, and it is, I fear, a sad commentary on my personal appearance that the only time I have been allowed to show myself on the screen as I really am should be in a film where, while bearing the name of Mr. Brink, I was in reality a personification of Death!

Possibly I may be able to find a place among those providing entertainment in some form or other for the troops. But those two organisations, E.N.S.A. and N.A.A.F.I.—it's extraordinary how wars seem to call collections of initials into being—are already doing splendid work, and, by the time I get home, it may perhaps happen that there will be no room for me. Not that what befalls me is of any importance. In any case, it is an ironical and inevitable feature of these times that, in this struggle for the liberty, not only of nations, but of individuals, each of us, a cog in a vast machine, voluntarily sinks his individuality for the time being for the sake of the common cause.

But while *we* are insignificant, the theatre which we players are proud to serve is of enduring importance. We hope and trust that, as the outcome of this war, we shall find ourselves at the dawn of a new and better era, in a world which is something finer, as Mr. Anthony Eden put it, "than a stale reflection of the old, bled white." In like manner we hope and believe that the theatre, too, will take on a fresh, stimulating, and vigorous life.

These are dark days for the theatre, it may be argued; dark in the literal and the figurative sense alike. In the last war, when air-raids were infrequent and blackouts far from complete, the theatres were filled to capacity, whether we went to see *Chu Chin Chow*, *The Bing Boys*, or *A Little Bit of Fluff*. Light, cheerful, and spectacular pieces were mostly the order of the day, and they did much to hearten us. We craved entertainment, and the theatres supplied it. This time it is not so easy. At the moment the majority are shut or playing, as it were, fitfully. If the air-raid threat becomes a reality, even the few now open may be compelled to close down. How, then, can we expect health and a measure of prosperity to return to the stage?

Surely this is an idle question. We are all hopeful that out of the evils of this present war good will ultimately come. Admittedly not in material things, least of all at first. High taxation and widespread unemployment may well prevail among us for a time. But with the spectre of war laid and the principles of good faith among nations re-established—for what else can be our aim?—then a better order will be forthcoming. And if this be set up in the vast theatre of the world, why should the smaller one be passed by?

The pessimist will raise his dreary head to croak that the circumstances are not parallel. But for international unrest, he will point out, the world, or a

88

great part of it, would have settled down to a period of reviving trade. The stage, on the other hand, was in the trough of a depression and could never regain the crest.

Theatres in the provinces, he will remind us, have become cinemas. In Leicester Square, Shakespeare, were he to revolve on his pedestal as a variant to turning in his grave, would see five picture theatres and not a single play-house. Touring companies have largely vanished. Thousands of the younger generation have never seen a stage play. Twenty million people go each week to the cinema, and those who do not, prefer listening to the wireless to paying hard-earned money for the privilege of sitting in a theatre, the comfort of whose seats compares unfavourably with the accommodation to be had in a cinema at, perhaps, a more convenient hour and certainly for a quarter of the price. The actor-manager who backed his own judgment and had a settled policy for his theatre has disappeared. A successful play is acted until there is no chance of its being kept alive by later revivals, and gives rise to a flood of imitations doomed to a failure which discredits the memory of the original. The dramatist writes with half an eye on the prospect of film rights, whilst the player has ceased to be picturesque or romantic, and glamour has left the stage for the film studio. Scientific invention, in short, has dealt the death-blow to a long-moribund theatre.

Much of this may be true. But the conclusion is profoundly false. The theatre is not dead. How can it be when repertory companies flourish in many parts, when thousands of enthusiasts in towns and villages give plays two or three times a year, and when the reading of plays for pleasure is, despite the enormous number of novels available, more common than even in Restoration days?

It is, I think, possible that the very difficulty of seeing a play in these present months may stimulate an interest of late grown dull. Frequent visits to the pictures rob the experience of novelty, and from this it is but a short step to satiety and to the consequent yearning to see actors of flesh and blood. This is no mere wishful thinking. Let us put it in this way. In Victorian times, when domestic life was more hedged in with restraints than it is today, people found an outlet for suppressed emotions in seeing on the stage characters whose passions and vicissitudes were, so to speak, larger than life.

In the years since 1918 it has been different. Barriers were broken down. Emotions, once observed at second hand, became personal experiences. Ideals were shattered and standards changed. The need for an outlet by means of the theatre was temporarily lost, and people, groping in a strange new world, took refuge in the cynical and the trivial. Heroics went out of fashion and the theatre made the grievous mistake of attempting a realism and sometimes a lavishness in which it was hopelessly outclassed by the cinema. Yet, even here the theatre did not altogether lose its hold. Avoidance of those fields where, thanks to its mechanical and technical advantages, the cinema necessarily reigns supreme, would make unmistakably clear the great asset which the theatre just as inevitably enjoys. It is that elusive something which has enabled the drama to survive previous rebuffs and which must ensure its continuance, and that without trespassing on the acknowledged possessions of the screen or the microphone.

And what is this something? It is beyond my powers to express it exactly.

It is, I think, in part that the cinema shows rather than suggests. It makes little demand on the imagination of the spectator. Nor does it encourage him to listen to the beauty of words, to respond to that subtle magic which, be the fault that of playwright or of player, has often been so woefully lacking in recent years. That must at all costs be in some form recaptured, for it is part of the essential appeal of drama.

There is, too, what, for want of a better word, we term "personality," something present in the theatre, but absent when the players are but talking shadows on a screen or unseen voices in a room. And the theatre is not merely a large room. It is not an assembly of passive onlookers. A play is something that only comes to life when it is acted, and acted, furthermore, before an audience that, originally more or less active participants in a form of ritual, still contribute something vital, not demanded of them in a cinema. It is not a kind of duty laid upon them: it is an inward urge that they feel themselves, the intensity of which varies with the merit of the piece and the skill of the performers.

Subdued naturalistic acting and playwrights who, even though they deal with a great theme, have sought to enlighten rather than to stir have, perhaps, caused this inward urge to decline. But it is there. No other medium of public performance than the stage has been able to bring about this mutual contagion between actor and audience. And for that reason, whatever the fate of this theatre or that player, despite the possible barrenness of any particular period, the theatre can never die.

I have been fortunate in playing a good many parts. I hope I may be privileged to play many more. But in default of my fellows or myself, others will take our places and others again after them. It must be so, for the theatre satisfies an eternal and abiding need.

DAPHNE DU MAURIER

Daughter and biographer of that great actor, Gerald du Maurier, MISS DAPHNE DU MAURIER has high claims in her own right as a novelist. Although she has only been writing for some seven or eight years, she has already given us " Jamaica Inn " and " Rebecca."

THE ESCORT

THERE is nothing remarkable about the *Ravenswing*, I can promise you that. She is between six and seven thousand tons, was built in 1926, and belongs to the Condor Line, port of register Hull. You can look her up in Lloyd's if you have a mind. There is little to distinguish her from hundreds of other tramp steamers of her particular tonnage. She had sailed that same route and travelled those same waters for the three years I had served in her, and she was on the job some time before that. No doubt she will continue to do so for many years more, and will eventually end her days peacefully on the mud like her predecessor, the old *Gullswing*, did before her; unless the U-boats get her first.

She has escaped them once, but next time we may not have our escort. Perhaps I had better make it clear, too, that I myself am not a fanciful man. My name is William Blunt, and I have the reputation of living up to it. I never have stood for nonsense of any sort, and have no time for superstition. My father was a Nonconformist minister, and maybe that had something to do with it. I tell you this to prove my reliability, but, for that matter, you can ask anyone in Hull. And now, having introduced myself and the ship, I can get on with my story.

We were homeward bound from a Scandinavian port in the early part of the autumn. I won't give you the name of the port—the censor might stop me—but we had already made the trip there and back three times since the outbreak of war. The convoy system had not started, in those first days, and the strain on the captain and myself was severe. I don't want you to infer that we were windy, or the crew either, but the North Sea in war-time is not a bed of roses, and I'll leave it at that.

When we left port that October afternoon, I could not help thinking it seemed a long way home, and it did not put me in what you would call a rollicking humour when our little Scandinavian pilot told us with a grin that a Grimsby ship, six hours ahead of us, had been sunk without warning.

The Nazi Government had been giving out on the wireless, he said, that the North Sea could be called the German Ocean, and the British Fleet could not do anything about it. It was all right for the pilot, he was not coming with us. He waved a cheerful farewell as he climbed over the side, and soon his boat was a black speck bobbing astern of us at the harbour entrance, and we were heading for the open sea, our course laid for home.

It was about three o'clock in the afternoon, the sea was very still and grey, and I remember thinking to myself that a periscope would not be easy to miss; at least we would have fair warning, unless the glass fell and it began to blow. However, it did the nerves no good to envisage something that was not going to happen, and I was pretty short with the first engineer when he started talking about the submarine danger, and why did not the Admiralty do something about it?

"Your job is to keep the old *Ravenswing* full steam ahead for home and beauty, isn't it?" I said. "If Winston Churchill wants your advice, no doubt he'll send for you." He had no answer to that, and I lit my pipe and went on to the bridge to take over from the captain.

I suppose I'm not out-of-the-way observant about my fellow-men, and I certainly did not notice then that there was anything wrong with the captain. He was never much of a talker at any time. The fact that he went to his cabin at once meant little or nothing. I knew he was close at hand, if anything should happen. It turned very cold, after nightfall, and later a thin rain began to fall. The ship rolled slightly as she met the longer seas. The sky was overcast with the rain, and there were no stars. The autumn nights are always black, of course, in northern waters, but this night the darkness seemed intensified. There would be small chance of sighting a periscope, I thought, under these conditions, and it might well be that we should receive no other intimation than the shock of the explosion. Someone said the other day that the U-boats carried a new type of torpedo, super-charged, and that explained why the ships attacked sank so swiftly.

The *Ravenswing* would founder in three or four minutes, if she was hit right amidships, and it might be that we should never even sight the craft that sank us. The submarine would vanish in the darkness; they would not bother to pick up survivors. They could not see them if they wanted to, not in this darkness. I glanced at the chap at the wheel; he was a little Welshman from Cardiff, and he had a trick of sucking his false teeth and clicking them back into place again every few minutes. We stood a pretty equal chance, he and I, standing side by side together on the bridge.

It was then I turned suddenly and saw the captain standing in the entrance to his cabin. He was holding on for support, his face was very flushed, and he was breathing heavily.

"Is anything wrong, sir?" I said.

"This damn pain in my side," he gasped; "I started it yesterday, and thought I'd strained myself, and now I'm doubled up with the thing. Got any aspirin?" Aspirin my foot, I thought. If he has not got acute appendicitis I'll eat my hat. I'd seen a man attacked like that before; he'd been rushed to hospital and operated on in less than two hours. They'd taken an appendix out of him swollen as big as a fist.

"Have you got a thermometer there?" I asked the captain.

"Yes," he said. "What's the use of that? I haven't got a temperature. I've strained myself, I tell you. I want some aspirin."

I took his temperature. It was a hundred and four. The sweat was pouring down his forehead. I put my hand on his stomach, and it was

92

rigid, like a brick wall. I helped him to his berth and covered him up with blankets. Then I made him drink half a glass of brandy neat. It may be the worst thing you can do for appendicitis, but when you are hundreds of miles from a surgeon and in the middle of the North Sea in war-time you are apt to take chances. The brandy helped to dull the pain, and that was the only thing that mattered. Whatever the result to the captain, it had but one result for me. I was in command of the *Ravenswing* from now on, and mine was the responsibility of bringing her safely home through those submarine-infested waters. I, William Blunt, had got to see this through.

It was bitterly cold. All feeling had long since left my hands and feet. I was conscious of a dull pain in those parts of my body where my hands and my feet should have been. But the effect was curiously impersonal. The pain might have belonged to somebody else, the sick captain himself even, back there in his cabin, lying moaning and helpless as I had left him last, some forty-eight hours before. He was not my charge; I could do nothing for him. The steward nursed him with brandy and aspirin, and I remember feeling surprised, in a detached sort of way, that he did not die.

" You ought to get some sleep. You can't carry on like this. Why don't you get some sleep? "

Sleep. That was the trouble. What was I doing at that moment but rocking on my two feet on the border-line of oblivion, with the ship in my charge, and this voice in my left ear the sound that brought me to my senses. It was Carter, the second mate. His face looked pinched and anxious.

" Supposing you get knocked up? " he was saying. " What am I going to do? Why don't you think of me? "

I told him to go to hell, and stamped up and down the bridge to bring the life back to my numbed feet, and to disguise the fact from Carter that sleep had nearly been victorious.

" What else do you think has kept me on the bridge for forty-eight hours but the thought of you? " I said, " and the neat way you let the stern hawser drop adrift, with the second tug alongside, last time we were in Hull. Get me a cup of tea and a sandwich, and shut your mouth," I said.

My words must have relieved him, for he grinned back at me and shot down the ladder like a jack-in-the-box. I held on to the bridge and stared ahead, sweeping the horizon for what seemed like the hundred thousandth time, and seeing always the same blank face of the sea, slate-grey and still. There were low-banked clouds to the westward, whether mist or rain I could not tell, but they gathered slowly without wind and the glass held steady, while there was a certain smell about the air, warning of fog. I swallowed my cup of tea and made short work of a sandwich, and was feeling in my pocket for my pipe and a box of matches when the thing happened for which, I suppose, I had consciously been training myself since the captain went sick some forty-eight hours before.

" Object to port. Three-quarters of a mile to a mile distant. Looks like a periscope."

The word came from the look-out on the fo'c'sle head, and flashed back to the watch on deck. As I snatched my glasses I caught a glimpse of the faces

93

of the men lining the ship's side, curiously uniform they were, half-eager, half-defiant.

Yes. There she was. No doubt now. A thin grey line, like a needle, away there on our port bow, leaving a narrow wake behind her like a jagged ripple. Once again I was aware of Carter beside me, tense, expectant, and I noticed that his hands trembled slightly as he lifted the glasses in his turn. I gave the necessary alteration in our course, telegraphed the corresponding change of speed down to the first engineer, and then took up my glasses once more. The change of course had brought the periscope right ahead, and for a few minutes or so the thin line continued on its way as though indifferent to our manœuvre, and then, as I had feared and foreseen, the submarine altered course, even as we had done, and the periscope bore down upon us, this time to starboard.

" She's seen us," said Carter.

" Yes," I said. He looked up at me, his brown eyes troubled like a spaniel puppy's. We altered course again and increased our speed, this time bringing our stern to the thin grey needle, so that for a moment it seemed as though the gap between us would be widened and she would pass away behind us, but, swift and relentless, she bore up again on our quarter, and little Carter began to swear, fluently and passionately, the futility of words a sop to his own fear. I sympathised, seeing in a flash, as the proverbial drowning man is said to do, an episode in my own childhood when my father had lectured me for lying and even as I remembered this picture of a long-forgotten past I spoke down the mouth-tube to the engine-room once more, and ordered yet another alteration in our speed. The watch below had joined the watch on deck. They lined the side of the ship, as though hypnotised by that unwavering grey line that crept closer, ever closer.

" She's breaking surface," said Carter. " Watch that line of foam."

The periscope had come abeam of us and had drawn ahead. It was now a little over a mile distant, on our port bow. Carter was right. She was breaking surface, even as he said. We could see the still water become troubled and disturbed, and then slowly, inevitably, the squat conning-tower appeared and the long lean form rose from the depths like a black slug, the water streaming from its decks.

" The bastards," whispered Carter to himself; " the filthy, stinking bastards." The men below me on the deck watched the submarine with a strange indifference, like spectators at some show with which they had no concern. I saw one fellow point out some technical detail of the submarine to the man by his side, and then light a cigarette. His companion laughed, and spat over the side of the ship into the water. I wondered how many of them could swim.

I gave the final order through to the engine-room, and then ordered all hands on deck, to boat stations. My next order would depend on the commander of the submarine.

" They'll shell the boats," said Carter; " they won't let us get away, they'll shell the boats."

" Oh, for God's sake," I began, the pallor of his face begetting in me a furious senseless anger, when suddenly I caught sight of the wall of fog that was rolling down upon us from astern. I swung Carter round by the shoulders to meet it. " Look there," I said, " look there," and his jaw dropped, and he

94

grinned stupidly. Already the visibility around us was no more than a cable's length on either side, and the first drifting vapour stung us with its cold sour smell. Above us the air was thick and clammy. In a moment our after shrouds were lost to sight. I heard one fellow strike up the opening chorus of a comic song in a high falsetto voice and he was immediately cursed to silence by his companions. Ahead of us lay the submarine, dark and immobile, the water still running from its sides, the decks as yet unmanned, and her long snout caught unexpectedly in a sudden shaft of light. Then the white fog that enveloped us crept forward and beyond : the sky descended, and our world was blotted out.

It wanted two minutes to midnight. I crouched low under cover of the bridge and flashed a torch on to my watch. No bell had been sounded since the submarine had first been sighted, some eight hours earlier.

We waited. Darkness had travelled with the fog, and night fell early. There was silence everywhere, but for the creaking of the ship as she rolled in the swell, and the thud of water slapping her sides as she lay over, first one side, then the other. Still we waited. The cold was no longer so intense as it had been. There was a moist, clammy feeling in the air. The men talked in hushed whispers beneath the bridge.

We went on waiting. Once I entered the cabin where the captain lay sick, and flashed my torch on to him. His face was flushed and puffy. His breathing was heavy and slow. He was sleeping fitfully, moaning now and again, and once he opened his eyes, but he did not recognise me. I went back to the bridge. The fog had lifted slightly, and I could see our forward shrouds and the fo'c'sle head. I went down on to the deck and leant over the ship's side. The tide was running strongly to the south. It had turned three hours before, and for the fourth time that evening I began to calculate our drift. I was turning to the ladder to climb to the bridge once more, when I heard footsteps running along the deck, and a man cannonaded into me.

" Fog's lifting astern," he said breathlessly, " and there's something coming up on our starboard quarter."

I ran back along the deck with him. A group of men were clustered at the ship's side, talking eagerly. " It's a ship all right, sir," said one; " looks like a Finnish barque. I can see her canvas."

I peered into the darkness with them. Yes, there she was, about a hundred yards distant, and bearing down upon us. A great three-masted vessel, with a cloud of canvas aloft. It was too late in the year for the grain ships. What was she doing in these waters in war-time? Unless she was carrying timber. Had she seen us, though? That was the point. Here were we, without lights, skulking in the trough of the sea because of that damned submarine, and now risking collision with some old timber ship. If only I could be certain that the tide and the fog had put a number of miles between us and the enemy. She was coming up fast, the old-timer. God knows where she found her wind—there was none on my left cheek that would blow a candle. If she passed us at this rate there would be fifty yards to spare, no more, and with that hell-ship waiting yonder in the darkness somewhere the Finn would go straight to Kingdom come.

" All right," I said, " she's seen us; she's bearing away." I could only make out her outline in the darkness as she travelled past abeam. A great, high-sided vessel she was, in ballast probably, or there would never have been so much of her out of the water. I'd forgotten they had such bulky after-decks. Her spars were not the clean things I remembered either; these were a mass of rigging, and the yards an extraordinary length, necessary, no doubt, for all that bunch of canvas.

"She's not going to pass us," said somebody, and I heard the blocks rattle and jump, and the rigging slat, as the great yards swung over. And was that faint high note, curious and immeasurably distant, the pipe of a boatswain's whistle? But the fog vapour was drifting down on us again, and the ship was hidden. We strained our eyes in the darkness, seeing nothing, and I was about to turn back to the bridge again when a thin call came to us from across the water.

"Are you in distress?" came the hail. Whether her nationality was Finnish or not, at least her officer spoke good English, even if his phrasing was a little unusual. I was wary though, and I did not answer. There was a pause, and then the voice travelled across to us once more. "What ship are you, and where are you bound?"

And then, before I could stop him, one of our fellows bellowed out, "There's an enemy submarine come to the surface about half a mile ahead of us." Someone smothered the idiot half a minute too late, and, for better for worse, our flag had been admitted. We waited. None of us moved a finger. All was silent. Presently we heard the splash of oars and the low murmur of voices. They were sending a boat across to us from the barque. There was something furtive and strange about the whole business. I was suspicious. I did not like it. I felt for the hard butt of my revolver, and was reassured. The sound of oars drew nearer. A long low boat like a west-country gig drew out of the shadows, manned by half a dozen men. There was a fellow with a lantern in the bows. Someone, an officer I presumed, stood up in the stern. It was too dark for me to see his face. The boat pulled up beneath us, and the men rested on their oars.

"Captain's compliments, gentlemen, and do you desire an escort?" enquired the officer.

"What the hell!" began one of our men, but I cursed him to be quiet. I leant over the side, shading my eyes from the light of the boat's lantern.

"Who are you?" I said.

"Lieutenant Arthur Mildmay, at your service, sir," replied the voice.

There was nothing foreign in his intonation, I could swear to that, but again I was struck by his phraseology. No snottie in the Navy ever talked like this. The Admiralty might have bought up a Finnish barque, of course, and armed her, like Von Lucknow did in the last war; but the idea seemed unlikely.

"Are you camouflaged?" I asked.

"I beg your pardon?" he replied, in some surprise. Then his English was not so fluent as I thought. Once again I felt for my revolver. "You're not trying to make a fool of me by any chance, are you?" I said sarcastically.

"Not in the least," replied the voice. "I repeat, the captain sends his compliments, and as you gave him to understand we are in the immediate vicinity of the enemy, he desires me to offer you his protection. Our orders are to escort any merchant ships we find to a port of safety."

FROM THE ORIGINAL BY EDMUND BLAMPIED

The Symbol

"And who issued those orders?" I said.

"His Majesty King George, of course," replied the voice. It was then, I think, that I felt for the first time a curious chill of fear. I remember swallowing hard. My throat felt very dry and I could not answer at once. I looked at the men around me, and they wore, one and all, a silly, dumb expression on their faces.

"He says the King sent him," said the fellow beside me, and then his voice trailed away uncertainly, and he fell silent.

I heard Carter tap me on the shoulder. "Send them away," he whispered. "There's something wrong; it's a trap."

The man kneeling in the bows of the gig flashed his lantern in my face, blinding me. The young lieutenant stepped across the thwarts and took the lantern from him. "Why not come aboard and speak to the captain yourself if you are in doubt?" he said.

Still I could not see his face, but he wore some sort of cloak round his shoulders, and the hand that held the lantern was long and slim. The lantern that dazzled me brought a pain across my eyes so severe that for a few moments I could neither speak nor think, and then, to my own surprise, I heard myself answer, "Very well, make room for me then in your boat."

Carter laid his hand on my arm. "You're crazy," he said; "you can't leave the ship."

I shook him off, obstinate for no reason, determined on my venture. "You're in charge, Carter," I said; "I shan't be long away. Let me go, you damn fool."

I ordered the ladder over the side, and wondered, with a certain irritation, why the stupid fellows gaped at me as they obeyed. I had that funny reckless feeling that comes upon you when you're half-drunk, and I wondered if the reason for it was my own lack of sleep for over forty-eight hours.

I landed with a thud in the gig, and stumbled to the stern beside the officer. The men bent to their oars, and the boat began to creep across the water to the barque. It was bitterly cold. The clammy mugginess was gone. I turned up the collar of my coat and tried to catch a closer glimpse of my companion, but it was black as pitch in the boat, and his features were hidden from me. I felt the seat under me, with my hand. It was like ice, freezing to the touch, and I plunged my hands deep in my pockets. The cold seemed to penetrate my great-coat and find my flesh. My teeth chattered, and I could not stop them. The chap in front of me, bending to his oar, was a great burly brute, with shoulders like an ox. His sleeves were rolled up above his elbow, his arms were bare. He was whistling softly between his teeth.

"You don't feel the cold then?" I asked.

He did not answer, and I leant forward and looked into his face. He stared through me, as though I did not exist, and went on whistling between his teeth. His eyes were deep-set, sunken in his head. His cheek-bones were very prominent and high. He wore a queer, stove-pipe of a hat, shiny and black.

"Look here," I said, tapping him on his knee, " I'm not here to be fooled, I can tell you that."

And then the lieutenant, as he styled himself, stood up beside me in the stern. "Ship ahoy," he called, his two hands to his mouth, and, looking up, I saw we were already beneath the barque, her great sides towering above us.

G   97

A lantern appeared on the bulwark by the ladder, and again my eyes were dazzled by the sickly yellow light.

The lieutenant swung on to the ladder, and I followed him, hand over fist, breathing hard, for the bitter cold caught at me and seemed to strike right down into my throat, as though I swallowed ice. I paused when I reached the deck, with a stitch in my side like a kicking horse, and in that queer half-light that came from the flickering lanterns I saw that this was no Finnish barque with a load of timber, no grain ship in ballast, but a raider bristling with guns. Her decks were cleared for action, and the men were there ready at their stations. There was much activity and shouting, and a thin high voice from for'ard calling out orders. There seemed to be a haze of smoke thick in the air, and a heavy sour stench, and with it all the cold dank chill I could not explain.

"What is it?" I called. "What's the game?" No one answered. Figures passed me and brushed me, shouting and laughing at one another. A lad of about thirteen ran by me, with a short blue jacket and long white trousers, while close beside me, crouching by his gun, was a great bearded fellow like my oarsmen of the gig, with a striped stocking cap upon his hat. Once again above the hum and confusion I heard the thin shrill piping of the boatswain's whistle, and, turning, I saw a crowd of jostling men running barefooted to the after-deck, and I caught the gleam of steel in their hands.

"The captain will see you, if you come aft," said the lieutenant.

I followed him, angry and bewildered. Carter was right, I had been fooled; and yet as I stumbled in the wake of the lieutenant I heard English voices shouting on the deck, and funny, unfamiliar English oaths.

We pushed through a door on the after-deck, and the musty rank smell became more sour and more intense. It was darker still. Blinking, I found myself at the entrance of a large cabin, lit only by flickering lantern light, and in the centre of the cabin was a long table, and a man was sitting there in a funny high-backed chair. Three or four other men stood behind him, but the lantern light shone on his face alone.

He was very thin, very pale, and his hair was ashen grey. I saw by the patch he wore that he had lost the sight of one eye, but the other eye looked through me in the cold abstracted way of someone who would get his business done, and has little time to spare.

"Your name, my man?" he said, tapping with his hand upon the table before him.

"William Blunt, sir," I said, and I found myself standing to attention, with my cap in my hands, my throat as dry as a bone, and that same funny chill of fear in my heart.

"You report there is an enemy vessel close at hand, I understand?"

"Yes, sir," I said; "a submarine came to the surface about a mile distant from us, some hours ago. She had been following us for half an hour before she broke surface. Luckily the fog came down and hid us. Since then we have not attempted to steam, but have drifted without lights."

He listened to me in silence. The figures behind him did not move. There was something sinister in their immobility and his, as though my words meant nothing to them, as though they did not believe me or did not understand.

"I shall be glad to offer you my assistance, Mr. Blunt," he said at last. I stood awkwardly, still turning my cap in my hands. He did not mean to make game of me, I realised that, but what use was his ship to me?

"I don't quite see," I began, but he held up his hand.

"The enemy will not attack you while you are under my protection," he said; "if you care to accept my escort, I shall be very pleased to give you safe-conduct to England. The fog has lifted, and luckily the wind is with us."

I swallowed hard. I did not know what to say.

"We steam at eleven knots," I said awkwardly, and when he did not reply I stepped forward to his table, thinking he had not heard. "Supposing the blighter is still there," I said; "he'll get the pair of us. She'll blow up like matchwood, this ship of yours. You stand even less chance than us."

The man seated by the table leant back in his chair. I saw him smile. "I've never run from a Frenchman yet," he said.

Once again I heard the boatswain's whistle, and the patter of bare feet overhead upon the deck. The lanterns swayed, in a current of air from the swinging door. The cabin seemed very musty, very dark. I felt faint and queer, and something like a sob rose in my throat which I could not control.

"I'd like your escort," I stammered, and even as I spoke he rose in his chair and leant towards me. I saw the faded blue of his coat, and the ribbon across it. I saw his pale face very close, and the one blue eye. I saw him smile, and I felt the strength of the hand that held mine and saved me from falling.

They must have carried me to the boat and down the ladder, for when I opened my eyes again, with a queer dull ache at the back of my head, I was at the foot of my own gangway, and my own chaps were hauling me aboard. I could just hear the splash of oars as the gig pulled away back to the barque.

"Thank God you're back!" said Carter. "What the devil did they do to you? You're as white as chalk. Were they Finns or Boche?"

"Neither," I said curtly; "they're English, like ourselves. I saw the captain. I've accepted his escort home."

"Have you gone raving mad?" said Carter.

I did not answer. I went up to the bridge and gave orders for steaming. Yes, the fog was lifting, and above my head I could see the first pale glimmer of a star. I listened, well content, to the familiar noises of the ship as we got under way again. The throb of the screw, the thrash of the propeller. The relief was tremendous. No more silence, no more inactivity. The strain was broken, and the men were themselves again, cheerful, cracking jokes at one another. The cold had vanished, and the curious dead fatigue that had been part of my mind and body for so long. The warmth was coming back to my hands and my feet. Slowly we began to draw ahead once more, ploughing our way in the swell, while to starboard of us, some hundred yards distant, came our escort, the white foam hissing from her bows, her cloud of canvas billowing to a wind that none of us could feel. I saw the helmsman beside me glance at her out of the tail of his eye, and when he thought I was not looking he wet his finger and held it in the air. Then his eye met mine, and fell again, and he whistled a song to show he did not care. I wondered if he thought me as mad as Carter did. Once I went in to see the captain. The steward was

99

with him, and when I entered he switched on the lamp above the captain's berth.

" His fever's down," he said; " he's sleeping naturally at last. I don't think we're going to lose him after all."

" No, I guess he'll be all right," I said.

I went back to the bridge, whistling the song I had heard from the sailor in the gig. It was a jaunty, lilting tune, familiar in a rum sort of way, but I could not put a name to it. The fog had cleared entirely, and the sky was ablaze with stars. We were steaming now at our full rate of knots, but still our escort kept abeam, and sometimes, if anything, she drew just a fraction ahead.

Whether the submarine was on the surface still, or whether she had dived, I neither knew nor cared, for I was full of that confidence that I had lacked before, and which, after a while, seemed to possess the helmsman in his turn, so that he grinned at me, jerking his head at our escort, and said, " There don't seem to be no flies on Nancy, do there? " and fell, as I did, to whistling that nameless jaunty tune. Only Carter remained sullen and aloof. His fear had given way to sulky silence, and at last, sick of the sight of his moody face staring through the chart-room window, I ordered him below, and was aware of a new sense of freedom and relief when he had gone.

So the night wore on, and we, plunging and rolling in the wake of our flying escort, saw never a sight of periscope or lean grey hull again. At last the sky lightened to the eastward, and low down on the horizon appeared the streaky pallid dawn. Five bells struck, and away ahead of us, faint as a whisper, came the answering pipe of a boatswain's whistle. I think I was the only one that heard it. Then I heard the weak tired voice of the captain calling me from his cabin. I went to him at once. He was propped up against his pillows, and I could tell from his face he was as weak as a rat, but his temperature was normal, even as the steward had said.

" Where are we, Blunt? " he said. " What's happened? "

" We'll be safely berthed before the people ashore have rung for breakfast," I said; " the coast's right ahead of us now."

" What's the date, man? " he asked. I told him.

" We've made good time," he said. I agreed.

" I shan't forget what you've done, Blunt," he said; " I'll speak to the owners about you. You'll be getting promotion for this."

" Promotion my foot ! " I said. " You don't need to thank me, but our escort away on the starboard bow."

" Escort? " he said, staring at me. " What escort? Are we travelling in a convoy? "

Then I told him the story, starting with the submarine, and the fog, and so on to the coming of the barque herself, and my own visit aboard her, and not missing out an account of my own nerves and jumpiness either. He listened to me, dazed and bewildered on his pillow.

" What's the name of your barque? " he said slowly, when I had finished.

I smote my hand on my knee. " It may be Old Harry for all I know; I never asked them," I said, and I began whistling the tune that the fellow had sung as he bent to his oars in the gig.

" I can't make it out," said the captain; " you know as well as I do there aren't any sailing-ships left on the British register."

I shrugged my shoulders. Why couldn't he accept the escort as naturally as I and the men had done?

"Get me a drink, and stop whistling that confounded jig," said the captain. I laughed, and gave him his glass.

"What's wrong with it?" I said.

"It's Lillibullero, centuries old. What makes you whistle that?" he said. I stared back at him, and I was not laughing any longer.

"I don't know," I said, "I don't know."

He drank thirstily, watching me over the rim of his glass. "Where's your precious escort now?" he said.

"On the starboard bow," I repeated, and I went forward to the bridge again and gazed seaward, where I knew her to be.

The sun, like a great red globe, was topping the horizon, and the night clouds were scudding to the west. Far ahead, like a long low smudge, lay the coast of England. But our escort had gone.

I turned to the fellow steering. "When did she go?" I asked.

"Beg pardon, sir?" he said.

"The sailing-ship. What happened to her?" I repeated.

The man looked puzzled, and cocked his eye at me in a curious way.

"I've seen no sailing-ship," he said. "There's a destroyer been abeam of us some time. She must have come up with us under cover of darkness. I've only noticed her since the sun rose."

I snatched up my glasses and looked to the west. The fellow was not dreaming. There was a destroyer with us, as he said. She plunged into the long seas, churning up the water and chucking it from her like a great white wall of foam. I watched her for a few minutes in silence, and then I lowered my glasses. The fellow steering gazed straight in front of him. Now daylight had come he seemed changed in a queer indefinable way. He no longer whistled jauntily, with a rakish, reckless air. He was his usual stolid seaman self.

"We shall be docked by nine-thirty. We've made good time," I said.

"Yes, sir," he said.

Already I could see a black dot far ahead, and a wisp of smoke. The tugs were lying off for us. Carter was in my old place on the fo'c'sle head. The men were at their stations. I, on the captain's bridge, would bring his ship to port. He called me to him, five minutes before the tugs took us in tow, when the first gulls were wheeling overhead.

"Blunt," he said, "I've been thinking. That captain fellow you spoke to in the night, on board that sailing-craft. You say he wore a black patch over one eye. Did he by any chance have an empty sleeve pinned to his breast as well?"

I did not answer. We looked at each other in silence. Then a shrill whistle warned me that the pilot's boat was alongside. Somewhere, faint and far, the echo sounded like a boatswain's pipe.

ANN BRIDGE

MISS ANN BRIDGE won the Atlantic Monthly Prize and instant recognition with her first novel, " Peking Picnic." Since then she has published one book of short stories and five other novels, as varied as they are delightful. It is a question on which side of the Atlantic Miss Ann Bridge's work gets the more enthusiastic welcome.

LOOKING BACK ON MAY THE SIXTH, 1935

LOOKING back on May the sixth, 1935, that day of sun and warmth so strangely interposed in the grimmest and harshest of English springs, blowing cold and grey from the north-west week after week, one has the feeling that that unexpected and spontaneous rejoicing of a whole nation, carefree and happy in a world shadowed by the storm-clouds of calamity, was like the day itself—a lovely thing, a perfect moment of consciousness suddenly vouchsafed to the most patient, the most pedestrian, the most inexpressive and subconscious of peoples. I am glad that I was alive to see it; it brings warmth into more wintry days to remember what I saw, what I heard—just in what manner England for once knew her soul and was glad.

I was at Oxford. The Bach Choir and the Oxford Musical Society had decided to celebrate simultaneously both His Majesty's Jubilee and the anniversaries of the two great musicians, Bach and Handel; and for a whole week of Festival the holy city of the humanities expressed its rejoicing in the clear, formal, and lovely strains of two centuries ago. But the great day was Jubilee Day itself, when in the eighteenth-century elegance of the Sheldonian Theatre the massed voices of youth and age sang not only Bach's most glorious motet, " Sing Ye to the Lord," but also the anthems which Handel had written for the Coronation of an earlier King George of England. I have heard mixed choirs sing in many parts of the world, but never anything lovelier than the quality of those sopranos at Oxford: the preponderance of girls' voices, young and high, gave it a freshness, a ringing clarity like the notes of birds at dawn.

But the day did not begin with the concert. That was in the afternoon. In the morning I drove a car crammed with girls in pretty summery frocks through the grey dignified streets—here and there blossoming trees, flowering over the ancient walls, reminded me of how Oxford, old and wise, for ever blooms afresh with the youth that fills her, century after century. Perennial magic of that perennial union, in the most beautiful of cities, of all that is most lovely and precious out of the past with all that is most youthful and ardent in the present. Quiller-Couch's wistful lines came into the mind:

> *Know you her secret none can utter?*
> *Hers of the Book, the tripled crown?*
> *Still on the spire the pigeons flutter,*
> *Still by the gateway flits the gown.*

We went up to a house in a beautiful garden on one of the hills above the city; there, between limes and lilacs and flowering cherries, the eye travelled down to Oxford's towers, spire and dome and pinnacle; and there, while the bells of Magdalen and the deeper notes of Great Tom at Christ Church came up to us through the sunshine, we listened over the wireless to the hum and shuffle of the waiting crowds in the London streets, and the joyous pealing of the bells of St. Clement's and St. Paul's. We heard the clatter of the feet of cavalry, the sharp voice of command; and then the roar of cheering, swelling like the sound of surf on a shore, as the King passed up Ludgate Hill and entered the Cathedral.

Listening to the service in St. Paul's, I was principally struck by one thing—the familiarity and antiquity of the *form* of the service. I had spent the early part of the spring in Germany and Italy, and in both countries I had attended various celebrations of a national character. Under these new dictatorships the formulas for rejoicing are new, and new songs are sung, like the *Horst Wessel Lied*—a rather uninspiring pæan—and the new verses to *Deutschland, Deutschland über alles*. But when Great Britain celebrated the Jubilee she used forms which were familiar to every English person since childhood—the prayers, the clauses, were part of the ordinary furniture of our minds, and when we sang the Te Deum we sang the very words which England used to rejoice in the victory over the Armada nearly three hundred and fifty years ago—words which have been used on every solemn occasion in the nation's history since that day. And recalling the rather febrile note of those Continental rejoicings, the undercurrent of uncertainty and strain, I could not but feel the contrast—what stability and strength there was in these ancient usages, with their centuries of memories behind them, their dear and customary simplicity today. The Old Hundredth Psalm—since Cromwell's time we have sung that when Kings were born or married, or battles won by sea or land, or the State delivered from any peril. And the Archbishop's sermon, brief, direct, and homely, was in key with all the rest. There were no flights of oratory or difficult turns of phrase—very simply and quietly he voiced what was in the nation's heart, and suddenly we knew what we were feeling. Later in the day we were to realise our emotions more fully, and recognise their nature with a certain surprise, but the Archbishop's sermon was the first intimation of them.

There was just one new thing in the service—one hymn which was not centuries old and hallowed by custom. This was "I Vow to Thee, My Country," written by Sir Cecil Spring-Rice, onetime British Ambassador at Washington, after his son had been killed in the war, and set by the late Gustav Holst to one of the noblest of his melodies. I quote it in full, because I like to recall what new song it was that we in England sang in the hour of our rejoicing:

103

I vow to thee, my country—all earthly things above—
Entire and whole and perfect, the service of my love,
The love that asks no question: the love that stands the test,
That lays upon the altar the dearest and the best:
The love that never falters, the love that pays the price,
The love that makes undaunted the final sacrifice.

And there's another country, I've heard of long ago—
Most dear to them that love her, most great to them that know—
We may not count her armies: we may not see her King—
Her fortress is a faithful heart, her pride is suffering—
And soul by soul and silently her shining bounds increase,
And her ways are ways of gentleness and all her paths are Peace.

Here, you see, was no pride of conquest, no dream of dominion, no rattling of sabres and sounding of drums. And as I listened to the voices of that vast concourse in St. Paul's, pouring out, with a sincerity of emotion which the wireless could not mask, their aspiration towards that city not built with hands, that invisible kingdom of the spirit which knows no earthly boundaries of race or speech, whose gates stand wide in welcome to all men of goodwill, I had a passionate wish that by some sudden Pentecostal illumination all the statesmen of all the countries of the earth could hear what I was hearing, and each " in his own tongue in which he was born " could know the words we were singing and the spirit in which they were sung. " Her ways are ways of gentleness and all her paths are Peace "—repeated, the words died away, lingeringly, into silence. It was the nation singing! And that was England's aspiration, in a world racked with disquiets, economic and political, feverish with suspicion and fear and distrust. I could just remember the Diamond Jubilee, and the tone of our rejoicings then—militant, arrogant, imperialistic, crude, in fact really rather juvenile; and in a flash of understanding I realised a new fact about my country: as a nation, Great Britain had grown up.

A little hushed, a little sobered by the splendour of the Cathedral service and the thoughts which it engendered, we passed out into the sunshine again, packed into various cars, and went down into Oxford to get some lunch before the concert in the Sheldonian. The concert over, the National Anthem sung, the conductor raised his baton for silence. " The choir and I," he said, " for our own pleasure, and to celebrate this day, are going to do Bach's ' Sing Ye to the Lord ' all over again. The audience can leave or stay, as they please." Many stayed—others, we among them, went out and sat in the sun on the flagstones under the grey walls of the lovely circular building, among the crowd of dons, musicians with their instruments, visitors, and undergraduates, settling what we should do next. We had heard London's celebrations over the wireless, we had taken part in Oxford's concert—now, we decided, we would see what the English countryside was making of the Jubilee. And to that end we arranged to go out and dine at Abingdon, where the Crown and Thistle (a thoroughly appropriate hostelry for a Jubilee dinner, we felt) offered a fairly sophisticated meal.

Abingdon lies on the river, about six miles out of Oxford—a beautiful little town of old red brick, approached by a long and noble bridge of grey stone, carrying the road across the willow-fringed water meadows and the quiet Thames; with a fine grey church, and a huge market-square adorned with an elegant eighteenth-century Town Hall. We chose Abingdon not only because of the probable merits of dinner at the Crown, but because it is the heart and centre of a large tract of agricultural country, lying between the river and the Downs, ill-served by road and by railway, and containing a population as simple, rustic, and unmodernised as almost any other in the South of England. When you go into the villages of South Oxfordshire, you go back sixty years, in customs, outlook, and speech. Now it is the habit of these villagers, on market days, Saturdays, and all occasions of holiday or importance, to go into Abingdon to hear the news, gather opinions, and see life generally, sitting in the small dark pubs or hanging about the bus stop in the square. And we assumed that on Jubilee Day they would probably have mustered there in force.

We were right. They had. As we drove along through spring woods sky-floored with bluebells, whose scent, piercingly sweet, floated in through the car windows and reached us as we sat, we overtook little parties walking cheerfully along the road—Father, rather stiff in his dark Sunday best, pushing the perambulator; Mother, gayer in hers, holding a child by either hand and calling to the others to " mind they motors, now! " By the time we reached the bridge the groups had thickened to a crowd, through which we could only move at a foot's pace. Slowly, carefully, we worked our way through the narrow streets to the square. The mellow brickwork of the houses of Abingdon had disappeared behind a sea of flags; the streets and pavements were indistinguishable, both alike thronged with humanity—here and there through the crowd moved figures in rich historical costumes, for Abingdon, we learned, had indulged in a pageant procession to illustrate her past glories. And over all the bells of the grey church pealed out ceaselessly, in a quick joyful rhythm that knocked on the heart and set the pulses dancing—Abingdon is a royal borough, and had decided to mark the fact by non-stop bell-ringing for twelve hours, from 7 a.m. to 7 p.m. Relay teams from the country churches round about, having rung their own Jubilee peals, came in to help the Abingdon ringers, and without an instant's pause or check that merry noise had gone on all day.

All this, and much more, we learned during our first hour in Abingdon. Having parked the cars, we descended upon the public-houses of the town, splitting up into twos and threes and entering those curious dark low rooms, blue with tobacco smoke and gloomy with old timbers, in which rural England takes its ease during its scanty hours of leisure. With our pints of Four X ale we sat in the ladies' parlour, the darts parlour, the private or the public bars, and entered into conversation with the assembled company wherever we happened to be. No one was drunk, but all were cheerful; by beer and by the greatness of the occasion tongues were—very slightly—loosened; and, as we had hoped, we heard what Oxfordshire thought about the Silver Jubilee.

The King and Queen, we learned, were " nice "; they were not at all " high "—on the contrary, they were " homely "; they worried about the unemployed and the people in hospitals; the Queen wore such lovely dresses, and was, besides, a good mother—" Ah, an' a grandmother too, bless the little Duchess! " Soberly, with queerly expressed but unmistakable satisfaction,

105

we passed on to philosophise, in the true public-house fashion, about England and international affairs. We in the darts parlour, between due applause to skilful throws, agreed what a good thing it was to have a king; we asked Mr. Brown, who was eighty-nine, if it was not a good thing to have a king, and Mr. Brown, who was a bit hard of hearing, having at last mastered the import of the question, gave it as his verdict that it was a very good thing to have a king—" so 'e be a good king. An' our King George *be* a good king! " Applause for Mr. Brown, applause for King George; more beer for the dart players, more beer for Mrs. Godfrey. " 'Tis Jubilee Day, Mrs. Godfrey—do 'ee have another, now! " Mrs. Godfrey did, while we went on to decide how pitiable was the lot of almost all foreigners, with their upstart dictators and cheerless republics, with no jolly family of princes to marry pretty wives and have children and do as their fathers did and be read about in the papers. The Prince of Wales, now! " 'E be a rare 'un," we said.

But what emerged from all this, with a clearness that startled some of our party, was that to these country people the royal family, the principle of king-ship, *meant* something: something real, valuable, and personally important to them, though for reasons which they were utterly incapable of formulating, otherwise than in such sentences as those reported above. There was affec-tion here, and pride—the strong possessive pride of ownership: " Our King," " Our Queen "; and the good folk of Oxfordshire were rejoicing in the Jubilee with something of the possessive pride of old servants in the achieve-ments of the son of the house. " Our " king had done well; he had lasted twenty-five years; he was a fine fellow, and we were all fine fellows too, and finer because of him; his Jubilee had made us realise ourselves, and what a fine place England was—and so we were ringing the bells right the clock round, and Mr. Brown and Mrs. Godfrey would each have another beer.

Now the unmistakableness, warmth, and spontaneity of this feeling came almost as a shock to many of us. For weeks and months beforehand the preparations and arrangements for the Jubilee had been written up in the press till the more sophisticated English were sick of the very sound of the word; and we had expected that when the day came the whole thing would be thor-oughly machine-made, artificial, and without reality of any kind, merely from over-preparation. It was not so. For the waiting crowds in London and the gathering of England's greatest in St. Paul's it had clearly not been so; we saw for ourselves that it was not so for the yokels gathered in the ancient public-houses of Abingdon. Nor was it really so for us. The Archbishop's sermon in the morning had begun to stir our feelings; those tireless pealing bells at Abingdon and the gaiety of the crowded little streets finished what his words began, and now, with a half-shy, half-amused surprise, we recognised in our-selves a real emotion: a quite active joy, a genuine dancing gaiety of spirit.

Suddenly, through the little dark rooms, the clink of glasses, the jolly laughter, and the slow laborious sentences, a word went round: " The King is coming on in the Square." Out we trooped, pint in hand, some of us, and joined the already dense throng on the cobblestones before the Town Hall, where a loud-speaker had been installed for the occasion, to hear the Gracious Speech. The first few seconds were moments of acute suspense, for the King's emotion was evident—so evident that it seemed doubtful if he would be able to go through with his self-imposed task. But he mastered it, and delivered his speech, addressed principally to the young, the children of the Empire. The local children of the Empire paid no attention whatever, but kept up a ceaseless display of acrobatics on the railings of the platform erected for the Mayor's address earlier in the day; but nobody minded that. "There, that's children all over!" The rest of the crowd listened with eager contentment to a very perfect little speech from their sovereign, perfect in its simplicity, directness, and most obvious sincerity—a speech which by some magic of insight, and with precisely that "homeliness" which we had heard praised in the Dog and Duck, responded to the simple temper of regard and affection and ownership which the day had so clearly evinced. "*Our* King," we had said—and the King in reply said, "*My* people." And nothing touched his people more than their King's emotion. "'E wur a bit full ['full' in Oxfordshire and Berkshire means 'near to tears'] to starrt wi'; I didn't think 'e'd manage it," said an old man to me at the close. "But 'e *did* manage it—fine, it wur. I could 'ear ivery worrd."

After the speech was over we went down on foot to the Crown and Thistle, where the dinner fully came up to expectation. And then came the question of the bonfire. We had been bidden to the official one on Boars Hill, presided over by the Lord-Lieutenant, at which all the county and the intelligentsia of Oxford would be present. Abingdon, again, was having her own bonfire; a huge pyre stood ready in an open space near the bridge. But we had no great taste for the intelligentsia, and from the flat water meadows of Abingdon we should see no bonfire but its own. No, said the romantic elements in the party, the Downs was the place; there were sure to be bonfires on the Downs, and we should see all the others for miles around. So we packed into the cars again, and once more set out to crawl through the thronged streets, filled from wall to wall with good-tempered, happy, perspiring faces. Out in the open country we raced across the levels, and swung up on to the long grey slopes of the Downs by the Newbury road. On the very crest, the road crosses that wide expanse of rutted turf, stretching for miles on either hand, known as the Ridgeway—one of the ancient British trackways which for several centuries before the Romans came had been one of the principal routes across Southern England, from east to west. Here we halted, and looked about us. It was only nine-thirty, and the chain of beacons was not to be lit till ten o'clock, but a rosy glare away to the east showed where some village up on the Chilterns had set its bonfire going too soon. Meanwhile there was no sign of preparations for a fire in our immediate vicinity, and we enquired of a passer-by where the nearest was to be found. He waved along the Ridgeway—a couple o' mile along there, by the Monument, there was to be a big one.

So began one of the most lovely episodes of a lovely day. We guessed where the beacon must be—by the Monument above Wantage, once King Alfred's capital; but to reach it by road would mean a détour of many miles, and we should certainly be late. So we turned the cars round and bumped off along the hard dry turf of the Ridgeway—for much nearer four miles than two, through the warm May night, sweet with the scent of the wild flowers which our headlights picked up. A thin moon hung low in the sky ahead of us; little jets of fireworks sprayed up now and then out of the darkness of the plain below, and from unseen village churches late peals of bells came up on the wind.

107

The going was rough and difficult, and we were travelling at considerable speed —but no difficulties could dim the thrill of driving to the Jubilee bonfire of King George the Fifth, in the year of grace 1935, along a track which had been a great highway at least three hundred years before the Romans came. Now we passed through beech woods, grey and mysterious, where the going was soft and the tyres skidded in the moist ground; now bounced across the unexpected gullies formed by cross-tracks. Presently a dim glare showed close ahead of us—we accelerated quickly, reckless of broken springs, and drew up by the Monument just as the pyre, thirty-five feet high, burst with a great roar into golden flame.

It was a notable bonfire. We sat on the short sweet turf, smoking, to watch it, or climbed the plinth of the Monument to count the glares from other fires along the Downs, to east and west. A great crowd had assembled, black silhouettes on the near side of the roaring mass, faces illumined to a golden varnished look on the other, and presently the whole company, some hundreds in number, joined hands in a vast circle, nearly a quarter of a mile across (for the strong wind made the pyre quite unapproachable on the leeward side), and moved slowly round singing "For Auld Lang Syne." When the circle broke up we found ourselves on the farther side of the fire from our cars; the crowd was melting away rapidly now, mostly to waiting motors on the Wantage road close by, and we made our way slowly back towards our own.

Cheerful strains drew us towards a small group to windward of the fire. A middle-aged countryman, slightly tipsy—the only human being that I saw drunk or anything approaching it through the whole of Jubilee Day— was sitting on the ground, a bowler hat tilted crookedly over one eye, singing "The Life and Death of Cock Robin," at the pitch of a rather beautiful voice, though in the burring Berkshire accent. The knot of supporters occasionally took him under the armpits and endeavoured to raise him to his feet. "Stand up, Bert—we shall 'ear 'ee better if 'ee stand up!" But Bert's legs and feet had melted, and hung limp and boneless below his body—the moment the supporting hands were relaxed, down he sank again to the ground, while his voice, without the slightest interruption, continued to inform the night that "All the birds of the air fell a-sighin' and a-sobbin', When they heard of the death of Poor Cock Robin." We passed on, charmed to think that the song which beer and loyalty combined had brought forth should be, not some modern jazz or wireless tune, but one of the more ancient English folk songs.

It was time to be thinking of getting home. Even on Jubilee Day there would be *some* limits to what girls' colleges allowed in the matter of hours! We got into the cars and drove back to Oxford—through Abingdon, silent and almost empty now; through the woods, where still the scent of the blue-bells came to us as we drove by; down the long slope of Boars Hill and in by St. Aldate's to the city. We had thought that the day was over, and could hold no more of surprise or delight or beauty; but we were wrong. We came into an Oxford such as we had never seen or dreamed of. Long graceful festoons of coloured lights garlanded the streets; most of the great buildings were floodlit: Tom Tower and the spire of St. Mary's and the tower and front of Magdalen College stood up, silent, white, and noble into the night sky, in all their perfection and dignity of form. They did not look like buildings of stone at all—they were like a vision of that other Oxford, the unseen city of the spirit, the mother of minds and souls, these white lovelinesses towering above the happy streets, where the dancing boys and girls had made the roadway their own. Everywhere they were dancing, or walked singing with linked arms; as the traffic moved slowly, or stood still in the dense throng, they swarmed on to the running boards of the cars, perched on the bonnets or even the roofs, laughing and singing still.

It was all utterly sweet-tempered, gay, and delightful; there was no rough-ness, no rowdiness—it was, as one elderly member of our party said, the *prettiest* crowd of merrymakers she had ever seen. The very police were smiling as they tried to move the jammed traffic forward between the sets of lancers, the country dances, and the reels which were going on in the middle of the road; and the motorists and the bus drivers laughed back. Goodness knew when they would be able to get on, or get home—but no one minded. Sitting idle at the wheel, awaiting the next chance to move, I realised that the elderly lady was murmuring to me through the din; I leaned towards her to catch her words.

" Do you realise," she said, " that we're seeing something that we've often heard about, and never seen—something we thought was dead ? "

" What's that ? " I asked, pushing the gear lever over—the car in front of us was beginning to creep forward.

" Merry England," she said.

JAN STRUTHER

*People often write letters to " The Times " asking for more
Crossword Puzzles. In addition to this, they now write asking
for more " Mrs. Miniver." Her creator is the writer who is
known by the pseudonym of JAN STRUTHER, but everybody
will feel quite sure that " Jan Struther " is a married woman
with a family ; and everybody will be right.*

MRS. MINIVER MAKES A LIST

"WILL ye be wanting anything more tonight, mem? " asked Mrs. Adie,
putting the coffee down by the fire and picking up Mrs. Miniver's
supper-tray.

" No, thank you, nothing at all. As soon as I've made out my list of
Christmas presents, I'm going straight to bed."

Mrs. Adie paused at the door, tray in hand.

" Ay," she said. " This is going to be a queer kind of Christmas for the
bairns, with their Daddy away."

" I dare say he'll get leave," said Mrs. Miniver hopefully.

" Mebbe ay, mebbe no." Mrs. Adie was not one to encourage wishful
thinking. " To say nothing," she added, " of having ten bairns in the house,
instead of three. My! It'll take me back to when I was a wean myself."

" Why, there weren't ten of you, were there? "

" Thirteen," said Mrs. Adie, wearing the particular expression that Clem
always called " Scotland Wins."

Mrs. Miniver was surprised, not so much by the information itself as by
the fact that Mrs. Adie had vouchsafed it. She was not in the habit of
talking about her own childhood. Indeed, she rather gave the impression
that she had never had one, but had simply risen from the foam, probably
somewhere just off the East Neuk of Fife.

" Well, I'll say good night, mem."

" Good night, Mrs. Adie. That was a lovely welsh rabbit."

Left alone, Mrs. Miniver poured out a cup of coffee and sat on the fender-
stool to drink it, roasting her back. Yes, it was going to be a queer Christmas
for everybody this year. To the parents left behind in the big cities it would
seem only half a Christmas; to the hard-pressed foster-parents in the country,
a double one. Out of her own seven evacuees at Starlings, only two, she knew,
had ever had a tree of their own. And Reen, the eldest—a shrill, wizened,
masterful little creature of twelve, who in the last two months had become
so touchingly less shrill and wizened (though no less masterful)—had never
even hung up her stocking. She was inclined to scoff at the idea of taking to
this custom so late in life.

"Ony kids do that," she said. "It's sissy."

"Vin still does it," said Mrs. Miniver. "He's nearly sixteen, and he's not in the least sissy."

"Are you sure?" asked Reen suspiciously.

"Quite sure," said Mrs. Miniver, without a twitch. (She must tell Vin this, next time she wrote.)

But it was too early yet to make plans about stockings. First of all, she must get on with that list of presents. She put down her coffee-cup and went resolutely over to the writing-table.

One of Mrs. Miniver's bad habits—which, like many bad habits, was only an exaggeration of a good one—was that she was apt to begin by being methodical and to end by being a magpie. It was, for instance, quite a sound idea to keep one's Christmas present list until the following year, so as to make sure that one didn't leave people out or give them the same thing twice running. But the worst of it was, she never could bring herself to throw away the old lists when they were done with; and as she had started the habit when she first married, she had now accumulated no less than seventeen of them. Not only did they take up an unnecessary amount of space in an already overcrowded drawer, but they caused her to waste time at a season of the year when time was most valuable: for whenever she opened the drawer to consult last year's list, she found herself quite unable to resist browsing through the earlier ones.

For the last eight years the opening names had not varied at all: *Clem, Vin, Judy, Toby, Nannie, Mrs. Adie, Mrs. Downce, Downce.* The ninth name had changed, at intervals of about two years, from Norah to Jessie, from Jessie to Gladys, and from Gladys to Ellen: for there seemed to be something fatally marriageable, as well as incurably trochaic, about the Minivers' house-parlourmaids. Even Ellen, as unglamorous a girl as you could wish to meet, who had come to them a few months ago completely heart-whole, had already acquired a young man. Clem, to whom Mrs. Miniver had broken this news in a letter, had written back saying, "For heaven's sake, next time, go for a dactyl or a monosyllable. They may have less S.A."

As the lists went farther back, however, important gaps appeared. Nine years ago there had been no Toby; twelve years ago, no Judy. Yet at each of these Christmases, she remembered, her universe (which would now be unthinkable without them) had seemed complete. As for Vin, he figured in all the lists except the first two; and as she traced his presents backwards from last year's spinning-rod through conjuring sets and Red Indian outfits to the woolly rabbit of fifteen years ago, she felt that she was seeing the whole story of his childhood in reverse, like one of those trick films where the spilt milk pours itself back into the jug.

She laid down the sheets on top of each other, one by one. Vin grew up again before her mind's eye : became three, four, in a sun-suit and a floppy linen hat; became seven, eight, in grey flannel shorts (so like, and yet so unlike, Toby); became twelve, thirteen, in long trousers; shot upwards past her elbow, her shoulder, her head; and finally grinned down at her from six inches above it (so like, and yet so unlike, Clem).

Parallel with this memory-film ran another, whose only visible track was the column of prices on the right-hand side of the page. Amplified by her recollection, these scribbled figures made a pretty accurate record of the Miniver family's material ups and downs. There was the lavishness of the first two years, based on youthful ignorance, a fixed salary, and a regular parental allowance; there were the soberer standards which became necessary when Clem started out on his own; there were the deceptive early successes, the too optimistic move to a larger house. Then the slump, the difficult years; the years when an acute appendicitis seemed to take a malevolent pleasure in coinciding with an ultimatum from the bank; when they tossed on the horns of the professional classes' eternal dilemma—whether to retrench openly, or to bluff things out for the sake of keeping up appearances in front of potential clients. The years when, after dining out, they said No, thanks, they'd rather walk and pick up a taxi, it would be so nice to get a breath of air; and when their Christmas presents to each other (since they couldn't cut down too drastically on anybody else's) dwindled by mutual consent into mere tokens, which they exchanged in front of the children with elaborate ceremony, delighted exclamations, and a great deal of coloured wrapping-paper. Not that they needed tokens; but it would have shocked the children if they had exchanged nothing at all.

Things had looked up again, eventually. Clem built an unusual country house for Sandro Baltman, and Sandro talked, and that set the ball rolling fast. By the time Toby was born they had been able to buy Starlings and to get the Downces to look after it. The tokens had expanded into proper presents again, and ever since then the total at the bottom of the right-hand column had been getting a little larger every year. But both of them, fortunately, had good memories: and when young married couples came to dine with them, they always said, " Yes, of course; you're sure to find one on the rank just round the corner."

Mrs. Miniver put the last sheet back on top of the others and clipped them all together again. No, she could not possibly throw them away: they contained too much of her life. Besides, however clear one's memories seemed to be, it did one no harm to polish them up from time to time. One is what one remembers: no more, no less.

She took a clean sheet of paper and wrote across the top in neat block capitals:

" CHRISTMAS 1939."

HOP PICKERS: FROM THE ORIGINAL BY DAME LAURA KNIGHT

" If I could take my England, and could wring
  One living moment from her simple year,
  One moment only, whether of place or time
  Then might I say, ' That which I love, I am '."

ERIC AMBLER

*MR. ERIC AMBLER, one of our younger novelists, has
written five brilliant thrillers, of which "Epitaph for a Spy"
and "The Mask of Dimitrios" have been outstandingly
successful. Ambler's special forte is the spy story, and this
contribution is an example of his work in his cleverest mood.*

THE ARMY OF THE SHADOWS

*IT is three years since Llewellyn removed my appendix; but we still meet occasionally.
I am dimly related to his wife: that, at least, is the pretext for the acquaintanceship.
The truth is that, during my convalescence, we happened to discover that we both
like the same musicians. Before the war we usually met when there was some Sibelius
being played and went to hear it together. I was a little puzzled when, about three
weeks ago, he telephoned with the suggestion that I should dine at his house that night.
There was not, I knew, a concert of any sort in London. I agreed, however, to grope
my way round to Upper Wimpole Street shortly before eight o'clock.*

*It was not until he had presented me with a brandy that I found out why I had been
invited to dinner.*

*"Do you remember," he said suddenly, "that I spent a week or so in Belgrade last
year? I missed Beecham doing the Second through it. There was one of those international medical bun fights being held there, and I went to represent the Association.
My German is fairly good, you know. I motored. Can't stick trains. Anyway, on
the way back a very funny thing happened to me. Did I ever tell you about it?"*

"I don't think so."

*"I thought not. Well"—he laughed self-consciously—"it was so funny now there's
a war on that I've been amusing myself by writing the whole thing down. I wondered
whether you'd be good enough to cast a professional eye over it for me. I've tried"—he
laughed again—"to make a really literary job of it. Like a story, you know."*

*His hand had been out of sight behind the arm of his chair, but now it emerged from
hiding holding a wad of typewritten sheets.*

*"It's typed," he said, planking it down on my knees. And then, with a theatrical
glance at his watch, "Good Lord, it's ten. There's a telephone call I must make. Excuse
me for a minute or two, will you?"*

*He was out of the room before I could open my mouth to reply. I was left alone
with the manuscript.*

*I picked it up. It was entitled A Strange Encounter. With a sigh, I turned
over the title page and began, rather irritably, to read:*

The Stelvio Pass is snowed up in winter, and towards the end of November
most sensible men driving to Paris from Belgrade or beyond take the long way
round via Milan rather than risk being stopped by an early fall of snow. But

H 113

I was in a hurry and took a chance. By the time I reached Bolzano I was sorry I had done so. It was bitterly cold, and the sky ahead was leaden. At Merano I seriously considered turning back. Instead, I pushed on as hard as I could go. If I had had any sense I should have stopped for petrol before I started the really serious part of the climb. I had six gallons by the gauge then. I knew that it wasn't accurate, but I had filled up early that morning and calculated that I had enough to get me to Sargans. In my anxiety to beat the snow I overlooked the fact that I had miles of low-gear driving to do. On the Swiss side and on the Sargans road where it runs within a mile or two of the Rhätikon part of the German frontier, the car spluttered to a standstill.

For a minute or two I sat there swearing at and to myself and wondering what on earth I was going to do. I was, I knew, the only thing on the road that night for miles.

It was about eight o'clock, very dark and very cold. Except for the faint creaking of the cooling engine and the rustle of the breeze in some nearby trees, there wasn't a sound to be heard. Ahead, the road in the headlights curved away to the right. I got out the map and tried to find out where I was.

I had passed through one village since I had left Klosters, and I knew that it was about ten kilometres back. I must, therefore, either walk back ten kilometres to that village, or forward to the next village, whichever was the nearer. I looked at the map. It was of that useless kind that they sell to motorists. There was nothing marked between Klosters and Sargans. For all I knew, the next village might be fifteen or twenty kilometres away.

An Alpine road on a late November night is not the place to choose if you want to sleep in your car. I decided to walk back the way I had come.

I had a box of those small Italian waxed matches with me when I started out. There were, I thought, about a hundred in the box, and I calculated that, if I struck one every hundred metres, they would last until I reached the village.

That was when I was near the lights of the car. When I got out of sight of them, things were different. The darkness seemed to press against the backs of my eyes. It was almost painful. I could not even see the shape of the road along which I was walking. It was only by the rustling and the smell of resin that I knew that I was walking between fir trees. By the time I had covered a mile I had six matches left. Then it began to snow.

I say "snow." It had been snow; but the Sargans road was still below the snow-line, and the stuff came down as a sort of half-frozen mush that slid down my face into the gap between my coat collar and my neck.

I must have done about another mile and a half when the real trouble began. I still had the six matches, but my hands were too numb to get them out of the box without wetting them, and I had been going forward blindly, sometimes on the road and sometimes off it. I was wondering whether I would get along better if I sang, when I walked into a telegraph post.

It was of pre-cast concrete and the edge was as sharp as a razor. My face was as numb as my hands and I didn't feel much except a sickening jar; but I could taste blood trickling between my teeth and found that my nose was bleeding. It was as I held my head back to stop it that I saw the light, looking for all the world as if it were suspended in mid-air above me.

114

It wasn't suspended in mid-air, and it wasn't above me. Darkness does strange things to perspective. After a few seconds I saw that it was showing through the trees on the hillside, up off the right of the road.

Anyone who has been in the sort of mess that I was in will know exactly how my mind worked at that moment. I did not speculate as to the origin of that God-forsaken light or as to whether or not the owner of it would be pleased to see me. I was cold and wet, my nose was bleeding, and I would not have cared if someone had told me that behind the light was a maniac with a machine-gun. I knew only that the light meant that there was some sort of human habitation near me and that I was going to spend the night in it.

I moved over to the other side of the road and began to feel my way along the wire fence I found there. Twenty yards or so farther on, my hands touched a wooden gate. The light was no longer visible, but I pushed the gate open and walked on into the blackness.

The ground rose steeply under my feet. It was a path of sorts, and soon I stumbled over the beginnings of a flight of log steps. There must have been well over a hundred of them. Then there was another stretch of path, not quite so steep. When I again saw the light, I was only about twenty yards from it.

It came from an oil reading-lamp standing near a window. From the shape of the window and the reflected light of the lamp, I could see that the place was a small chalet of the kind usually let to families for the summer season or for the winter sports. That it should be occupied at the end of November was curious. But I didn't ponder over the curiosity: I had seen something else through the window besides the lamp. The light from a fire was flickering in the room.

I went forward up the path to the door. There was no knocker. I hammered on the wet, varnished wood with my fist and waited. There was no sound from inside. After a moment or two I knocked again. Still there was no sign of life within. I knocked and waited for several minutes. Then I began to shiver. In desperation I grabbed the latch of the door and rattled it violently. The next moment I felt it give and the door creaked open a few inches.

I think that I have a normal, healthy respect for the property and privacy of my fellow-creatures; but at that moment I was feeling neither normal nor healthy. Obviously, the owner of the chalet could not be far away. I stood there for a moment or two, hesitating. I could smell the wood smoke from the fire, and mingled with it a bitter, oily smell which seemed faintly familiar. But all I cared about was the fire. I hesitated no longer and walked in.

As soon as I was inside I saw that there was something more than curious about the place, and that I should have waited.

The room itself was ordinary enough. It was rather larger than I had expected, but there were the usual pinewood walls, the usual pinewood floor, the usual pinewood staircase up to the bedrooms, and the usual tiled fireplace. There were the usual tables and chairs, too: turned and painted nonsense of the kind that sometimes finds its way into English tea-shops. There were red gingham curtains over the windows. You felt that the owner probably had lots of other places just like it, and that he made a good thing out of letting them.

No, it was what had been added to the room that was curious. All the furniture had been crowded into one half of the space. In the other half, standing on linoleum and looking as if it were used a good deal, was a printing press.

The machine was a small treadle platten of the kind used by jobbing printers for running off tradesmen's circulars. It looked very old and decrepit. Alongside it on a trestle-table were a case of type and a small proofing press with a locked-up forme in it. On a second table stood a pile of interleaved sheets, beside which was a stack of what appeared to be some of the same sheets folded. The folding was obviously being done by hand. I picked up one of the folded sheets.

It looked like one of those long, narrow business-promotion folders issued by travel agencies. The front page was devoted to the reproduction, in watery blue ink, of a lino-cut of a clump of pines on the shore of a lake, and the display of the word "TITISEE." Page two and the page folded in to face it carried a rhapsodical account in German of the beauties of Baden in general and Lake Titisee in particular.

I put the folder down. An inaccessible Swiss chalet was an odd place to choose for printing German travel advertisements; but I was not disposed to dwell on its oddity. I was cold.

I was moving towards the fire when my eye was caught by five words printed in bold capitals on one of the unfolded sheets on the table: " DEUTSCHE MÄNNER UND FRAUEN, KAMERADEN! "

I stood still. I remember that my heart thudded against my ribs as suddenly and violently as it had earlier that day on the Stelvio when some crazy fool in a Hispano had nearly crowded me off the road.

I leaned forward, picked the folder up again, and opened it right out. The message began on the second of the three inside pages.

" GERMAN MEN AND WOMEN, COMRADES! We speak to you with the voice of German Democracy, bringing you news. Neither Nazi propaganda nor the Gestapo can silence us, for we have an ally which is proof against floggings, an ally which no man in the history of the world has been able to defeat. That ally is Truth. Hear then, people of Germany, the Truth which is concealed from you. Hear it, remember it, and repeat it. The sooner the Truth is known, the sooner will Germany again hold up its head among the free nations of the world."

Then followed a sort of news bulletin consisting chiefly of facts and figures (especially figures) about the economic condition of Germany. There was also news of a strike in the Krupp works at Essen and a short description of a riot outside a shipyard in Hamburg.

I put it down again. Now I knew why these " travel advertisements " were being printed in an inaccessible Swiss chalet instead of in Germany itself. No German railway official would distribute these folders. That business would be left to more desperate men. These folders would not collect dust on the counters of travel agencies. They would be found in trains and in trams, in buses and in parked cars, in waiting-rooms and in bars, under restaurant plates and inside table napkins. Some of the men that put them there would be caught and tortured to betray their fellows; but the distribution would go on. The folders would be read, perhaps furtively discussed. A little more truth would seep through Goebbels' dam of lies to rot still further the creaking foundations of Nazidom.

Then, as I stood there with the smell of wood smoke and printing ink in my nostrils, as I stood staring at that decrepit little machine as if it were the very voice of freedom, I heard footsteps outside.

I suppose that I should have stood my ground. I had, after all, a perfectly good explanation of my presence there. My car and the blood from my nose would confirm my story. But I didn't reason that way. I had stumbled on a secret, and my first impulse was to try to hide the fact from the owner of the secret. I obeyed that impulse.

I looked round quickly and saw the stairs. Before I had even begun to wonder if I might not be doing something excessively stupid, I was up the stairs and opening the first door I came to on the landing. In the half-light I caught a glimpse of a bed; then I was inside the room with the door slightly ajar. I could see across the landing and through the wooden palings along it to the top of the window at the far side of the room below.

I knew that someone had come in: I could hear him moving about. He lit another lamp. There was a sound from the door and a second person entered.

A woman's voice said in German, " Thank God, Johann has left a good fire."

There was an answering grunt. It came from the man. I could almost feel them warming their hands.

" Get the coffee, Freda," said the man suddenly. " I must go back soon."

" But Bruno is there. You should take a little rest first."

" Bruno is a Berliner. He is not as used to the cold as I am. If Kurt should come now he would be tired. Bruno could only look after himself."

There was silence for a moment. Then the woman spoke again.

" Do you really think that he will come now, Stephan? It is so late." She paused. Her voice had sounded casual, elaborately casual; but now, as she went on, there was an edge to it that touched the nerves. " I can keep quite calm about it, you see, Stephan. I wish to believe, but it is so late, isn't it? You don't think he will come now, do you? Admit it."

He laughed, but too heartily. " You are too nervous, Freda. Kurt can take care of himself. He knows all the tricks now. He may have been waiting for the first snow. The frontier guards would not be so alert on a night like this."

" He should have been back a week ago. You know that as well as I do, Stephan. He has never been delayed so long before. They have got him. That is all. You see, I can be calm about it even though he is my dear husband." And then her voice broke. " I knew it would happen sooner or later. I knew it. First Hans, then Karl, and now Kurt. Those swine, those——"

She sobbed and broke suddenly into passionate weeping. He tried helplessly to comfort her.

I had heard enough. I was shaking from head to foot; but whether it was the cold or not, I don't know. I stood back from the door. Then, as I did so, I heard a sound from behind me.

I had noticed the bed as I had slipped into the room, but the idea that there might be someone in it had not entered my head. Now, as I whipped round, I saw that I had made a serious mistake.

Sitting on the edge of the bed in which he had been lying was a very thin, middle-aged man in a nightshirt. By the faint light from the landing I could see his eyes, bleary from sleep, and his grizzled hair standing ludicrously on end. But for one thing I should have laughed. That one thing was the large automatic pistol which he held pointed at me. His hand was as steady as a rock.

"Don't move," he said. He raised his voice. "Stephan! Come quickly!"

"I must apologise . . ." I began in German.

"You will be allowed to speak later."

I heard Stephan dash up the stairs.

"What is it, Johann?"

"Come here."

The door was pushed open behind me. I heard him draw in his breath sharply.

"Who is it?"

"I do not know. I was awakened by a noise. I was about to get up when this man came into the room. He did not see me. He has been listening to your conversation. He must have been examining the plant when he heard you returning."

"If you will allow me to explain . . ."

"You may explain downstairs," said the man called Stephan. "Give me the pistol, Johann."

The pistol changed hands and I could see Stephan, a lean, rawboned fellow with broad, sharp shoulders and dangerous eyes. He wore black oilskins and gum-boots. I saw the muscles in his cheeks tighten.

"Raise your hands and walk downstairs. Slowly. If you run, I shall shoot immediately. March."

I went downstairs.

The woman, Freda, was standing by the door, staring blankly up at me as I descended. She must have been about thirty and had that soft rather matronly look about her that is characteristic of so many young German women. She was short and plump, and as if to accentuate the fact, her straw-coloured hair was plaited across her head. Wisps of the hair had become detached and clung wetly to the sides of her neck. She too wore a black oilskin coat and gum-boots.

The grey eyes, red and swollen with crying, looked beyond me.

"Who is it, Stephan?"

"He was hiding upstairs."

We had reached the foot of the stairs. He motioned me away from the door and towards the fire. "Now, we will hear your explanation."

I gave it with profuse apologies. I admitted that I had examined the folders and read one. "It seemed to me," I concluded, "that my presence might be embarrassing to you. I was about to leave when you returned. Then, I am afraid, I lost my head and attempted to hide."

Not one of them was believing a word that I was saying: I could see that from their faces. "I assure you," I went on in exasperation, "that what I am telling . . ."

"What nationality are you?"

"British. I . . ."

"Then speak English. What were you doing on this road?"

"I am on my way home from Belgrade. I crossed the Yugoslav frontier yesterday and the Italian frontier at Stelvio this afternoon. My passport was stamped at both places if you wish to . . ."

"Why were you in Belgrade?"

"I am a surgeon. I have been attending an international medical convention there."

"Let me see your passport, please."

"Certainly. I have . . ." And then with my hand in my inside pocket, I stopped. My heart felt as if it had come right into my throat. In my haste to be away after the Italian Customs had finished with me, I had thrust my passport with the Customs carnet for the car into the pocket beside me on the door of the car.

They were watching me with expressionless faces. Now, as my hand reappeared empty, I saw Stephan raise his pistol.

"Well?"

"I am sorry." Like a fool I had begun to speak in German again. "I find that I have left my passport in my car. It is several kilometres along the road. If . . ."

And then the woman burst out as if she couldn't stand listening to me any longer.

"Don't you see? Don't you see?" she cried. "It is quite clear. They have found out that we are here. Perhaps after all these months Hans or Karl has been tortured by them into speaking. And so they have taken Kurt and sent this man to spy upon us. It is clear. Don't you see?"

She turned suddenly, and I thought she was going to attack me. Then Stephan put his hand on her arm.

"Gently, Freda." He turned to me again, and his expression hardened. "You see, my friend, what is in our minds? We know our danger, you see. The fact that we are in Swiss territory will not protect us if the Gestapo should trace us. The Nazis, we know, have little respect for frontiers. The Gestapo have none. They would murder us here as confidently as they would if we were in the Third Reich. We do not underrate their cunning. The fact that you are not a German is not conclusive. You may be what you say you are; you may not. If you are, so much the better. If not, then, I give you fair warning, you will be shot. You say that your passport is in your car several kilometres along the road. Unfortunately, it is not possible for us to spare time tonight to see if that is true. Nor is it possible for one of us to stand guard over you all night. You have already disturbed the first sleep Johann has had in twenty-four hours. There is only one thing for it, I'm afraid. It is undignified and barbaric; but I see no other way. We shall be forced to tie you up so that you cannot leave."

"But this is absurd," I cried angrily. "Good heavens, man, I realise that I've only myself to blame for being here; but surely you could have the common decency to . . ."

"The question," he said sternly, "is not of decency, but of necessity. We have no time tonight for six-kilometre walks. One of our comrades has been delivering a consignment of these folders to our friends in Germany. We hope and believe that he will return to us across the frontier tonight. He may need our help. Mountaineering in such weather is exhausting. Freda, get me some of the cord we use for tying the packages."

I wanted to say something, but the words would not come. I was too angry. I don't think that I've ever been so angry in my life before.

She brought the cord. It was thick grey stuff. He took it and gave the pistol to Johann. Then he came towards me.

I don't think they liked the business any more than I did. He had gone a bit white and he wouldn't look me in the eyes. I think that I must have been white myself; but it was anger with me. He put the cord under one of my elbows. I snatched it away.

" You had better submit," he said harshly.

" To spare your feelings? Certainly not. You'll have to use force, my friend. But don't worry. You'll get used to it. You'll be a good Nazi yet. You should knock me down. That'll make it easier."

What colour there was left in his face went. A good deal of my anger evaporated at that moment. I felt sorry for the poor devil. I really believe that I should have let him tie me up. But I never knew for certain; for at that moment there was an interruption.

It was the woman who heard it first—the sound of someone running up the path outside. The next moment a man burst wildly into the room.

Stephan had turned. " Bruno! What is it? Why aren't you at the hut? "

The man was striving to get his breath, and for a moment he could hardly speak. His face above the streaming oilskins was blue with cold. Then he gasped out,

" Kurt! He is at the hut! He is wounded—badly! "

The woman gave a little whimpering cry and her hands went to her face. Stephan gripped the new-comer's shoulder.

" What has happened? Quickly! "

" It was dark. The Swiss did not see him. It was one of our patrols. They shot him when he was actually on the Swiss side. He was wounded in the thigh. He crawled on to the hut, but he can go no further. He . . ."

But Stephan had ceased to listen. He turned sharply. " Johann, you must dress yourself at once. Bruno, take the pistol and guard this man. He broke in here. He may be dangerous. Freda, get the cognac and the iodine. We shall need them for Kurt."

He himself went to a cupboard and got out some handkerchiefs, which he began tearing feverishly into strips, which he knotted together. Still gasping for breath, the man Bruno had taken the pistol and was staring at me with a puzzled frown. Then the woman reappeared from the kitchen carrying a bottle of cognac and a small tube of iodine of the sort that is sold for dabbing at cut fingers. Stephan stuffed them in his pockets with the knotted handkerchiefs. Then he called up the stairs, " Hurry, Johann. We are ready to leave."

It was more than I could bear. Professional fussiness, I suppose.

" Has any one of you," I asked loudly, " ever dealt with a bullet wound before? "

They stared at me. Then Stephan glanced at Bruno.

" If he moves," he said, " shoot." He raised his voice again. " Johann! "

There was an answering cry of reassurance.

"Has it occurred to you," I persisted, "that even if you get him here alive, which I doubt, as you obviously don't know what you're doing, he will need immediate medical attention? Don't you think that one of you had better go for a doctor? Ah, but of course; the doctor would ask questions about a bullet wound, wouldn't he? The matter would be reported to the police."

"We can look after him," he grunted. "Johann! Hurry!"

"It seems a pity," I said reflectively, "that one brave man should have to die because of his friends' stupidity." And then my calm deserted me. "You damn fool!" I shouted. "Listen to me. Do you want to kill this man? You're going about it the right way. I'm a surgeon, and this is a surgeon's business. Take that cognac out of your pocket. We shan't need it. The iodine too. And those pieces of rag. Have you got two or three clean towels?"

The woman nodded stupidly.

"Then get them, please, and be quick. And you said something about some coffee. Have you a flask for it? Good. Then we shall take that. Put plenty of sugar in it. I want blankets, too. Three will be enough, but they must be kept dry. We shall need a stretcher. Get two poles or broomsticks and two old coats. We can make a stretcher of sorts by putting the poles through the sleeves of them. Take this cord of yours too. It will be useful to make slings for the stretcher. And hurry! The man may be bleeding to death. Is he far away?"

The man was glowering at me. "Four kilometres. In a climbing hut in the hills this side of the frontier." He stepped forward and gripped my arm. "If you are tricking us . . ." he began.

"I'm not thinking about you," I snapped. "I'm thinking about a man who's been crawling along with a bullet in his thigh and a touching faith in his friends. Now get those poles, and hurry."

They hurried. In three minutes they had the things collected. The exhausted Bruno's oilskins and gum-boots had, at my suggestion, been transferred to me. Then I tied one of the blankets round my waist under my coat, and told Stephan and Johann to do the same.

"I," said the woman, "will take the other things."

"You," I said, "will stay here, please."

She straightened up at that. "No," she said firmly, "I will come with you. I shall be quite calm. You will see."

"Nevertheless," I said rather brutally, "you will be more useful here. A bed must be ready by the fire here. There must also be hot bricks and plenty of blankets. I shall need, besides, both boiled and boiling water. You have plenty of ordinary salt, I suppose?"

"Yes, *Herr Doktor*. But . . ."

"We are wasting time."

Two minutes later we left.

I shall never forget that climb. It began about half a mile along the road below the chalet. The first part was mostly up narrow paths between trees. They were covered with pine needles and, in the rain, as slippery as the devil. We had been climbing steadily for about half an hour when Stephan, who had been leading the way with a storm lantern, paused.

"I must put out the light here," he said. "The frontier is only three kilometres from here, and the guards patrol to a depth of two kilometres. They must not see us." He blew out the lamp. "Turn round," he said then. "You will see another light."

I saw it, far away below us, a pin-point.

"That is our light. When we are returning from Germany, we can see it from across the frontier and know that we are nearly home and that our friends are waiting. Hold on to my coat now. You need not worry about Johann behind you. He knows the path well. This way, *Herr Doktor*."

It was the only sign he gave that he had decided to accept me for what I said I was.

I cannot conceive of how anyone could know that path well. The surface soon changed from pine needles to a sort of rocky rubble, and it twisted and turned like a wounded snake. The wind had dropped, but it was colder than ever, and I found myself crunching through sugary patches of half-frozen slush. I wondered how on earth we were going to bring down a wounded man on an improvised stretcher.

We had been creeping along without the light for about twenty minutes when Stephan stopped and, shielding the lamp with his coat, relit it. I saw that we had arrived.

The climbing hut was built against the side of an overhanging rock face. It was about six feet square inside, and the man was lying diagonally across it on his face. There was a large bloodstain on the floor beneath him. He was semi-conscious. His eyes were closed, but he mumbled something as I felt for his pulse.

"Will he live?" whispered Stephan.

I didn't know. The pulse was there, but it was feeble and rapid. His breathing was shallow. I looked at the wound. The bullet had entered on the inner side of the left thigh just below the groin. There was a little bleeding, but it obviously hadn't touched the femoral artery and, as far as I could see, the bone was all right. I made a dressing with one of the towels and tied it in place with another. The bullet could wait. The immediate danger was from shock aggravated by exposure. I got to work with the blankets and the flask of coffee. Soon the pulse strengthened a little, and after about half an hour I told them how to prepare the stretcher.

I don't know how they got him down that path in the darkness. It was all I could do to get down by myself. It was snowing hard now in great fleecy chunks that blinded you when you moved forward. I was prepared for them to slip and drop the stretcher; but they didn't. It was slow work, however, and it was a good forty minutes before we got to the point where it was safe to light the lamp.

After that I was able to help with the stretcher. At the foot of the path up to the chalet, I went ahead with the lantern. The woman heard my footsteps and came to the door. I realised that we must have been gone for the best part of three hours.

"They're bringing him up," I said. "He'll be all right. I shall need your help now."

She said, "The bed is ready." And then, "Is it serious, *Herr Doktor*?"

"No." I didn't tell her then that there was a bullet to be taken out.

It was a nasty job. The wound itself wasn't so bad. The bullet must have been pretty well spent, for it had lodged up against the bone without doing any real damage. It was the instruments that made it difficult. They came from the kitchen. He didn't stand up to it very well, and I wasn't surprised. I didn't feel so good myself when I'd finished. The cognac came in useful after all.

We finally got him to sleep about five.

"He'll be all right now," I said.

The woman looked at me and I saw the tears begin to trickle down her cheeks. It was only then that I remembered that she wasn't a nurse, but his wife.

It was Johann who comforted her. Stephan came over to me.

"We owe you a great debt, *Herr Doktor*," he said. "I must apologise for our behaviour earlier this evening. We have not always been savages, you know. Kurt was a professor of zoology. Johann was a master printer. I was an architect. Now we are those who crawl across frontiers at night and plot like criminals. We have been treated like savages, and so we live like them. We forget sometimes that we were civilised. We ask your pardon. I do not know how we can repay you for what you have done. We . . ."

But I was too tired for speeches. I smiled quickly at him.

"All that I need by way of a fee is another glass of cognac and a bed to sleep in for a few hours. I suggest, by the way, that you get a doctor in to look at the patient later today. There will be a little fever to treat. Tell the doctor he fell upon his climbing axe. He won't believe you, but there'll be no bullet for him to be inquisitive about. Oh, and if you could find me a little petrol for my car . . ."

It was five in the afternoon and almost dark again when Stephan woke me. The local doctor, he reported, as he set an enormous tray of food down beside the bed, had been, dressed the wound, prescribed, and gone. My car was filled up with petrol and awaited me below if I wished to drive to Zürich that night. Kurt was awake and could not be prevailed upon to sleep until he had thanked me.

They were all there, grouped about the bed, when I went downstairs. Bruno was the only one who looked as if he had had any sleep.

He sprang to his feet. "Here, Kurt," he said facetiously, "is the *Herr Doktor*. He is going to cut your leg off."

Only the woman did not laugh at the jest. Kurt himself was smiling when I bent over to look at him.

He was a youngish-looking man of about forty with intelligent brown eyes and a high, wide forehead. The smile faded from his face as he looked at me.

"You know what I wish to say, *Herr Doktor*?"

I took refuge in professional brusqueness. "The less you say, the better," I said, and felt for his pulse. But as I did so his fingers moved and gripped my hand.

"One day soon," he said, "England and the Third Reich will be at war. But you will not be at war with Germany. Remember that, please, *Herr Doktor*. Not with Germany. It is people like us who are Germany, and in our way we shall fight with England. You will see."

I left soon after.

At nine that night I was in Zürich.

123

Llewellyn was back in the room. I put the manuscript down. He looked across at me.
" Very interesting," I said.

"I'd considered sending it up to one of these magazines that publish short stories," he said apologetically. " I thought I'd like your opinion first, though. What do you think ? "

I cleared my throat. " Well, of course, it's difficult to say. Very interesting, as I said. But there's no real point to it, is there ? It needs something to tie it all together."

" Yes, I see what you mean. It sort of leaves off, doesn't it ? But that's how it actually happened." He looked disappointed. " I don't think I could invent an ending. It would be rather a pity, wouldn't it ? You see, it's all true."

" Yes, it would be a pity."

" Well, anyway, thanks for reading it. Funny thing to happen. I really only put it down on paper for fun. Have another brandy ? " He got up. " Oh, by the way. I was forgetting. I heard from those people about a week after war broke out. A letter. Let's see now, where did I put it ? Ah, yes."

He rummaged in a drawer for a bit, and then, tossing a letter over to me, picked up the brandy bottle.

The envelope bore a Swiss stamp and the postmark was Klosters, September 4th, 1939. The contents felt bulky. I drew them out.

The cause of the bulkiness was what looked like a travel agent's folder doubled up to fit the envelope. I straightened it. On the front page was a lino-cut of a clump of pines on the shore of a lake and the word " TITISEE." I opened out the folder.

" GERMAN MEN AND WOMEN, COMRADES! " *The type was worn and battered.* " Hitler has led you into war. He fed you with lies about the friendly Polish people. In your name he has now committed a wanton act of aggression against them. As a consequence, the free democracies of England and France have declared war against Germany. Comrades, right and justice are on their side. It is Hitler and National Socialism who are the enemies of peace in Europe. Our place as true Germans is at the side of the democracies *against* Hitler, *against* National Socialism. Hitler cannot win this war. But the people of Germany must act. All Germans, Catholics, Protestants, and Jews, must act now. Our Czech and Slovak friends are already refusing to make guns for Hitler. Let us stand by their sides. Remember . . ."

I was about to read on when I saw that the letter which accompanied the folder had fluttered to the carpet. I picked it up. It consisted of a few typewritten lines on an otherwise blank sheet of paper.

" Greetings, *Herr Doktor.* We secured your address from the Customs carnet in your car and write now to wish you good luck. Kurt, Stephan, and Bruno have made many journeys since we saw you and returned safely each time. Today, Kurt leaves again. We pray for him as always. With this letter we send you Johann's newest work so that you shall see that Kurt spoke the truth to you. We are of the army of the shadows. We do not fight for you against our countrymen; but we fight with you against National Socialism, our common enemy. *" Auf Wiedersehen.*

" FREDA, KURT, STEPHAN, JOHANN, AND BRUNO."

Llewellyn put my glass down on the table beside me. " Help yourself to a cigarette. What do you think of that ? Nice of them, wasn't it ? " he added. " Sentimental lot, these Germans."

HOWARD MARSHALL

MR. HOWARD MARSHALL is distinguished as a writer; and as a commentator on the English scene in sport and service he has no peer.

THE FISHERMAN'S ENGLAND

"AND what," said the vicar, " are we fighting for? "

Well, there were many answers to that question. Rather abstract answers, most of them, it is true. And it was not until my eyes strayed to the old map that I saw how to avoid fruitless argument.

It is a beautiful old map. It hangs on the wall of my cottage. It was drawn and bravely coloured in 1649.

It shows the county of HANTONIA (*vulgo Hantshire*), and upon it are traced, leading from the OCEANUS BRITANNICUS, the mouths of Hampshire's noble rivers. The Avon, the Test, the Itchen, the Stour—there they flow, boldly marked, the strongest lines upon the map. And from them wander the little streams, meandering down forgotten valleys between the great chalk hills.

There are other rivers in England. Fine rivers. I have fished in many of them. But these rivers of Hampshire gave me sufficient answer to the vicar.

Indeed, whenever the talk turns to war-aims, my mind goes back to that old map, and beyond it to the gentle water-meadows of my county.

We may wage a war for great ideals. Freedom is a stirring word. The intellectual may find an ideology for which he will lay down his life.

To the ordinary man, however, war is a simpler matter. If he must fight, let it be for his country. For a corner of his country, maybe. For the water-meadows of Hampshire, say I.

There we are upon ground which we can understand. We want no Gestapo counting the spots on our trout. We will tolerate no " Verbotens " on the stile which leads to the water-side.

So it is simple and straightforward. And when you come to analyse it, freedom includes the right to wander through the meadows on an April evening.

My England, perhaps, is not yours. This enchanted isle of ours has many disguises. You may see it most clearly on a misty autumn morning, when hounds are moving off along the woodland ride. A cricket field under the July sun, and the smell of freshly mown grass, and the sound of rooks in the elm trees—this may be your England.

You may find it in the surge of surf round Cornish headlands, or in the desolate cry of the curlew on northern moors.

So many aspects of England there are, so many moods of enchantment. But for me one alone is supreme. The England of the fisherman—of hidden valleys and bird-song, of wayside inns and good companionship.

125

The rivers of England—follow them on the map. Not that old map of mine, but one of those modern affairs which pay far too much attention to the motorist's speed tracks.

Leave the roads alone for once, and follow the winding water-ways, and see how rich England is in fertile valley country. Look at them spread before you—peaty becks of the north country—the quiet waters of the Midlands —great rivers like Trent and Severn, Thames and Wye—the slow streams of Norfolk—the Ouse curling sleepily through Bedfordshire—the chalk streams of Hampshire and Wiltshire—all have their lovers, and all hold delight abounding.

For myself, when I can escape, like a schoolboy playing truant, it is southwards I head. Not to the lordly rivers, for Test and Itchen, Wylye and Kennet are beyond the purse of the general run of anglers.

If, at the benevolent behest of some wealthy friend, the humble fisherman may snatch a day now and again in those exclusive water-meadows, he counts himself fortunate, but Test and Itchen do not limit his horizon. He is, indeed, happier on some smaller stream, where he may fish alone.

Here he has his modest triumphs. They encourage him to keep on fishing, and so to haunt the lost England which only the angler knows.

It lies, this England, in forgotten folds in the hills, where the snipe go drumming on April evenings; it lies behind the golden withies along the reed-fringed bank. And the road to it begins in the quiet mind.

Only the man who moves quietly through the fields with his rod as a magic wand may discover this enchantment, this country within a country, this England of water-meadow and silver stream.

Quietness: that is the secret of the fisherman. He must tread softly and move gently; he must dress inconspicuously and become part of the background of willow and withy if he is to succeed.

It grows upon him, a quietness of mind no less than movement. And he will be accepted by the river creatures—the water-vole and the meadow birds will show no fear of him. I have had a kingfisher pause in his brilliant passage to perch on my rod, and that was a compliment I cherished.

So the angler moves silently into his kingdom, and takes England unawares, with barriers down. The villages of the valley are his, the thatched cottages, and the gardens bright with flowers. The country folk are his friends.

I have a friend who is a meadsman. A drowner, they call him, and he and his ancestors for generations have worked in Hampshire water-meadows. And whenever he wishes to be emphatic, he pauses and says, " It's true, as sure as I stand on English ground."

He seeks no stronger guarantee of his sincerity. English ground suffices him, and there is the fisherman's creed.

I have in my little cottage room two aldermanic roach stuffed in glass cases. Fine roach they are, both exceeding the cherished two pounds, one by no less than seven and a half ounces.

Any roach fisherman will tell you that such fish are worthy of a glass case, and yet they are there, not so much because they are large, as for the memories they revive when I look at them.

Memories of the English scene, and here let me say that the angler does not wait upon England in her fairest moods. He seeks her rivers in deep

126

winter as often as in spring, and watches the rhythm of seasons round the year.

They remind me, these roach, of the Hampshire Avon, that swift and majestic river. One was caught at dawn in an August so wet that the Avon roared down in towering flood. There was an eddy where fish would gather out of the swirling press of heavy water, and there the float dipped as the first grey light struck across the fields, and my two-pounder set my rod arching and quivering.

The other roach—the grandfather—betrayed his presence by the merest flicker of my quill float in the middle of a December snowstorm, with a north-easter driving the flakes into my eyes.

No day for fishing—the skies were leaden, heavy with snow—there was snow-broth in the dark water—the withies sighed and creaked in the wind—the river surface was whipped into waves—and it was cold, bitterly cold.

On such a day only an unreasoning optimist would hope to catch fish, but all anglers are optimists and all rules have exceptions.

Roach in plenty I caught that day, and big chub and fat dace, but my abiding reward is the memory of grey winter in an English valley.

I have fished for roach in so many different rivers, and not only rivers—in wayside ponds, in broads and meres and private lakes, even in the reservoirs of the Metropolitan Water Board, and to my mind the roach is the finest quarry of all.

Salmon are very well, and trout are better. Grayling on a misty October morning have their charm, and tench at dawn in high summer are worth the catching. Leave me the modest roach, though, the handsome, cunning, red-finned roach, and I am well content.

Is there anything, I wonder, more typically English than a summer evening's roach fishing ?

The punt is moored across the river where a streamy run will carry the red-tipped quill float drifting down between the weed-beds. The sun drops behind the elms which guard the distant village, and against that golden glow the squat tower of the church stands shadowed and solid.

In the meadows cattle move slowly among the deep grasses, and swallows dip to the surface of the stream, wheeling and swinging in wide, glancing curves. And always there are the pleasant river voices, the gurgle of water past the mooring chains, the murmur of the weir, with now and again the swift dip of the float, the tightening on a fighting fish, the exhilaration of achievement, and then again that peace which only the valleys of England hold.

All this I explained to the vicar as best I could, but the fisherman is hard put to it when he must analyse his happiness in elusive words. It is compounded of so many sights and sounds, this happiness, of such golden and indefinably precious memories. It represents to him a way of life, a heritage of tranquillity and loveliness for which no sacrifice could be too great.

HUMFREY JORDAN

The Merchant Navy has found its chronicler in MR. HUMFREY JORDAN, whose reputation as a novelist was firmly established by " The Commander Shall," followed by " Sea Way Only." For this gift book, Mr. Jordan has written a short story in the same tradition and with a specially intriguing title.

THE BOATSWAIN YAWNED

IN the first-class dining saloon of the *Lake Victoria*, which would seat two hundred diners, there was only one table occupied. About the table was a pool of light, the rest of the saloon was scarcely lit and full of shadows. At the only occupied table Mr. James Walters, a director of the Lake Steamship Company, dined with the senior officers of the ship on the night before departure. This was a ritual affair: in turn one of the directors so dined on each eve of departure of one of their passenger ships from Tilbury for the Far East. All the senior officers, the heads of departments, were there except the surgeon: he had made a specious excuse and had got away with it to the envy of the others. These feasts with one of the owners, when the ship was lifeless and waiting, pausing between the administrations of the shore staff, which had just ended, and the attentions of her own company, which would begin shortly, were considered necessary by the Board and accepted as inevitable by the officers impressed for the occasion. At them it was the custom for the owner present to impart special instructions for the voyage ahead. That evening, as he discoursed to a politely attentive audience of economic difficulties and international unrest, Mr. James Walters' manner had been that of a man about to impart important secrets; but the meal had ended and he had got up from the table without imparting more than platitudes. Being on their best behaviour, not one of his audience had said what was in all their minds, " For God's sake, man, get on with it."

As a steward placed coffee before them in the Smoking Room, Mr. Walters sprang a surprise.

" You are all," he announced, " having a liqueur with me. Give them names."

That was a new, although pleasing, item of ritual. As they named their liqueurs—the Commander, the Chief Officer, and the Chief brandy, the Purser, who had a sweet tooth, cointreau—they wondered what was coming. Since a director was buying them drinks, it was a good bet that he was about to ask them for a spot, or several spots, of extra labour. They listened somewhat anxiously for what should come.

When the steward was out of earshot, Captain Mortimer raised his glass of brandy.

FROM THE ORIGINAL BY BIP PARES

" When Faith is kneeling by his bed of death,
    And Innocence is closing up his eyes—
    Now if thou would'st, when all have given him over
    From death to life thou might'st him yet recover "

"Here's luck, sir," he said, trying by those simple words to convey, without offence, to an owner that there were limits to patience.

Whether he realised what the Commander wished or not, Mr. Walters came at last to the point. He blew gently upon the end of the cigar which he had just lighted; he selected his words with nice care.

"The *Lake Constance*," he said, "was in collision with a tanker today. Between them they almost succeeded in closing the Suez Canal."

If he had wished for comment, he was disappointed. Four men, whose lives were the service of ships, gazed at him in silent concern. Trouble had come to a ship and to men whom they knew, but they were volunteering nothing to an owner about that trouble.

"It appears"—Mr. Walters spoke judicially—"that the tanker was entirely at fault. The damage done was slight. The Canal is now clear."

He paused. The four men remained silent, their faces giving nothing away. They knew that there was more to it than that. They knew rightly; there was. Mr. Walters ceased to be judicial; he became forceful.

"This," he declared, " is the fourth mishap to one of our ships within three weeks. Each of the others has received and this one will receive full publicity in the papers. There are nasty jokes about, already, as you know. This afternoon four passages with you were cancelled."

He paused again. The continued silence was getting on his nerves. He brought his hand down with a slap on the table in front of him.

"It has got to cease. You understand me. Cease."

They did understand him. Such commands were normally given on such occasions. Silence was safe. But Mr. Walters was not going to have more silence.

"Well, Mortimer," he demanded, "I'm waiting for you to say something."

Captain Mortimer smiled. He was a dapper, slight, smallish man with very bright, alert, brown eyes.

"Run of bad luck, sir. All companies have them."

Mr. James Walters was the most popular member of the Board; with most of the ships' officers in his employ he was regarded as very nearly human. Conquering his annoyance he showed how near to humanity he was. Signing to the steward he gave the order, "The same again." When the drinks were on the table and the steward back in the bar, he leaned forward.

"Exactly," he admitted. "But with the world and sea trade in the state they are we can't afford bad luck. Simply can't afford it. There's talk and we are losing passengers. You've got to change that run of bad luck. Stop it. The *Lake Victoria* has got to make a completely successful voyage, without complaints or trouble. If there is any trouble—and believe me I do realise something about your difficulties—it has got to be hidden from passengers. So," he stretched out a hand for his glass, " here's to a good voyage."

They all drank to that. When they put down their glasses Mr. Walters stood up.

"I must be getting back to London," he said. "Break that run of luck. At all costs passengers must be kept smiling and full of faith in us. If not, things have got so bad that we shall have to start laying up ships. The *Lake Victoria* would be the first for that."

I

There it was—the sting in the tail. Passengers had got to be kept smiling, whatever the sea might send, or the company of the *Lake Victoria* would be out of a job. That was sufficiently serious to put four men, who lived by their jobs alone, on a little more than their best behaviour as they completed the final ritual of the feast: seeing the owner off.

To limit access to the ship at night there was only the forward gangway down. As four anxious officers and an owner approached it a cheerful, somewhat high, quick voice sounded clearly from the shore end.

" Funny thing, Sam," it said, " but the beer don't taste quite right to me tonight. So I come along 'ome like."

In spite of his anxiety Captain Mortimer smiled at the Chief Officer, Bell. The high, quick voice was that of the Boatswain, Truefit. He always came aboard sooner than he need on the night before sailing; he always, in exactly the same words, made the same excuse to the quartermaster on duty. He was a noticeable figure of a man, standing five feet no inches. It was said of him, of course untruly, that he was as broad as he was long, that if a square frame were placed around him his head and feet would touch the top and bottom, his shoulders the sides. So, he had always been known as Square Truefit. He was immensely powerful; absurdly short but not deformed. His voice was hard worked and his energy out of all soundings. As the group of officers and owner reached the head of the gangway, the Boatswain was coming briskly up. He was so short that his head, on which he wore, cocked sideways, a magnificent dove-grey felt hat, hardly reached above the side rails.

" Parlez," sang Mr. Truefit, cheerfully but scarcely as the composer would have wished it, " moi d'amour."

He reached the head, still singing, breaking off to point the moral of his song to the seaman on duty.

" Not 'alf, George," he said, " you don't wish that she wouldn't parlez of it to you neither. You could do . . ."

Recognising the group approaching, he ended his discourse with George and raised his magnificent hat.

" If, sir," he addressed the captain, " I'd known you was there, I'd 'ave spared you the grand opera like. There's some as criticises me singing. Good night, sir."

He passed on to his quarters and Mr. James Walters smiled.

" The Boatswain, isn't he ? " he asked. " Lit up for the occasion, eh ? " The Commander of the *Lake Victoria* shook his head.

" Not he, sir. There isn't the liquor in this town which would light him. That's his nature."

" It's really dreadful," Mr. Walters complained, " the way I forget names. A curse. I know our cheerful friend, of course, but his name has vanished. He's a good man, too, if I remember."

" Truefit," Mortimer explained ; " for obvious reasons they call him Square. Square Truefit. He is a good man. After forty years at sea I'm not given to slinging praise easily; but Truefit almost comes up to my idea of what a boatswain should be."

" High praise that."

Mr. Walters seemed astonished at the height of it.

" I'll go higher," Mortimer declared. " I'll say that Truefit couldn't let his captain or his ship down. Just couldn't. It isn't in the fellow's nature."

.   .   .   .

As the seven strokes on the bell on the bridge were echoed by seven strokes on the bell on the forecastle head they were followed by the call of the look-out, softened and beautified by the night, that the lights burned bright, that all was well. That call in that setting seemed the only one possible. Beneath the clear shine of stars, with the ship gently talking on a windless sea, wrapped in the hot peace of a perfect tropic night, anything but that call " All's well " would have appeared an outrage on decency.

The *Lake Victoria* was thirty hours from Aden outward bound. It had been a voyage without events, a dull voyage. A blow crossing the Bay, which was to be expected in February, another off the mouth of the Adriatic and passing Crete. The ship had not half her complement of passengers, something else to be expected in February, outward bound; but so far they seemed reasonably contented passengers. That they should be contented and be kept contented had been passed round as an urgent order. The Commander had started the passing before Mr. James Walters had left the dock; it had reached downwards and had impressed the bell-boys before the first passenger came aboard next morning. The Boatswain had handed it personally to all members of both watches.

" If," he declared, " it should so 'appen that we was to drop both pro-pellers into deep water, this ship would 'ave to be sailed to 'er port without a bleedin' passenger seeing no difference whatever. Straight from the owners that is—and for you. Smiling passengers. That's it. So take it and keep it. Put it away safely in them solid blocks of ivory what tops off so many of your necks."

The jokes of smiling passengers in the Canal, their request to be shown the exact spot where the *Lake Constance* had done her bit, urgent demands to know whether the *Lake Victoria* could not do anything herself, had set a severe strain upon all ranks and ratings. Yet, in spite of strain, the *Lake Victoria* was out in the Indian Ocean without giving real cause for the removal of one smile from the face of any passenger. On that fine night all did look well.

Mitchell, the supernumerary Third Officer, left the bridge soon after seven bells to complete his rounds. When he had gone below, Laird, the Second Officer, took a stellar sight. There was a beautiful horizon and he was finding his watch dull; so he did not hurry himself. Leisurely he fixed the ship's position; with neatness and deliberation he put a pencilled cross upon the chart. He was adding the time and date when the sound of hurrying footsteps on the ladder scattered his leisurely mood. Mitchell was panting as he came into the charthouse.

" Fire," he said, " in the forward hold. You can smell it and feel it but not hear it yet."

" Sure ? Been down yourself ? "

" Yes. I've left the Bosun down there."

" Right. Take the bridge. Send round the alarm. Warn everybody that passengers must not suspect a thing. I'll call the Old Man."

Even in that moment when the two men faced the thing which they dreaded so much more than the fury of the sea, the order to keep passengers smiling was not forgotten. The Commander remembered it as, a few minutes later, he hurried, in his pyjamas as he had jumped from his bed, forward.

"Pass it round, Bell," he told his Chief Officer, whose pyjamas were much more gaudy than his own, "that, if any man getting to his station wakes a passenger, I'll log him."

As the Commander and the Chief Officer arrived Truefit emerged from Number One hatch. He had contrived to get his face very dirty, but his cheerfulness and his garrulity were unabated.

"Well, Bosun?" The Commander was urgent.

Truefit drew the back of his left hand across his shining, dirty face.

"You could say that it's 'ot down there, sir," he declared. "But it ain't took right 'old yet. I'd put a bob on that."

"Any idea of where or what?" Captain Mortimer was not going to rush a man he trusted, but to keep him exactly to the point.

Scratching his head and closing his eyes Truefit thought. The effort caused his face to pucker. He had a queer, an almost uncanny trick of carrying in his head the contents of the holds of the ships he served; where officers might have to consult documents to make certain, he turned to his memory. The men who knew and valued that trick of his waited anxiously. They saw him, his eyes still tightly closed, sniff at his hands and clothing; and they knew that he did not do it just to exasperate them.

"Paper," he said, and opened screwed-up lids to show his eyes very bright and assured. "I knew I'd get that smell in time. It's all them cases of books we're carrying. They'll smoulder slow until opened up, they will. There's nothing much to 'urt below 'em; but there's flimsy stuff atop. Women's dresses, ain't they, Mr. Bell?"

The Chief Officer nodded. Led by Truefit, his memory confirmed that.

"Both the books and the cases of dresses will take some getting at, sir," he told his captain.

Captain Mortimer was very sure of that. Deep down in the hold while they all thought that the voyage was going so well two cases had been working together in the bad weather in the Bay and off Crete. A spark, perhaps, or intense heat from friction. Anyhow, this: a ship at sea on fire. He did not think that they would find that the Boatswain had been wrong in his diagnosis. It would, of course, be difficult to get at. That was the way of such things. But—packed paper did smoulder slowly. There was that comfort.

"I'm going to trust to your nose, Bosun," he said, "making trouble if it's proved a liar. Mr. Mitchell will take charge here for the moment. Mr. Bell, I want you to go round and see that no news of this gets to the passengers. Send the Surgeon up to me, please. I'll be down again when you know more about the reliability of the Bosun's nose. Carry on."

He turned from the hatch and made his way topsides alone. There was a lonely decision facing him: whether he should turn and steam for a port or whether he should carry on though his ship might burn at sea.

The early passengers at breakfast found the Commander in his place, an alert, dapper figure with his smile as ready as usual and his accustomed morning greetings. He ate his meal without hurry; so did the Chief, the Doctor, the Purser and his assistants. The Chief Officer was not down, nor were any of the watchkeepers; but that often happened at breakfast so their absence aroused no interest. There were, however, people at breakfast who did not usually breakfast early. There was, also, an item of news on a dull voyage. The passengers feeding before their usual time had been turned out of their cabins, which were all forward, and accommodated in others—more comfortable and more expensive ones farther aft. The reason was chicken-pox. Some children—no passenger had happened to notice their arrival—had come aboard at Aden. They had gone at once to bed in their cabins forward. Next morning they had not been well. Now there was no doubt of them having chicken-pox, and they had gone into isolation and would remain there. As a precaution all passengers berthed forward, served by the same stewards and stewardesses, had been moved to other, better cabins and the alleyways leading to the presumably infected part of the ship had been closed with carbolic sheets. That the passengers had swallowed without suspicion the mythical children and their ailment was a source of much satisfaction to the anxious men who had invented the children. Passenger jokes about the Lake Line's excessive coddling and carbolic sheets were very well received. If they would remain content to smell carbolic and not be forced to smell fire, all would be well.

His breakfast deliberately finished, Captain Mortimer strolled from the saloon, nodding and exchanging the time of day as he passed tables. He lingered for a few minutes on the promenade deck chatting with more passengers. Then, avoiding the appearance of hurry until he was out of passengers' sight, he went forward.

Canvas screens had been rigged so that Number One hatch was hidden from passengers. From behind the screens there came the clanging of metal and a most penetrating and offensive stench. The Commander hurried to investigate.

A very stout seaman, his dungaree trousers and singlet clinging to his body almost as wetly as though he had been bathing, sat panting on the after part of the hatch cover, which had not been removed. From time to time he struck the steel of the combing resounding blows with a hammer. Beside him the Boatswain was joining two ends of manilla; his short, stubby, callous fingers worked with surprising nimbleness. As the Commander appeared Truefit transferred a marline-spike to his left hand and saluted; he then went on with his job. The stout seaman slid off the hatch cover, his great paunch threatening to burst the leather belt which held it in place.

" What the devil is this ? " Captain Mortimer demanded. " This appalling smell ? "

" Fish glue, mostly, sir, but there's other things besides."

" What do you mean, fish glue ? "

Truefit showed the yellow stumps of teeth in a wide grin: an economical man he kept his false set for shore-going and great occasions.

" Them books," he explained, " was beginning to make themselves noticeable like. So I says to the carpenter ' Chips,' I says, ' you got to make a smell for to keep the passengers from smelling burning books.' Chips 'e says, ' Right you are, Square, I'll make a smell.' And 'e fetches that there portable forge and from time to time 'e pitches a 'andful of glue and wotnot into the fire. And 'e makes the smell."

" Yes "—the Commander did not allow himself to smile—" he does. And

133

what is Morley doing? Why was he playing at drums with that hammer?"

The stout seaman looked abashed; he hitched the leather belt more securely round his stomach. Truefit, however, explained with pride.

"Morley," he said, " 'is 'aving a spell, sir. The man what's 'aving a spell does a trick of camyflage."

"Camouflage for what and why? You're getting yourself tied up, Bosun."

"Camyflage for us digging out they books, sir. Going around, I manages to 'ave a word or two with passengers. I tells them that we 'ave a proper job on 'ere, welding metal it is, and we are using something patent wot is un-pleasant on the nose. They swallows it—'ole. So there's Chips' smell to 'ide the books and this 'ere clanging to make certain they don't 'ear what we really is up to. Your orders, sir. You says ' Keep the perishers fooled and grinning.' "

The Commander allowed himself to smile.

"It's a mercy you work while you talk, Truefit," he laughed. " I'll find out later whether passengers swallow as easily as you think. Belay that hammer, Morley, till I've got below. I don't want my ear-drums cracked."

Below he found that the work of getting at the fire was going very slowly. The heat was increasing, but there was no indication of any immediate danger that the imprisoned glow would turn to consuming flame. Shifting cargo, preparing to quench the glow, was very difficult; yet it went forward without attracting passengers' attention to the reality. They did seem to have swal-lowed and to have found a completely satisfying meal the explanation, the smell, and the noise with which the Boatswain had provided them.

The Chief Officer commented on that as he had a drink with his captain to fortify them before they went down to dinner in the saloon. Mortimer had made his lonely choice. He would not play for safety; he would carry on. If things went right, the owners' wishes would have been fulfilled: passengers would not know that the *Lake Victoria* shared in the Company's run of bad luck. If things went wrong, and despite care and forethought and planning and labouring they might, there could be a major, a horrible disaster. With the alternatives in his mind Mortimer made his choice, and, having made it, stuck to it.

To lessen the chance of passengers becoming suspicious he and the Chief Officer must dine as usual in the saloon, an ordeal when their anxious minds were so far away from small talk. Fortifying themselves for the ordeal their talk summed up the progress, or lack of it, of the day's work.

"There isn't a doubt now," Bell declared as he put down his empty glass, "that Truefit's nose was right from the start. It's the books. Also the stench and hammering are proving the right dope. Competent little devil although he wags his tongue so much."

"I told Mr. Walters," Mortimer said, moving to the door, "that he was pretty near a real bosun. I stick to that. It isn't in him to let us and the ship down. He'll work all night and be full of talk and bright ideas in the morning."

Although he was far from being the only man who worked all night, Truefit was full of energy and talk in the morning. When many men, in temper and in looks, were showing signs of strain, he seemed tireless. He was effective, although obscene, in dealing with pessimism. With passengers he had another bright idea.

Soon after breakfast that day the rumour spread that the mythical chicken-pox of the mythical children from Aden was really small-pox. It grew and tales of the discomforts of quarantine added to passengers' gloom. The Doctor, very angry because his chicken-pox invention, which had seemed to him ingenious and effective, had been so distorted, went about denying. His denials cut no ice. Yet by lunch time the rumour was dead.

With most passengers the Boatswain was popular. His odd appearance, his quick, high talk, his amazing flow of yarns and information attracted them. Towards noon that morning he was button-holed by a massive dame and her escort of two elderly male gossips. They, all three, wanted stable information; they wanted confirmation of the report which the elderly gossips would have liked to have originated but had not, that there was small-pox in the ship. Although he did not show it, Truefit was very tired. The small-pox tale was new to him, but in spite of his fatigue he realised the harm which it might do to passengers' smiles. He let his imagination go.

"Seen the Doctor, ma'am?" he asked the massive dame.

When she had replied that she had and that he was looking very worried, the Boatswain wagged a stubby finger at her.

"There you are, ma'am," he assured her. "I saw 'im too, not five minutes ago, looking like he'd got a pain. So it ain't small-pox."

"I fail," the elder of the elderly gossips objected, " to follow that reasoning."

"This way, ma'am," Truefit explained. "The Doctor 'e's a proper one for small-pox. Afore 'e came to sea 'e was a prosperous detective of it. What they calls a re-seeker. 'E's wrote a book about it. If 'e 'ears of a case of small-pox 'e's off and 'e's 'appy. Last voyage 'omeward at Colombo 'e 'opped it into the jungle to see something what turned out only to be lice bites after all and near as damn it missed 'is ship. There ain't no small-pox aboard because if there was the Doctor 'e'd be grinning that wide the top of 'is 'ead would be loose."

When the massive dame reported these biographical details to the Doctor, his reception of them caused the matter of small-pox to slump in the gossip market; and the Boatswain's readiness as an imaginative liar was appreciated by his superiors.

Shortly after five that afternoon Captain Mortimer stood at the back of a group on the boat deck watching the important affair of the finals of the mixed doubles of ball tennis. He was extremely tired but relieved. The fire, after little more than thirty-six hours of toil, had been got at and subdued; the danger to the ship was past. The passengers, except two of the players of ball tennis, were in excellent temper; there had been no more rumours to disturb them; the fire and the labours of anxious men fighting it had been kept secret. That evening there was the prize-giving for the games competitions and a dreadful amateur entertainment by passengers to follow it. He and his officers would have to stay to the bitter end of that show, but after it they would sleep. He was thinking of that sleep, while clapping the players because other people were clapping them, when a messenger running up the companion caught his eye.

The Commander slipped quietly away from the back of the group. Below he caught up the Chief Officer and the Doctor who were hurrying to the forward hold. It seemed that there had been a fall of cargo in the tunnel which had been made to get at the fire and that Mitchell had been imprisoned. As the three officers climbed over cargo in the hold they saw the Boatswain push a seaman roughly aside from the mouth of the tunnel.

"Staring!" he said, fiercely, "s'elp me your proper place is be'ind a counter slopping out frillies to the lovelies. Out of it. Now then Alf Morley, look slippy."

As he talked he passed a bight at the end of a rope over his head and shoulders and settled it round his chest; he took another rope in his hand; he turned to the fat seaman, who was bracing his back against a crate ready to heave it up to increase the size of the tunnel opening, and he smiled.

"You be careful, Alf!" he admonished. "Don't you get falling about. We doesn't want the smell of burnt fat atop of everything. Now—'eave and away we goes . . ."

Still talking he disappeared down the tunnel.

Much talk was his nature; he used jesting words because, like so many men in danger, he found them easier; yet none of the men who saw him disappear doubted that he knew that he might not come out of that hole alive.

They heard snatches of his continued talk, muffled but characteristic, high and quick. "I'm acomin', sir . . . 'ere I be . . . stuffy, ain't it . . . couldn't you move, sir, couldn't you . . . I'll 'ave to get below you then . . ."

The voice became more muffled, almost indistinguishable. One of the ropes jerked. A call that had desperation in it came up: "'Eave! And smartly."

While men heaved smartly, bringing up Mitchell to the mouth of the tunnel, there was no more talking from below.

Mitchell had a broken jaw, broken ribs, and a broken ankle. He looked doped, but managed to mutter:

"Truefit fell . . . below me . . . he'll choke—quicker."

But before he muttered that the Commander and the fat seaman, Morley, relieved of his Atlantean performance, were hauling in on the other rope.

When they got him out of the tunnel Truefit's face was almost blue-black; his eyes bulged from his head; his great chest struggled madly to expel foul gases from his lungs and to bring in the air of life. They laid him where fresh air could blow upon him and stood by. There was nothing else to do; but his struggle for life frightened them as they watched it. He won his fight. When he had retched and coughed, horribly, and spat, he lay still with his eyes shut: a queer, stunted little figure, panting.

Opening his eyes, he sat up and spat again, noisily. The Commander leaned over him.

"Feeling better, Truefit?" he asked.

The little Boatswain struggled, shakily, to his feet.

"I'm fine, sir," he announced.

As he said it his expression changed. Consciousness and memory had returned to a man by nature careful and economical.

"But," he said, aggrieved, "I've split me pants."

Watching the little man being helped up the ladder out of the hatch, the Commander spoke to the Chief Officer.

136

" Uncommon near the genuine article, Bell," he declared.

. . . .

From the centre of the improvised stage, which had provided the Boatswain, the Carpenter, and several hands with additional work, the Commander faced the passengers in the forward lounge. He was making a speech which he had made before and would make again. Reaction—for the fire was out, finished, and the passengers still ignorant and smiling—had made the ordeal of the prize-giving and amateur entertainment very grim. Like so many of his ship's company he was desperately tired. Yet he knew his speech by heart and it seemed to be going down well. He had come to the place where he stressed the value of good shipmates and conveyed to the batch in front of him that they were something exceptional in the goodness line.

" I'm not slinging bouquets," he was saying, " but I do know when I've struck lucky. . . ."

They were taking it down well, so well that he allowed his eyes to stray for a second from their faces. A sound in the wings had attracted his attention; he glanced towards it. Out of sight of the audience a small, tired figure waited patiently to superintend scene-shifting for amateurs. Suddenly it closed its eyes, raised clenched fists, stretching like a child, opened a large mouth to show the stumps of yellow teeth. The Boatswain yawned prodigiously.

So, before he could prevent himself, did the Commander in the centre of the stage. It was not such a prodigious yawn. Mortimer got his jaws shut with a snap when they were only half stretched. Yet it was quite enough. The speech finished very flat. The passengers had got a grouse, which too many of them would use instead of smiles. " Damn the fellow," they would be saying, " there is no need for him to show us to our faces how bored he is."

Really, Captain Mortimer decided as he sat down in his armchair in the front row prepared to be vociferous in his applause of amateur efforts, by doing a silly infectious thing like that at the wrong moment the Boatswain had let him down badly. He had never believed that Truefit could do that.

ALFRED NOYES

MR. ALFRED NOYES is properly described as an epic poet. " Drake " and " The Torch-bearers " are works on the grand scale and rightly regarded as his great contribution to English letters. But an equal vigour characterises his shorter poems, many of them familiar to the younger of us since our schooldays.

A CHILD'S GALLOP

The refrain in the following poem is a child's version of an old nursery song in the patois of Languedoc.

WHERE the great hills meet the sky,
Where the wheeling plovers cry,
Where the foxglove belfries burn
Crimson over seas of fern,—
Head uplifted, face alight,
Eyes and stirrups glittering bright,
Rides my little girl of girls
With a tempest in her curls;
Heels thrust down, and mouth a rose,
Hear her singing as she goes:
    Allons ! Allons, chivalet !
    A la fièro dal Coulet,
    Porterai un gros couteau !
    Allons, allons, moun chivau !

See, her charger turns again,
Flowing tail and tossing mane,
Like a wave with stormy crest,
And a glory in its breast,
Knowing that an elf of nine
Rules it now by right divine.
Hear the warrior hoof-beats come,
Clattering like a kettle-drum !
Hear her singing, low and loud,
To the skylark and the cloud:
    Allons ! Allons, moun chivau,
    A la guerro je m'en vau !
    Pat-a-trica, pat-a-tra !
    La nous ferons tout tramblà !

ALFRED NOYES

THE STRANGER

THERE was a man born deaf and blind,
And he had midnight in his mind.
His wrinkled skin, by warmth and cold,
Knew if the year was young or old;
But light and music meant no more
To him, than a wall, or a locked door.
There was no window to that wall,
No key to that locked door at all.

All day long in his porch he sat,
And none knew what he was staring at.
He sat so still, so silent there,
That—one late noon—a hunted hare
Leapt with a little whimpering cry
Into his lap, while hounds went by.

Under his cloak his old hands pressed
Its panting body against his breast.
He felt its heart against his own
Beating in piteous unison.
He hid it close; and, whispering, said,
" *Poor little one, don't be afraid!* "

Then he looked up, and he looked round,
And saw no light, and heard no sound.

Yet, while his pity soothed its fear,
And the wild hounds bayed on elsewhere,
A Stranger, ere that day grew dim,
Paused—looked long—and pitied *him*;
Then, gently as the sun's last ray,
Touched, with his hand, and went his way.

Was it his own blind gentleness
Had given the Power its chance to bless;
His own blind love that, altering fate,
Had made the Master's by-path straight?
From the dark house they heard a cry—
I see a tree against the sky!
Lord, Lord, what wonderful thing is this
That fills the earth and sky with bliss?

Christ God, according to Thy word,
The blind man saw, the deaf man heard.

O. DOUGLAS

O. DOUGLAS is the pen-name of Miss Anna Buchan, novelist-sister of John Buchan, now Lord Tweedsmuir. Her stories have unfailing charm. Everyone knows " Penny Plain " and "The Proper Place," and Priorsford is one of the best-loved places in modern fiction.

SUCH AN ODD WAR!

ON the afternoon of the day Britain declared herself at war, Jean Bidborough with her husband and family, sat on the lawn at Mintern Abbas and tried to find her bearings.

To Jean the peace of green turf and smooth river seemed a mockery. War had begun. A flame had been lit and no one knew when it would be extinguished.

She turned to her husband, who was sitting with his hands in his pockets, staring before him, and asked, " What will it mean, Biddy? "

" Changes, Jean."

" I know you will want to go? "

" Of course. As a matter of fact, Leithen promised me a job some time ago. You wouldn't want me to stay, darling? "

" I wouldn't keep you, Biddy. You'd be miserable not working."

" You will find lots to do," said her husband. " I suppose we'd better offer Mintern Abbas as a hospital? "

" Oh! " Jean looked startled. " Yes, I suppose so. A convalescent place, don't you think? It's better suited for that."

The three children, Peter and Quentin and their sister Alison, were lying on the grass, and Quentin, looking up, asked in a casual way, " Will they begin to bomb us just at once, Peter? "

" Shouldn't think so. Too busy with the Poles. Daddy, we'll send help to Poland, won't we? "

" It's difficult to see how we can," his father said gravely.

" Couldn't we send aeroplanes, simply fleets of them? "

" Oh," said Jean, " don't talk of these things; they've been the beginning of all the trouble. The man who invented the combustion engine, and made aeroplanes and submarines possible, was the greatest enemy of the human race."

" Mummy! " Peter's voice was shocked. " Planes are wonderful things. I'm going to be an airman when I'm old enough—nineteen, and I'm sixteen now—Daddy, the war won't be over in three years, will it? Surely Hitler can keep it going longer than that. Once a war lasted thirty years," he added hopefully, " so I think I've a good chance."

"Me too," said Quentin; "I'll be an airman, Peter. Alison can only be a nurse. Ho! Florence Nightingale."

Alison, whose head was bent over a book, did not even look up at this taunt, and her mother said, "What are you reading, darling?"

Alison gave a long sigh as she said, "I'm trying to make myself laugh with *What Katy Did*, but nothing seems very funny today. Why had there to be a war, Mummy?"

"I don't know, Alison. It was the last thing in the world anyone wanted. But we've got to go through with it now, and everyone can, and must, help. Last war we kept saying 'Business as usual,' but this time nothing's as usual. For one thing, our homes have been touched, we are blacked out."

"That's fun," said Peter. "Daddy, come and see the blue lamp in my room; it gives about as much light as a match."

"And," his mother went on, "there's the evacuation."

"That would have been fun," Peter cried; "it was too bad our lot didn't come. Do you suppose they're lost?"

"They'll probably turn up tomorrow. Everything is ready for them, anyway. They are to have their midday meal all together in the hall that was the old barn. I hope that will work all right, and they'll be very comfortable in the cottages."

"Oh, Mummy, they will," said Alison, "and the two that live with Mrs. Bainbridge will get the loveliest toffee made with condensed milk. She once gave me some. I wish we hadn't to go to school, and we could give the children such a good time."

This put an idea into Peter's head. "Daddy, isn't it a pity to go to school in war-time? Such a waste. The masters could all be fighting and the schools used for barracks, and we'd work on the land. Quentin's growing brussels-sprouts in his garden, anyway, and we'd dig up the lawn and plant potatoes. We'd lose very little by not going to school. You can't think, Daddy, how *little* we learn at school."

"I've a very good notion from your reports how little *you* learn, my son. No, I'm afraid you must all go back to school, and you can help your country by trying to give as little trouble as you can, and learning as hard as you can. When this war comes to an end we're pretty sure of one thing—that there'll be precious little money left. You'll all have to stand on your own feet, and make your own way, and the better educated you are, the better you will get on."

This sounded very dull, and, rather dashed, Peter and Quentin, followed more slowly by Alison, set off for the lake. Their parents looked after them in silence.

Presently Jean said, "Biddy, I suppose it means that everyone goes? Mhor, a soldier, will be away first, and Jock, poor Jock, who couldn't hurt the least crawling thing, will have to leave Agnes and their Thomas, and learn to kill his fellow-men, and David too——"

"I don't think David will ever have to go. He is much too useful a man in his own line."

"Betty will be thankful. . . . Mhor is only twenty-six. Do you remember what a funny little boy he was? His passion for trains! How he kissed the man's hand when he was allowed to pull the chain that made the engine

141

squeal, and the letter he wrote to the lion at the Zoo beginning, ' Dear Loin ' ? ' "

" But he's still here, darling," Lord Bidborough protested; " there's no need for such an obituary tone. This war isn't going to be so bad for soldiers as the last one. It's the civilians who may suffer. I'm thankful to think I'm leaving you in such a safe place. There is nothing to bring raiders near Mintern Abbas."

" But, Biddy, I'm not going to stay here when you are away. When you are here, and the children, it's home, and I love it, but without you it's only a big empty house. Besides, if it's a hospital, I shall only be in the way."

" But, darling, where will you go ? To The Rigs ? I thought so."

" Yes, I think I could bear a war better at Priorsford than anywhere else. The mere sight of the hills gives me courage. And I'd be near Pamela and Lewis at Laverlaw, and I'm sure they'll take us all there when the children come for Christmas. Don't you think that would be a good arrangement, Biddy ?—Oh, here comes Sylvia ! "

Sylvia Howard came slowly from the house to where her cousin and his wife sat. She had been staying at Mintern Abbas for a month, not a very welcome guest, Jean felt guiltily, for she was not a particularly pleasant person. Aged about forty-five, she was handsome in an untidy way. A discontented mouth spoiled her face, and she had so many complaints against life that her conversation was far from inspiriting.

" Have this chair, Sylvia."

Miss Howard sank into the chair offered her, and said, " The more one thinks of it, the more terrible it seems."

There was something in the way Sylvia dramatised a situation that made her hearers, even on the most serious occasions, become flippant.

" The war, d'you mean ? " Lord Bidborough asked.

" What else could I mean ? After nearly two thousand years of Christianity, to come to this ! How shameful ! "

" Have a cushion," said her cousin. " Jean and I are trying to make plans."

" Plans ? Won't you and Jean stay quietly here and look after things ? That seems to me your first duty."

" Our idea is to offer this place for a convalescent hospital. I hope to get a job, and Jean thinks she would like to go to her old home in Scotland while I'm away and the children are at school."

Miss Howard leant forward and took one of Jean's hands in hers. " No need to do that, dear Jean. I shall stay with you."

Lord Bidborough broke in hastily, " That's very good of you, Sylvia, but I'd be happier thinking of Jean in her old home. You see, Pamela and Lewis will be quite near her and the children will go for holidays. Besides, you will want to get something to do—drive an ambulance, or nurse, or something."

" Oh, my dear, if you knew how these women in uniform tire me, so smug and pleased with themselves, tearing about in cars, molesting people on the telephone, as if the war were got up entirely for their benefit. No, indeed, my war work will be inconspicuous, but helpful. I shall look after Jean. I'll go with you to Priorsford, Jean. I don't care for Scotland. I must frankly admit that I like neither the people nor the climate, but at a time like this one must not think of oneself. I shall go. London will be impossible, and Scotland at least is safe."

With the feeling that she was in a nightmare, Jean stared at her self-sacrificing relative by marriage. She had nothing to say, neither had her husband.

The silence was broken by an excited shout, and Quentin came streaking towards them, crying breathlessly, " Mummy! Daddy! Three planes coming this way, and Peter says p'r'aps it's Adolf! "

By the end of September, when the children were back at school, the evacuees comfortably parked in the village, and Mintern Abbas dismantled and made ready for its new rôle, Jean turned her face towards Priorsford. She was accompanied by Sylvia Howard.

They had corner seats in an empty first-class carriage, and Miss Howard was congratulating herself that there was a restaurant car on the train.

" Being fed regularly is so important," she said.

" We've got sandwiches and fruit with us," Jean reminded her.

" Oh, I know, dear, but I *never* feel comfortable after a sandwich luncheon."

Miss Howard smiled wanly, and went on, " Of course, *nothing* would make me grumble at a time like this when our brave men are in danger. Isn't this a strangely uninteresting war? So little seems to happen."

" Isn't that a good thing? If things were happening we'd have lists of casualties? "

" And how dreadful that would be! But what I was going to say is that I do feel the authorities make us quite unnecessarily uncomfortable. These blackouts, and all the fuss about evacuating children—almost hysterical, I call it, quite unlike British calm in the face of danger."

Jean took up the *Spectator*, and said, " We're so often a day behind the fair that I think we were determined to take no risks this time. How were we to know that we wouldn't be bombed at once? " and, not waiting for a reply, she began to read.

" How lucky you are, dear Jean, to be able to read in the train; already my head aches to distraction, and we haven't even got to Crewe. Why should an express go slower in a war, I wonder; and so many unexplained stops? I'm afraid we have to change. Have we, Jean? "

" I'm afraid we have, and at Symington, of all places! You know the saying about Symington? ' Neither man's meat, nor dog's meat, nor a place to sit down.' That isn't quite true, though. There's certainly nothing to eat, but there's generally a good fire in the waiting-room. In happier times we would have had a car to meet us, but Pamela and Lewis are away, and won't be back for a day or two, and with petrol rationed I didn't like to order a car from Priorsford."

Miss Howard sighed. " And when do we reach Priorsford? "

" We should be there before eight o'clock. We'll have the early luncheon, and then you should lie down and have a sleep; tea will cheer us, and Symington will soon come. Unfortunately we've to cross a bridge at Symington to get the Priorsford train, but I've brought a torch, and we ought to manage all right."

The travellers arrived intact, and were wakened next morning by bright sunshine. Jean went to ask how her guest had slept, and found her enjoying a hearty breakfast.

"You're looking well," said Jean. "I hope the headache's gone? Such a divine morning! Isn't it fun to come to a new place in the dark and see it in morning sunshine?"

"So many hills," said Miss Howard. "The town seems quite surrounded by them. Does that not make it rather enervating?"

Jean laughed. "Wait till you feel it swept by bitter north-east winds! Sometimes it's almost impossible to cross Tweed Bridge in winter. Spring and autumn are Priorsford's specially lovely times. Come for a walk, Sylvia."

"Not now, dear?"

"Oh no, about eleven, perhaps? I'm going now to have a talk with my dear Mrs. McCosh."

"She's quite an old family servant, isn't she?"

"And an old family friend. She was with us when we were children. I don't think I could have managed without her. You see, I was pretty young to be in charge of a house, even this tiny house, and three boys."

"Yes, and then Pamela came here, didn't she?"

"She took rooms in Bella Bathgate's cottage, and we became great friends. Then Biddy came to see Pam, and our story began. Well, I'll leave you in peace. Come down when you please."

Mrs. McCosh had much to tell. Priorsford, that cheerful little town, looked gay with the sun turning the yellowing leaves to gold, but war had laid its hand even on that favoured place. Every house was full of people who had left danger zones; the Hotel-Hydro had changed from a luxurious haven for the rich to a hospital, and was already full of the sick and wounded. Every hall had been taken, and was either filled with soldiers or used for A.R.P. work, while many private houses held children from the cities, the evacuees that have been the subject of so much talk.

"Priorsford's been lucky!" said Mrs. McCosh. "There's nothing wrong wi' the bairns that have come here, nothing to make a fuss about. They're mebbe no very well dressed, but they're clean, and they've settled down wonderful quietly. Did I tell ye Bella Bathgate's got two? Oh, ay, two wild laddies. You must awa and hear Bella's breath on them."

"But—she's the last person I'd have expected to take in children," said Jean. "She's so afraid of her house."

"She used to be, but you go in and see her. Bella's changed."

When Miss Howard appeared, in very smart tweeds, she and Jean started off together.

"Isn't it amazing the difference the sun makes?" said Jean, as they stood at the garden gate. "Even now, with so much anxiety weighing on us all, one's heart jumps up in the most unreasonable way. 'I to the hills will lift mine eyes.' That's Cademuir, and Lee Pen, and over there are the Shiel Green Kips."

"What odd names!" said Sylvia. "It's no use telling me the names of hills—I never know them again when I see them. Where are we going now? To the town?"

144

FROM THE ORIGINAL BY ARTHUR WRAGG

" They have taken away my Lord, and I know not where they have laid Him "

"Would you mind coming with me first to see my friend Miss Bella Bathgate? This should be a time to catch her, before they have their dinner. It's just over here."

Miss Bathgate opened the door, looking very like herself. Her long upper lip was as intimidating as ever, her hair was dragged back into a small coil, she wore a large white linen apron over her dark dress. "Come into the room," she said. "My, but I'm glad to see ye again, Miss Jean, I mean Lady Bidborough."

"This is a cousin, Miss Howard, who is kindly keeping me company," Jean said.

"Pleased to meet you," said Miss Bathgate.

The moment they entered the room Jean realised that the cherished apartment had suffered a change. A writing-table stacked with papers stood where no writing-table was wont to be, the ornaments had vanished from the mantelpiece, the whatnot was not there, and over all hung the smell of tobacco.

Jean turned and looked at Miss Bathgate, who nodded, and said, "Ay, ma lodger's a man this time; Major Parker's his name. He's doing some army job here."

"And I hear you have taken two evacuees. Are they nice boys?"

"Oh, there's nothing wrong with them except that they're aye there."

"Yes, it must make a difference, looking after them, cooking for them——"

"Ay, and washing and mending for them, and knitting stockings for them, and teaching them manners—they'd none—and seeing that their lessons are done, and hearing their prayers."

"Had they been taught to say prayers?"

"They had not, but I soon learned them. And, mind you, they're no bad laddies. Jimmy's the worst; he eggs Donald on, and they're that uproarious that I think the house is coming down about my ears. I whiles think I was daft to have put ma name down, for I could have let ma rooms at a big price—everybody's wantin' rooms in Priorsford now—but if I can make two laddies healthier and better, it's a help to ma country."

"Do you find," said Miss Howard, speaking very slowly and distinctly, as if she were speaking to a foreigner—"do you find that these children will eat sensible food? I'm told they all want things out of tins."

"They like ma food fine," said Miss Bathgate. "I doubt if they've ever had enough to eat all their lives afore. They sup their porridge and milk, and eat bread and butter and an egg and a sausage to their breakfasts, and get good hot broth and meat and vegetables to their dinner, and I don't stint them in sweet things, for sugar's necessary to children. You'd think they'd settled down for life. I heard Jimmy talking about what he'd do next year and the next again. I thought to maself, Oh, mercy! How long d'you think the war'll last? I've taken them for the duration."

"Who can say?" Jean leant forward, smiling at her old friend. "Miss Bathgate, I believe you'd be sorry if it stopped tomorrow and your boys left you."

Bella Bathgate drew down her long upper lip as she said, "Sorry? Me! With ma house being ruined afore my eyes, and me getting up at all hours to get them away to school, and not able to go to the Guild Work-party, and never getting any peace till they're in their beds, wearing maself out . . . Mercy! Here's the Major. What'll we do? "

" Let's brave it out," said Jean boldly. " Introduce him."

But Miss Bathgate's mind was a blank for the moment. She stood dumb while a young-middle-aged man stood in the doorway, surprised to find his room crowded with females. Jean went forward, holding out her hand, and explaining who she was and why she was there. She said, " Miss Bathgate is an old friend. I lived as a child across the road in The Rigs. I hear we are to be neighbours for a time. I hope you will come over to see us, if you can spare the time. What about luncheon tomorrow? "

" Very kind, very kind, I'm sure. If I'm not kept—one never knows in these days, so much confusion—I'll be delighted to lunch with you tomorrow."

" That's very nice. One o'clock. Good morning."

Miss Bathgate accompanied them to the front door.

" Ye'd be surprised to find me with a man in ma room, but I just thought with a war on, and no saying what Hitler would be up to with his capers, bombs, and that, and I know fine I'll never get ma gas-mask on, I'd be the better of a man, seeing I had the boys, anyway. But eh, Miss Jean, I never thought to be mixed up with the military! "

" Jean," said Miss Howard, when they were once more on the high road, " *do* you think that poor man will be comfortable in that cottage? "

Jean laughed. " Well, Miss Bathgate is what is known as a ' good plain cook,' with the accent on the plain. That's why I asked him to luncheon. Pamela lived there, but she never cares much what she eats; a man is different. He seems a very commanding sort of gentleman, don't you think? "

" Rather good-looking, I thought."

" Oh, quite. Sylvia, do you know who is approaching? No less a person than the Dictator of Priorsford, Mrs. Duff-Whalley."

Sylvia saw only a smallish, oldish woman, with a sharp face, walking up the hill in a purposelike manner.

She stopped. " Bless me, Lady Bidborough! Have *you* flown for refuge to Priorsford? We were never so popular; all kinds and conditions are here, every corner full. Are you at Laverlaw? "

" No," said Jean, " I'm at The Rigs. When the children come we'll all go to Laverlaw, but I am very happy to be in my old home. Sylvia—Miss Howard, Mrs. Duff-Whalley—is keeping me company. We've just been calling on Bella Bathgate."

" Are you going home now? I might come in for a chat. I happen to have a free hour, and that, let me tell you, is a very unusual thing. I've been rushed into doing so much."

Jean obediently turned, and the three women walked back to The Rigs. There, Mrs. Duff-Whalley settled herself into a chair and talked for almost an hour without drawing breath.

She had much to say about the faults and failings of the Government, the foolish method in which the war was being conducted, the muddling ways of Britain, and finally she reached the evacuation scheme. " Was there ever such an ill-thought-out scheme! Sending those filthy children——"

Here Jean interrupted. " I wish people hadn't talked and written as they did about them. Just think of the feelings of these children, rejected by one billet after another! It wasn't *their* fault."

" And what of the poor householders who had to take them? that was a scandal if you like. People who were proud of their homes having to burn their bedding after they got rid of the children."

" If they had better houses," Jean began.

" Oh! don't say that. Put them in new houses and they have them like pigsties in six months. *I* know."

To change the subject Jean asked if there were any evacuees in The Towers, her visitor's own home.

" Of course there are, three boys and two girls. How could I refuse them with all these rooms standing empty? Besides, as you know, I've got three little grandsons, and I just thought if they had wanted a home . . . But, see here, since you're so sympathetic with dirty children, will you take two that arrived today? A batch came out from Edinburgh, and it's been difficult to find places for them. Why shouldn't you? You've room to spare, and it would give you and your friend something to do."

Jean looked at Miss Howard and saw in her face nothing but horror at the suggestion, then, " Wait a moment," she said. " I must see what Mrs. McCosh says."

In a few minutes she was back. " Mrs. McCosh merely says, ' The poor lambs,' so that's all right. When will they come? "

" They're waiting," said Mrs. Duff-Whalley. " May I use your telephone? I'll tell the teacher in charge to bring them at once."

Jean rushed back to the kitchen. " Jock's room," she said. " It has two beds and a big cupboard for their things."

Presently, Jean, watching from the window, saw two stolid-looking small boys stamping up the garden path, a fair-haired girl brooding over them like a providence. Jean ran to open the door, smiling widely.

They were introduced, " This is John (shake hands) and Gavin." Each wore a label and carried a bundle; both looked as if they found themselves adrift in strange seas.

" They'll be all right," said the fair-haired girl. " I'm glad to get a home for them. They're rather a pathetic pair. The mother's in hospital, and nobody knows anything about the father. I'm afraid you'll find they've been rather neglected. Well, I must go. No, I can't wait for lunch. Thank you very much. Good-bye, boys."

Two days later Pamela Elliot, Jean's sister-in-law and Sylvia's cousin, arrived at The Rigs.

" We got back last night," she explained, " after a weary journey; we felt very bad about not being here to welcome you, but it just couldn't be managed. How did you find things? "

" Perfect. Is everything right with you? "

" Much as usual. Even a European war doesn't disturb Laverlaw Glen. Of course we have our evacuees; they stir things up a bit—a mother and three children. The children, two boys and a girl, are very happy. They go to school in the Glen and love it. But poor Mrs. Cossar, who has never in her life been away from the city, except for a bus ride in summer (her house is

147

somewhere about the Lawnmarket) is appalled by the wildness of the place. How anyone could live there from choice passes her comprehension. She can't stand the look of the hills—' shapeless-looking things ' she calls them."

Jean laughed. " As bad as Dr. Johnson with his ' shocking protuberances! ' But it's a big change from the Lawnmarket to Laverlaw. She'll miss terribly her cosy stair-head talks, and daunders round the shops, and tasty fish and chips! "

" Oh, you needn't speak so feelingly, Jean. Mrs. Cossar's very well off, if she knew it. She has two bedrooms, and a nice sunny living-room, with an electric stove as well as a fire, and she's made very welcome by the servants and shares many meals with them. They've taught her to ride a bicycle, and mean to bring her in to Priorsford to the cinema when there's an afternoon performance. The children have no desire to leave the Glen. The Laverlaw Water is an enchantment to them; they've been in and out of it since ever they came, and if they haven't caught any fish, neither have they caught a cold. D'you know they'd never seen a cow milked! They thought milk came out of tins and apples out of barrels."

" I know, we have some at Mintern Abbas whose whole lives have been lived in a city. At first they didn't know what to make of it; you'd have thought they were frightened and suspicious, but very soon they were completely at home. Pam, did you know Mrs. Duff-Whalley had taken five children ? "

" I pity them! "

" No. I don't think you need. You know how devoted she is to her own grandchildren, they will have softened her heart to all children. And she sees to it too that other people do their duty; she suggested that I should take two little boys."

" Absurd! Of course you refused. That woman's as ruthless as the Gestapo."

" Pam, you never could stand the Priorsford Dictator, could you ? She once terrified me, but now I quite enjoy her. Of course I took the boys; no one else wanted them. They're pathetic little people, dirty and neglected. Mrs. McCosh scrubbed them thoroughly and burned their clothes. Fortunately she had stored away some of Peter's and Quentin's clothes, outgrown, but still quite good, so she dressed them ' from the skin ' as she put it. When they went off to school this morning in warm suits and overcoats, and whole shoes on their feet, they were stiff with pride. They kept stroking themselves! They talk a little to Mrs. McCosh, but, so far, have nothing to say to me. Little Gavin (five and a half) has a Mongolian look—he is my idea of the present Dalai Lama—but John (seven) is a good-looking boy. Bring your children down to see them; it'll do them good to play."

" Yes, that would be fun. But where, may I ask, is Sylvia ? "

" She'll be in to tea. At the moment she is taking a walk with Bella Bathgate's lodger, Major Parker. We had him to lunch yesterday, and Sylvia and he got on very well together, and he suggested showing her some place she asked about. I'm thankful for anything that fills the time for her. It's depressing to have anyone sit about looking discontented. I knew she'd be bored, but she *would* come."

" I'll take her to Laverlaw if you say the word, though I am afraid a wild glen is not Sylvia's idea of pleasure, any more than it's Mrs. Cossar's! By the way, is Mrs. McCosh your only attendant nymph, so to speak?"

"We've a sedate damsel who does the table, and housework. But Mrs. McCosh is, as ever, my rock. In a changing world she stands steady. I think that's why the little boys stay close to her."

In the middle of October there was a party at The Rigs, quite a large party, Pamela from Laverlaw with four evacuees, Mrs. Duff-Whalley with her five, Bella Bathgate with her two, were all received by Jean and her two, with Mrs. McCosh hovering in the background. The children, very quiet at first, became animated over tea, and were very ready to " dook " for apples and be taught games. Bella Bathgate's Jimmy was the leading spirit, and more than once Bella had to rebuke him. The small John, admiring his spirit, followed him closely.

"Where do *you* bide?" Jimmy asked.

"Here," said John.

"Wi' that woman?" nodding towards his hostess. "What's her name?"

"'Canna mind, but the one in the kitchen's Mrs. McCosh."

Jimmy regarded his hostess, and said, "She's no' a Tartar like our Bella. Bella started beatin' me last night for I tell't a lee. Bella's beatin's!" He gave a laugh of kindly scorn. "They wouldna hurt a bug."

The night after the party Jean wrote a long letter to her husband.

". . . Your letter this morning made me very happy. The hope that you may come for Christmas has changed everything. I've been trying to keep from thinking more than a day forward, but now I can let myself dream about Christmas.

"Today Sylvia and I were in Edinburgh for a few hours. We heard some queer noises, and saw little white puffs of smoke away up in the blue of the sky; people stood in groups and looked at them, and we thought our men were practising. It was our first air-raid! We've been expecting it since the moment war began, and we didn't know it when we saw it! It was really quite serious, and at least fifteen of our sailors were killed. The men of the Auxiliary Air Force went up, people who in ordinary life are lawyers and stockbrokers and farmers. I am told there was a thrilling chase over the Pentlands, when an Edinburgh lawyer brought down a German plane. Can you imagine such a thing happening? Such an odd war! as Sylvia says.

"Last night, we had a party for our evacuees. I think they were happy, but they play with gravity, and they don't say funny things, as so many seem to do. I read somewhere a very nice reply to a teacher, who asked a child what he knew of the cuckoo. He said, ' Naething. Excep' he doesna lay his ain eggs.'

"At the party, my small Gavin (The Dalai Lama) got tired, and, to my immense astonishment, climbed on to Mrs. Duff-Whalley's lap and leant against her most confidingly. That wicked Pamela said it reminded her of the Bible saying about the child and the cockatrice!

"But this war does the oddest things. I'm not at all sure that it isn't going to give Sylvia a husband to her liking. Major Parker, Bella Bathgate's lodger. The bond between them, as far as I can see, is a mutual love of grousing. They are convinced that everything is wrong everywhere, and they thoroughly enjoy prophesying the end of civilisation.

"Another thing I notice about the war is that it is changing the natures of some people.

"Bella Bathgate, who always put her own comfort first, now slaves for her two wild evacuees, and leaves even the most tempting gossip with Mrs. McCosh to 'say good night to my boys.'

"Mrs. Duff-Whalley, so cordially disliked by many for her overbearing way, has, quite obviously, won the trust and affection of her small charges.

"Lewis Elliot, always one of the best, but inclined to care more for books than his fellow-men, is building huts in his Glen, and making plans for taking children every summer. He says, 'To think it took a European war to make me realise the iniquity of bringing children up to know only city streets.'

"No one can expect to get through this war comfortably, but I think most of us are not only accepting the limitations set by war conditions, but we're finding amusement in them. Let Herr Adolf Hitler beware of that laughter!

"All my love and most of my thoughts, darling,

"Your

JEAN."

HOWARD SPRING

For many years MR. HOWARD SPRING, of the " Evening Standard," has been among the first six of our literary critics. Just lately, his own novel " O Absalom ! " reversed the rôle and put him in the hands of the reviewers. He emerged with flying colours.

CHRISTMAS HONEYMOON

WE were married on December 22nd, because we had met on the 21st. It was as sudden as that. I had come down from Manchester to London. Londoners like you to say that you come up to London; but we Manchester people don't give a hoot what Londoners like. We know that we, and the likes of us, lay the eggs, and the Londoners merely scramble them. That gives us a sense of superiority.

Perhaps I have this sense unduly. Certainly I should never have imagined that I would marry a London girl. As a bachelor, I had survived thirty Manchester summers, and it seemed unlikely to me that, if I couldn't find a girl to suit me in the north, I should find one in London.

I am an architect, and that doesn't make me love London any the more. Every time I come down to the place I find it has eaten another chunk of its own beauty, so as to make more room for the fascias of multiple shops.

All this is just to show you that I didn't come to London looking for a bride; and if I had been looking for a bride, the last place I would have investigated would be a cocktail party. But it was at a cocktail party in the Magnifico that I met Ruth Hutten.

I had never been to a cocktail party in my life before. We don't go in much for that sort of thing in Manchester: scooping a lot of people together and getting rid of the whole bang shoot in one do. It seems to us ungracious. We like to have a few friends in, and give them a cut off the joint and something decent to drink, and talk in a civilised fashion while we're at it. That's what we understand by hospitality. But these cocktail parties are just a frantic St. Vitus gesture by people who don't want to be bothered.

I shouldn't have been at this party at all if it hadn't been for Claud Tunstall. It was about half-past six when I turned from the lunatic illumination of Piccadilly Circus, which is my idea of how hell is lit up, and started to walk down the Haymarket. I was wondering in an absent-minded sort of way how long the old red pillars of the Haymarket Theatre would be allowed to stand before some bright lad thought what fun it would be to tear them down, when Claud turned round from reading one of the yellow playbills, and there we were, grinning and shaking hands.

Claud had something to grin about, because the author's name on the play-

151

bill was his. It was his first play, and it looked as though it wouldn't matter to Claud, so far as money went, if it were his last. The thing had been running for over a year; companies were touring it in the provinces and Colonies; and it was due to open in New York in the coming year. No wonder Claud was grinning; but I think a spot of the grin was really meant for me. He was the same old Claud who had attended the Manchester Grammar School with me and shared my knowledge of its smell of new exercise books and old suet pudding.

Claud was on his way to this party at the Magnifico, and he said I must come with him. That's how these things are: there's no sense in them; but there would have been no sense either in trying to withstand Claud Tunstall's blue eyes and fair tumbling hair and general look of a sky over a cornfield.

That's going some, for me, and perhaps the figure is a bit mixed, but I'm not one for figures at any time. Anyway, it explains why, five minutes later, I was gritting my teeth in the presence of great boobies looking like outsizes in eighteenth-century footmen, yelling names and looking down their noses.

We stood at the door of a room, and I was aware of the gold blurs of chandeliers, and a few dozen apparent football scrums, and a hot blast of talk coming out and smacking our faces, so I deduced this was the party all right. One of the boobies yelled: " Mr. Claud Tunstall and Mr. Edward Oldham," and from what happened it might just as well have been " The Archangel Gabriel and one Worm." Because, the moment we were over the threshold, all the scrums loosened up and girls descended on Claud like a cloud of bright, skittering, squawking parrakeets, flashing their red nails at him, unveiling their pearly portals in wide grins, and bearing him off towards a bar where a chap in white was working overtime among all the sweet accessories of Sin. I never saw him again.

Well, as I say, I might have been a worm, no use at all to parrakeets, but that lets in the sparrows. I was just turning slowly on my own axis, so to speak, in the space that was miraculously cleared round me, when I saw a girl looking at me with an appreciative gleam in her brown eye. She was the brownest girl I ever saw—eyes, skin, and hair—homely as a sparrow, and just as alert.

As our eyes met, there came fluting out of one of the scrums a high-pitched female voice: " No, Basil, I'm teetotal, but I can go quite a long way on pahshun fruit."

The pronunciation of that *pahshun* was indescribable; it seemed the bogus essence of the whole damn silly occasion; and the brown girl and I, looking into one another's eyes, twinkled, savouring together the supreme idiocy. Instinctively we moved towards one another, the twinkle widening to a smile, and I found myself getting dangerously full of similes again, for when she smiled the teeth in her brown face were like the milky kernel of a brown nut.

We sat together on a couch at the deserted end of the room, and I said: " Let me get you something to drink. What would you like ? Though whatever it is, it would taste nicer in civilised surroundings."

" I agree," she said simply. " Come on."

And so, ten minutes after I had entered the Magnifico, I was outside again, buttoning my overcoat warmly about me, and this girl was at my side. It was incredible. This is not the sort of thing I usually do; but it had happened so spontaneously, and to be out there in the street, with a little cold wind blowing about us, was such a relief after that gaudy Bedlam, that the girl and I turned to one another and smiled again. I could see she was feeling the same about it as I was.

Our eyes were towards the dazzle of Piccadilly Circus, when she turned and said, "Not that way," so we went the other way, and down those steps where the Duke of York's column towers up into the sky, and then we were in the park. To be walking there, with that little wind, and the sky full of stars huddling together in the cold, and the bare branches of the trees standing up against the violet pulsing of the night—this was indescribable, incredible, coming within a few minutes upon that screeching aviary.

Ruth Hutten was a typist—nothing more. Her father had been one of those old fogies who rootle for years and years in the British Museum to prove that Ben Jonson had really inserted a semi-colon where the 1739 edition or what not has a full-stop. Things like that. Somehow he had lived on it, like a patient old rat living on scraps of forgotten and unimportant meat. Ruth had lived with him—just lived, full of admiration for the old boy's scholarship, typing his annual volume, which usually failed to earn the publisher's advance.

When he died, the typewriter was all she had; and now she typed other people's books. She had been typing a long flaming novel about Cornwall by Gregoria Gunson; and Gregoria (whom I had never heard of before, but who seemed a decent wench) had said, "I'll take you along to a party. You'll meet a lot of people there. Perhaps I can fix up some work for you."

So there Ruth Hutten was, at the Magnifico, feeling as much out of it as I did, and as glad to escape.

She told me all this as we walked through the half-darkness of the park, and I, as naturally, told her all about myself. She was hard up, but I had never known anyone so happy. And I don't mean gay, bubbling, effervescent. No; you can keep that for the Magnifico. I mean something deep, fundamental; something that takes courage when you're near the limit as Ruth was.

To this day I don't know London as well as Londoners think everyone ought to know the place. I don't know where we had supper; but it was in a quiet place that everybody else seemed to have forgotten. There was a fire burning, and a shaded lamp on the table. The food was good and simple, and no one seemed to care how long we stayed. I wanted to stay a long time. I had a feeling that once Ruth got outside the door, shook hands, and said " Good night," I should be groping in a very dark place.

I crumbled a bit of bread on the table, and without looking at her I said: " Ruth, I like you. I've never liked anyone so much in my life. Will you marry me ? "

She didn't answer till I looked up, and when our glances met she said, " Yes. If you and I can't be happy together, no two people on earth ever could."

This was five years ago. We have had time to discover that we didn't make a mistake.

We were married at a registry office the next morning. The taxi-driver, who looked like one of the seven million exiled Russian princes, and the office charwoman, who had a goitre and a hacking cough, were the witnesses. I

153

tipped them half a sovereign each. I cling to these practical details because I find them comforting in view of the mad impracticality of what was to follow. Please remember that I am an unromantic northerner who couldn't invent a tale to save his life. If I tried to do so, I should at once begin to try and fill it with this and that—in short with Something. The remarkable thing about what happened to me and Ruth was simply that Nothing happened. If you have never come up against Nothing you have no idea how it can scare you out of your wits. When I was a child I used to be afraid of Something in the dark. I know now that the most fearful thing about the dark is that we may find Nothing in it.

It was Ruth's idea that we should spend the few days of our honeymoon walking in Cornwall. Everything was arranged in a mad hurry. Not that there was much to arrange. We bought rucksacks, stuffed a change of under-clothing into them, bought serviceable shoes and waterproofs, and we were ready to start.

Walking was the idea of both of us. This was another bond: you could keep all the motor-cars in the world so far as we were concerned, and all the radio and daily newspapers, too; and we both liked walking in winter as much as in summer.

Cornwall was Ruth's idea. She had Cornwall on the brain. Her father had done some learned stuff on Malory; and her head was full of Merlin and Tintagel and the Return of Arthur. Gregoria Gunson's novel helped, too, with its smugglers and romantic inns and the everlasting beat of surf on granite coasts. So Cornwall it was—a place in which neither of us had set foot before.

We made our first contact with Cornwall at Truro. Night had long since fallen when we arrived there on our wedding day. I have not been there since, nor do I wish ever to return. Looking back on what happened, it seems appropriate that the adventure should have begun in Truro. There is in some towns something inimical, irreconcilable. I felt it there. As soon as we stepped out of the station, I wished we were back in the warm, lighted train which already was pulling out on its way to Penzance.

There was no taxi in sight. To our right the road ran slightly uphill; to our left, downhill. We knew nothing of the town, and we went to the left. Soon we were walking on granite. There was granite everywhere: grey, hard, and immemorial. The whole town seemed to be hewn out of granite. The streets were paved with it, enormous slabs like the lids of ancestral vaults. It gave me the feeling of walking in an endless graveyard, and the place was silent enough to maintain the illusion. The streets were lit with grim economy. Hardly a window had a light, and when, here and there, we passed a public-house, it was wrapped in a pall of decorum which made me wonder whether Cornishmen put on shrouds when they went in for a pint.

It did not take us long to get to the heart of the place, the few shopping streets that were a bit more festive, gay with seasonable things; and when we found an hotel, it was a good one. I signed the book, " Mr. and Mrs. Edward Oldham, Manchester," and that made me smile. After all, it was something to smile about. At this time last night, Ruth and I had just met, and now " Mr. and Mrs. Edward Oldham."

Ruth had moved across to a fire in the lounge. She had an arm along the mantelpiece, a toe meditatively tapping the fender. She looked up when I approached her and saw the smile. But her face did not catch the contagion. "Don't you hate this town?" she asked.

"I can put up with it," I said, "now that I'm in here, and now that you're in here with me."

"Yes," she answered, "this is all right. But those streets! They gave me the creeps. I felt as if every stone had been hewn out of a cliff that the Atlantic had battered for a thousand years and plastered with wrecks. Have you ever seen Tewkesbury Abbey?"

The irrelevant question took me aback. "No," I said.

"I've never seen stone so saturated with sunlight," said Ruth. "It looks as if you could wring summers out of it. The fields about it, I know, have run with blood, but it's a happy place all the same. This place isn't happy. It's under a cold enchantment."

"Not inside these four walls," I said, "because they enclose you and me and our supper and bed."

We fled from Truro the next morning. Fled is the word. As soon as breakfast was over we slung our rucksacks on to our backs and cleared out of the granite town as fast as our legs would take us. December 23rd, and utterly unseasonable weather. The sky was blue, the sun was warm, and the Christmas decorations in the shops had a farcical and inappropriate look. But we were not being bluffed by these appearances. We put that town behind us before its hoodoo could reimpose itself upon our spirits.

And soon there was nothing wrong with our spirits at all. We were travelling westward, and every step sunk us deeper into a warm enchantment. Ruth had spoken last night of a cold enchantment. Well, this was a warm enchantment. I hadn't guessed that, with Christmas only two days ahead, any part of England could be like this. We walked through woods of evergreens and saw the sky shining like incredible blue lace through the branches overhead. We found violets blooming in warm hedge bottoms, and in a cottage garden a few daffodils were ready to burst their sheaths. We could see the yellow staining the taut green. We had tea at that cottage, out of doors! I thought of Manchester, and the fog blanketing Albert Square, and the great red trams going through it, slowly, like galleons, clanging their warning bells. I laughed aloud at the incredible, the absurd things that could happen to a man in England. One day Manchester. The next London. The next marriage, Truro, and the cold shudders. The next—this! I said all this to Ruth, who was brushing crumbs off the table to feed the birds that hopped tamely round her feet. "It makes me wonder what miracle is in store for tomorrow," I said. "And, anyway, what is Cornwall? I've always thought it was beetling cliffs and raging seas, smugglers, wreckers, and excisemen."

We entered the cottage to pay the old woman, and I went close up to the wall to examine a picture hanging there. It was a fine bit of photography: spray breaking on wicked-looking rocks. "That's the Manacles," the old girl said. "That's where my husband was drowned."

The Manacles. That was a pretty fierce name, and it looked a pretty fierce place. The woman seemed to take it for granted. She made no further comment. "Good-bye, midear," she said to Ruth. "Have a good day."

We did, but I never quite recaptured the exaltation of the morning. I felt that this couldn't last, that the spirit which had first made itself felt in the hard

155

grey streets of Truro had pounced again out of that hard grey name: the Manacles. It sounded like a gritting of gigantic teeth. We were being played with. This interlude in fairyland, where May basked in December, was something to lure us on, to bring us within striking reach of—well, of what? Isn't this England? I said to myself. Isn't Cornwall as well within the four walls of Britain as Lancashire?

We breasted a hill, and a wide estuary lay before us, shining under the evening sun. Beyond it, climbing in tier upon tier of streets, was Falmouth. I liked the look of it. " This is where we stay to-night," I said to Ruth. " We shall be comfortable here."

A ferry took us across the harbour. Out on the water it was cold. Ruth pointed past the docks, past Pendennis Castle standing on the hill. " Out there is the way to Land's End," she said.

I looked, and low down on the water there was a faint grey smudge. Even a Manchester man would know that that was fog, creeping in from the Atlantic.

All night long we heard the fog-horns moaning, and it was very cold.

I hate sleeping in an airless room, but by midnight the white coils of fog, filling every crevice, and cold as if they were the exhalation of icebergs, made me rise from bed and shut the window. Our bedroom hung literally over the sea. The wall of the room was a deep bay, and I had seen how, by leaning out of the window, one could drop a stone to the beach below. Now I could not see the beach. I could not see anything. If I had stretched my arm out into the night the fingers would have been invisible. But though I could not see, I could hear. The tide had risen, and I could hear the plash of little waves down there below me. It was so gentle a sound that it made me shudder. It was like the voice of a soft-spoken villain. The true voice of the sea and of the night was that long, incessant bellow of the fog-horns. The shutting of the window did nothing to keep that out.

I drew the curtains across the window, and, turning, saw that a fire was laid in the grate. I put a match to it. Incredible comfort! In ten minutes we felt happier. In twenty we were asleep.

There seemed nothing abnormal about Falmouth when we woke in the morning. A fairly stiff wind had sprung up. The fog was torn to pieces. It hung here and there in dirty isolated patches, but these were being quickly swept away. There was a run on the water. It was choppy and restless, and the sky was a rag-bag of fluttering black and grey. Just a normal winter day by the seaside: a marvellous day for walking, Ruth said.

At the breakfast-table we spread out the map and considered the day's journey. This was going to be something new again. There had been the grey inhospitality of Truro; the Arcadian interlude; the first contact with something vast and menacing. Now, looking at the map, we saw that, going westward, following the coast, we should come to what we had both understood Cornwall to be: a sparsely populated land, moors, a rock-bound coast. It promised to be something big and hard and lonely, and that was what we wanted.

We put sandwiches into our rucksacks, intending to eat lunch out of doors. We reckoned we should find some sort of inn for the night.

A bus took us the best part of ten miles on our westward journey. Then it struck inland, to the right. We left it at that point, climbed a stile, walked through a few winter-bare fields, and came to a path running with the line of the coast.

Now, indeed, we had found traditional Cornwall. Here, if anywhere, was the enchanted land of Merlin and of Arthur—the land that Ruth dreamed about. Never had I found elsewhere in England a sense so overpowering both of size and loneliness. To our left was the sea, down there at the foot of the mighty cliffs along whose crest we walked. The tide was low, and the reefs were uncovered. In every shape of fantastic cruelty they thrust out towards the water, great knives and swords of granite that would hack through any keel, tables of granite on which the stoutest ship would pound to pieces, jaws of granite that would seize and grind and not let go. Beyond and between these prone monsters was the innocent yellow sand, and, looking at the two—the sand and the reefs—I thought of the gentle lapping of the water under my window last night, and the crying of the fog-horns, the most desolate crying in the world.

Southward and westward the water stretched without limit; and inland, as we walked steadily forward all through the morning, was now a patch of cultivation, now the winter stretch of rusty moor with gulls and lapwings joining their lamentations as they glided and drooped across it, according to their kind. From time to time a cluster of trees broke the monotony of the inland view, and I remember rooks fussing among the bare boughs. Rooks, lapwings, and gulls: those were the only birds we saw that day.

It was at about one o'clock that we came to a spot where the cliff path made a loop inland to avoid a deep fissure into which we peered. In some cataclysm the rocks here had been torn away, tumbling and piling till they made a rough giant's stairway down which we clambered to the beach below. We ended up in a cove so narrow that I could have thrown a stone across it, and paved with sand of an unbelievable golden purity. The sun came through the clouds, falling right upon that spot. It was tiny, paradisal, with the advancing tide full of green and blue and purple lights. We sat on the sand, leaned against the bottom-most of the fallen granite blocks, and ate our lunch.

We were content. This was the loveliest thing we had found yet. Ruth recalled a phrase from the novel she had typed for Miss Gregoria Gunson. " And you will find here and there a paradise ten yards wide, a little space of warmth and colour set like a jewel in the hard iron of that coast." Far-fetched, I thought, but true enough.

It was while we were sitting there, calculating how long that bit of sun could last, that Ruth said, " We wanted a lonely place, and we've found it, my love. Has it struck you that we haven't seen a human being since we got off the bus ? "

It hadn't, and it didn't seem to me a matter of concern. I stretched my arms lazily towards the sun. " Who wants to see human beings ? " I demanded. " I had enough human beings at the Magnifico to last me a very long time."

" So long as we find some human beings to make us a bit of supper to-night . . ."

" Never fear," I said. " We'll do that. There! Going . . . Going . . . Gone."

157

The sun went in. We packed up, climbed to the cliff top, and started off again.

At three o'clock the light began to go out of the day. This was Christmas Eve, remember. We were among the shortest days of the year. It was now that a little uneasiness began to take hold of me. Still, I noticed, we had seen no man or woman, and, though I kept a sharp lookout on the country inland, we saw no house, not a barn, not a shed.

We did not see the sun again that day, but we witnessed his dying magnificence. Huge spears of light fanned down out of the sky and struck in glittering points upon the water far off. Then the clouds turned into a crumble and smother of dusky red, as though a city were burning beyond the edge of the world, and when all this began to fade to grey ashes I knew that I was very uneasy indeed.

Ruth said: " I think we ought to leave this cliff path. We ought to strike inland and find a road—any road."

I thought so, too, but inland now was nothing but moor. Goodness knows, I thought, where we shall land if we embark on that.

" Let us keep on," I said, " for a little while. We may find a path branching off. Then we'll know we're getting somewhere."

We walked for another mile, and then Ruth stopped. We were on the brink of another of those deep fissures, like the one we had descended for lunch. Again the path made a swift right-hand curve. I knew what Ruth was thinking before she said it. " In half an hour or so the light will be quite gone. Suppose we had come on this in the dark ? "

We had not found the path we were seeking. We did not seek it any more. Abruptly, we turned right and began to walk into the moor. So long as we could see, we kept the coast behind our backs. Soon we could not see at all. The night came on, impenetrably black and there would be no moon.

It was now six o'clock. I know that because I struck a match to look at the time, and I noticed that I had only three matches left. This is stuck in my mind because I said, " We must be careful with these. If we can't find food, we'll find a smoke a comfort."

" But, my love," said Ruth, and there was now an undoubted note of alarm in her voice, " we *must* find food. Surely, if we just keep on we'll see a light, or hear a voice, or come to a road——"

She stopped abruptly, seized my arm, held on to prevent my going forward. I could not see her face, but I sensed her alarm. " What is it ? " I asked.

" I stepped in water."

I knelt and tested the ground in front of me with my hands. It was a deep oozy wetness; not the clear wetness of running water. " Bog," I said; and we knew we could go forward no longer. With cliff on the one hand and the possibility of stumbling into a morass on the other, there seemed nothing for it but to stay where we were till heaven sent us aid or the dawn came up.

I put my arm round Ruth and felt that she was trembling. I want to put this adventure down exactly as it happened. It would be nice to write that her nerves were steady as rock. Clearly they weren't, and I was not feeling very good either. I said as gaily as I could, " This is where we sit down, smoke a cigarette, and think it out."

We went back a little so as to be away from the bog, and then we plumped down among the heather. We put the cigarettes to our lips and I struck a match. It did not go out when I threw it to the ground. In that world of darkness the little light burning on the earth drew our eyes, and simultaneously we both stood up with an exclamation of surprised delight. The light had shown us an inscribed stone, almost buried in the heather. There were two matches left. Fortunately, we were tidy people. We had put our sandwich papers into the rucksacks. I screwed these now into little torches. Ruth lit one and held it to the stone while I knelt to read. It seemed a stone of fabulous age. The letters were mossy and at first illegible. I took out a penknife and scraped at them. " 2 Miles——" we made out, but the name of this place two miles off we do not know to this day. I scraped away, but the letters were too defaced for reading, and just as the last of the little torches flared to extinction the knife slipped from my hand into the heather. There was nothing to do but leave it there.

We stood up. Two miles. But two miles to where, and two miles in what direction? Our situation seemed no happier, when suddenly I saw the stones.

I had seen stones like them on the Yorkshire moors, round about the old Brontë parsonage. But were they the same sort of stones, and did they mean the same thing? I was excited now. "Stay here," I said to Ruth, and I stepped towards the first stone. As I had hoped, a third came into view in line with the second, and, as I advanced, a fourth in line with the third. They were the same: upright monoliths set to mark a path, whitewashed half-way up so that they would glimmer through the dark as they were doing now, tarred on their upper half to show the way when snow was on the ground. I shouted in my joy: "Come on! Supper! Fires! Comfort! Salvation!" but Ruth came gingerly. She had not forgotten the bog.

But the stones did not let us down. They led us to the village. It must have been about nine o'clock when we got there.

Half-way through that pitch-black two-mile journey we were aware that once more we were approaching the sea. From afar we could hear its uneasy murmur growing louder, and presently threaded with a heart-darkening sound: the voice of a bell-buoy tolling its insistent warning out there on the unseen water.

As the murmur of the sea and the melancholy clangour of the bell came clearer we went more warily, for we could not see more than the stone next ahead; and presently there was no stone where the next stone should be. We peered into the darkness, our hearts aching for the light which would tell us that we were again among houses and men. There was no light anywhere.

"We have one match," I said. "Let us light a cigarette apiece and chance seeing something that will help us."

We saw the wire hawser: no more than the veriest scrap of it, fixed by a great staple into the head of a post and slanting down into darkness. I first, Ruth behind me, we got our hands upon it, gripping for dear life, and went inching down towards the sound of water.

So we came at last to the village. Like many a Cornish village, it was built at the head of a cove. The sea was in front; there was a horse-shoe of cliffs; and snuggling at the end was a half-moon of houses behind a seawall of granite.

All this did not become clear to us at once. For the moment, we had no other thought than of thankfulness to be treading on hard cobbles that had been laid by human hands, no other desire than to bang on the first door and ask whether there was in the place an inn or someone who would give us lodging for the night.

Most of the cottages were whitewashed; their glimmer gave us the rough definition of the place; and I think already we must have felt some uneasy presage at the deathly mask of them, white as skulls with no light in their eyes.

For there was no living person, no living thing, in the village. That was what we discovered. Not so much as a dog went by us in the darkness. Not so much as a cock crowed. The tolling from the water came in like a passing bell, and the sea whispered incessantly, and grew to a deep-throated threatening roar as the tide rose and billows beat on the sand and at last on the seawall; but there was no one to notice these things except ourselves; and our minds were almost past caring, so deeply were we longing for one thing only—the rising of the sun.

There was nothing wrong with the village. It contained all the apparatus of living. Bit by bit we discovered that. There was no answer to our knocking at the first door we came to. There was nothing remarkable in that, and we went on to the next. Here, again, there was no welcome sound of feet, no springing up of a light to cheer us who had wandered for so long in the darkness.

At the third house I knocked almost angrily. Yes; anger was the feeling I had then: anger at all these stupid people who shut down a whole village at nine o'clock, went to their warm beds, and left us standing there, knocking in the cold and darkness. I thudded the knocker with lusty rat-tat-tats; and suddenly, in the midst of that noisy assault, I stopped, afraid. The anger was gone. Plain fear took its place. At the next house I *could* not knock, because I knew there was no one to hear me.

I was glad to hear Ruth's voice. She said, surprisingly, " It's no good knocking. Try a door."

I turned the handle and the door opened. Ruth and I stepped over the threshold, standing very close together. I shouted, " Is there anyone at home ? " My voice sounded brutally loud and defiant. Nothing answered it.

We were standing in the usual narrow passageway of a cottage. Ruth put out her hand and knocked something to the floor from a little table. " Matches," she said; and I groped on the floor and found them. The light showed us a hurricane lantern standing on the table. I lit it, and we began to examine the house, room by room.

This was a strange thing to do, but at the time it did not seem strange. We were shaken and off our balance. We wanted to reassure ourselves. If we had found flintlocks, bows and arrows, bronze hammers, we might have been reassured. We could have told ourselves that we had wandered, bewitched, out of our century. But we found nothing of the sort. We found a spotless cottage full of contemporary things. There was a wireless set. There was last week's *Falmouth Packet*. There were geraniums in a pot in the window; there were sea-boots and oilskins in the passage. The bed upstairs was made, and there was a cradle beside it. There was no one in the bed, no child in the cradle.

160

"Outside the storms of war may blow and the land may be lashed with the fury of its gales, but in our own hearts ...there is peace."

Ruth was white. "I want to see the pantry," she said, inconsequentially I thought.

We found the pantry, and she took the cloth off a breadpan and put her hand upon a loaf. "It's warm," she said. "It was baked to-day." She began to tremble.

We left the house and took the lantern with us. Slowly, with the bell tolling endlessly, we walked through the curved length of the village. There was one shop. I held up the light to its uncurtained window. Toys and sweets, odds and ends of grocery, all the stock-in-trade of a small general store, were there behind the glass. We hurried on.

We were hurrying now, quite consciously hurrying; though where we were hurrying to we did not know. Once or twice I found myself looking back over my shoulder. If I had seen man, woman, or child I think I should have screamed. So powerfully had the death of the village taken hold of my imagination that the appearance of a living being, recently so strongly desired, would have affected me like the return of one from the dead.

At the centre of the crescent of houses there was an inn, the Lobster Pot, with climbing geraniums ramping over its front in the way they do in Cornwall; then came more cottages; and at the farther tip of the crescent there was a house standing by itself. It was bigger than any of the others; it stood in a little garden. In the comforting daylight I should have admired it as the sort of place some writer or painter might choose for a refuge.

Now I could make it out only bit by bit, flashing the lantern here and there; and, shining the light upon the porch, I saw that the door was open. Ruth and I went in. Again I shouted, "Is anyone here?" Again I was answered by nothing.

I put the lantern down on an oak chest in the small square hall, and that brought my attention to the telephone. There it was, standing on the chest, an up-to-date microphone in ivory white. Ruth saw it at the same moment, and her eyes asked me, "Do you dare?"

I did. I took up the microphone and held it to my ear. I could feel at once that it was dead. I joggled the rest. I shouted, "Hallo! Hallo!" but I knew that no one would answer. No one answered.

We had stared through the windows of every cottage in the village. We had looked at the shop and the inn. We had banged at three doors and entered two houses. But we had not admitted our extraordinary situation in words. Now I said to Ruth, "What do you make of it?"

She said simply, "It's worse than ghosts. Ghosts are something. This is nothing. Everything is absolutely normal. That's what seems so horrible."

And, indeed, a village devastated by fire, flood, or earthquake would not have disturbed us as we were disturbed by that village which was devastated by nothing at all.

Ruth shut the door of the hall. The crashing of the sea on granite, the tolling of the bell, now seemed far off. We stood and looked at one another uneasily in the dim light of the hurricane lamp. "I shall stay here," said Ruth, "either till the morning or till something happens."

She moved down the hall to a door which opened into a room at the back. I followed her. She tapped on the door, but neither of us expected an answer, and there was none. We went in.

L   161

Nothing that night surprised us like what we saw then. Holding the lantern high above my head, I swung its light round the room. It was a charming place, panelled in dark oak. A few fine pictures were on the walls. There were plenty of books, some pieces of good porcelain. The curtains of dark-green velvet fringed with gold were drawn across the window. A fire was burning on the hearth. That was what made us start back almost in dismay—the fire.

If it had been a peat fire—one of those fires that, once lit, smoulder for days—we should not have been surprised. But it was not. Anyone who knew anything about fires could see that this fire had been lit within the last hour. Some of the coals were still black; none had been consumed. And the light from this fire fell upon the white smooth texture of an excellent linen cloth upon the table. On the table was supper, set for one. A chair was placed before the knife and fork and plates. There was a round of cold beef waiting to be cut, a loaf of bread, a jar of pickles, a fine cheese, a glass, and a jug containing beer.

Ruth laughed shrilly. I could hear that her nerves were strained by this last straw. "At least we shan't starve," she cried. "I'm nearly dying of hunger. I suppose the worst that could happen would be the return of the bears, demanding 'Who's been eating my beef? Who's been drinking my beer?' Sit down. Carve!"

I was as hungry as she was. As I looked at the food the saliva flowed in my mouth, but I could as soon have touched it as robbed a poor-box. And Ruth knew it. She turned from the table, threw herself into an easy chair by the fire, and lay back, exhausted. Her eyes closed. I stood behind the chair and stroked her forehead till she slept. That was the best that could happen to her.

That, in a way, was the end of our adventure. Nothing more happened to us. Nothing *more*? But, as you see, nothing at all had happened to us. And it was this nothingness that made my vigil over Ruth sleeping in the chair the most nerve-destroying experience of all my life. A clock ticking away quietly on the chimney-piece told me that it was half-past nine. A tear-off calendar lying on a writing-table told me that it was December 24th. Quite correct. All in order.

The hurricane-lamp faded and went out. I lit a lamp, shaded with green silk, that stood on the table amid the waiting supper. The room became cosier, even more human and likeable. I prowled about quietly, piecing together the personality of the man or woman who lived in it. A man. It was a masculine sort of supper, and I found a tobacco jar and a few pipes. The books were excellently bound editions of the classics, with one or two modern historical works. The pictures, I saw now, were Medici reprints of French Impressionists, all save the one over the fireplace, which was an original by Paul Nash.

I tried, with these trivial investigations, to divert my mind from the extraordinary situation we were in. It wouldn't work. I sat down and listened intently, but there was nothing to hear save the bell and the water—water that stretched, I reminded myself, from here to America. This was one of the ends of the world.

At one point I got up and locked the door, though what was there to keep out? All that was to be feared was inside me.

The fire burned low, and there was nothing for its replenishment. It was nearly gone, and the room was turning cold, when Ruth stirred and woke. At that moment the clock, which had a lovely silver note, struck twelve. "A merry Christmas, my darling," I said.

Ruth looked at me wildly, taking some time to place herself. Then she laughed and said, " I've been dreaming about it. It's got a perfectly natural explanation. It was like this. . . . No. . . . It's gone. I can't remember it. But it was something quite reasonable."

I sat with my arm about her. " My love," I said, " I can think of a hundred quite reasonable explanations. For example, every man in the village for years has visited his Uncle Henry at Bodmin on Christmas Eve, taking wife, child, dog, cat, and canary with him. The chap in this house is the only one who hasn't got an Uncle Henry at Bodmin, so he laid the supper, lit the fire, and was just settling down for the evening when the landlord of the Lobster Pot thought he'd be lonely, looked in, and said: ' What about coming to see *my* Uncle Henry at Bodmin ? ' And off they all went. That's perfectly reasonable. It explains everything. Do you believe it ? "

Ruth shook her head. " You must sleep," she said. " Lay your head on my shoulder."

We left the house at seven o'clock on Christmas morning. It was slack tide. The sea was very quiet, and in the grey light, standing in the garden at the tip of the crescent, we could see the full extent of the village with one sweep of the eye, as we had not been able to do last night.

It was a lovely little place, huddled under the rocks at the head of its cove. Every cottage was well cared for, newly washed in cream or white, and on one or two of them a few stray roses were blooming, which is not unusual in Cornwall at Christmas.

At any other time, Ruth and I would have said, " Let's stay here." But now we hurried, rucksacks on backs, disturbed by the noise of our own shoes, and climbed the path down which we had so cautiously made our way the night before.

There were the stones of black and white. We followed them till we came to the spot where we found the stone with the obliterated name. " And, behold, there was no stone there, but your lost pocket-knife was lying in the heather," said a sceptical friend to whom I once related this story.

That, I suppose, would be a good way to round off an invented tale if I were a professional story-teller. But, in simple fact, the stone *was* there, and so was my knife. Ruth took it from me, and when we came to the place where we had left the cliff path and turned into the moor, she hurled it far out and we heard the faint tinkle of its fall on the rocks below.

" And now," she said with resolution, " we go back the way we came, and we eat our Christmas dinner in Falmouth. Then you can inquire for the first train to Manchester. Didn't you say there are fogs there ? "

" There are an' all," I said broadly.

" Good," said Ruth. " After last night, I feel a fog is something substantial, something you can get hold of."

163

DOROTHY WHIPPLE

MRS. WHIPPLE is, by comparison with some of her fellow-contributors to this book, one of the newer novelists of the day, but from the day that " Greenbanks " was published, she has been recognised as an author of quality, of grace, and of a charm that always delights.

NO ROBBERY
A FABLE FOR THE TIMES

MRS. GREEN and Mrs. Bromley lived side by side in two small houses under the shade of one great ash-tree.

" What a lovely tree! " Mrs. Green exclaimed when she first came.

" Oh, you'll find it a nuisance," said Mrs. Bromley darkly. " What with leaves dropping in autumn and bird-droppings all the year round. I'm for ever cleaning up after that tree. It's a great nuisance, I warn you."

But nothing seemed to be a nuisance to Mrs. Green. Mrs. Bromley didn't think that was normal.

" Thoughtless, that's what she is," said Mrs. Bromley. " Not a thought in her head."

It was a very charming head. Mrs. Green was young, slender, pretty—like a little girl. It astonished everybody in the lane to find that she had a boy of two and a half. Mrs. Green had shining fair hair which she was always doing in different ways, sometimes letting it swing loose, sometimes tying it up with a ribbon, sometimes doing it up on top like an Edwardian lady.

" The time she must spend on that hair," said Mrs. Bromley.

All the summer Mrs. Green went about in slacks and shorts, her little boy straddled on her hip. Nothing seemed to worry her. She was always gay. Giddy, Mrs. Bromley called it.

Mrs. Bromley was ashamed when Mrs. Green came out in shorts to speak to the butcher, the baker, and the other vanmen who brought their supplies to the lane.

From which it will be gathered that Mrs. Bromley belonged to an older generation. She did. She was a widow with a son rapidly nearing Militia age, and perhaps that pressed on Mrs. Bromley and made her rather sour.

At any rate, the summer was an anxious time for any thinking person, or so Mrs. Bromley said. The times might not affect Mrs. Green, but they affected her. She read the newspapers closely and did all she was told to do. Housewives were advised to lay in stocks of food, and Mrs. Bromley began.

She warned Mrs. Green. She cut pieces from the papers and gave them to Mrs. Green to read. But she had a strong suspicion that Mrs. Green did not read them, so she took to reading them to Mrs. Green herself, over the hedge in the afternoons. She could see, however, that she was making no impression.

Mrs. Green went on rolling on the grass with her child. Even on Monday mornings, when Mrs. Bromley was rubbing and wringing in her wash-house, Mrs. Green would be rolling on the grass with her little boy and laughing so hard that Mrs. Bromley had to look out to see what she was laughing at. Nothing, as far as Mrs. Bromley could make out, except that the child was sitting on his mother's stomach. Mrs. Bromley couldn't see anything particularly funny in that. She wouldn't have liked anybody to sit on hers.

During that summer, Mrs. Green continued to sing about the garden and play with her child, while Mrs. Bromley, most afternoons, made tiresome journeys into the town, which was two miles away, to buy things from the shops. When she came toiling up the lane with her baskets and carriers, Mrs. Green would run out in her shorts.

"Hello," she would cry. "Laden again! Let me help you in."

Through the summer days, Mrs. Bromley made jams, jellies, chutneys. She bottled vegetables; she clarified fat and stored it in jars. She laid in tins of this and tins of that, she laid in everything. And when her store cupboards were full, she brought in Mrs. Green to look at them and take a lesson.

"Ah," said Mrs. Green mischievously. "I shall know where to come."

And she would too, thought Mrs. Bromley. The cheek!

Mrs. Bromley knew the old fable of the ant and the grasshopper. The ant who toiled all summer long, as she had done, and the grasshopper who did nothing but fiddle and enjoy itself like Mrs. Green. And when winter came and there was no food, the grasshopper came to beg of the ant, just as Mrs. Green would come to beg of her. Well, she would get the same answer, determined Mrs. Bromley, looking forward to that time.

Even now, Mrs. Green borrowed.

"Could you lend me one egg?" she would ask, putting her bright head over the fence. "Just for John's lunch? I'll pay you back when the grocer's been."

"Could you lend me one slice of stale bread to toast for Jim's baked beans? Ours is too new."

She asked in such a way that Mrs. Bromley found it hard to refuse her. But what a housekeeper, she thought.

When Mrs. Green did her housework, Mrs. Bromley couldn't think. She was out not only practically all the day, she was out before breakfast. Every fine morning, about half-past seven, the Green family would emerge from their gate on bicycles—Mrs. Green on hers, her hair swinging, far too much leg, according to Mrs. Bromley, showing in shorts; Mr. Green with John on his handlebars, and like that they would go for a ride.

"I suppose the poor husband doesn't get any breakfast," thought Mrs. Bromley, seeing him rush off to work in his car a few moments after their return.

She had to admit, all the same, that the Greens looked remarkably well, in spite of Mrs. Green's sketchy housekeeping. The child was sturdy and well kept. They all looked very happy. Mrs. Bromley could only conclude that they had all been very hardy *to begin with*. Time would tell on them, she said darkly.

War was declared on a bright Sunday morning, and a few moments after the declaration of war, the lane had its first air-raid warning. Wardens in tin hats appeared as if by magic in the lane, sending children from their play into the houses. Mrs. Green went into the garden and swung her son up into her arms, kissing him. She was carrying him into the house, her face serious for once, when Mrs. Bromley, gas-mask in hand, approached the hedge.

"Are you all right, Mrs. Bromley?" called Mrs. Green. "Or will you and Charlie come in to us?"

"We are all right, thank you," said Mrs. Bromley rather stiffly. She had prepared a refuge as she had prepared everything else, and she thought it was rather hard lines that she should have to ask the Greens in to use up the oxygen, just because they had not prepared a refuge of their own. "I was coming to ask you to come in to us," she said.

"Thank you very much," said Mrs. Green, "but we'd rather stay in our own house, you know, in case a bomb starts a fire or anything. See you later," said Mrs. Green, with one of her smiles, and going into her house she closed the door.

The lane waited, silent, empty under the radiant sky, in which, so the lane had been warned, enemy planes might appear at any minute. They did not appear, and by and by the all-clear signal was given. Five minutes later, the Greens emerged from their gate on bicycles and went for a ride as if nothing had happened. Mrs. Bromley was astounded. It seemed such an extraordinary thing to do.

The black-out orders were given and Mrs. Bromley, fussing and clucking like an anxious hen, made incessant journeys into the town to buy, with great difficulty, her material. She measured and cut out and machined and got all her windows successfully blacked-out. There is no doubt that Mrs. Bromley was a model citizen. But Mrs. Green and her husband pinned up brown paper every night and when this got torn, as it did, the police came round. Mrs. Bromley would have been very ashamed, she knew, to receive a visit from the police, but Mrs. Green only laughed as she recounted how the police had come into the house and helped her to pin up more paper.

It was autumn and the leaves fell thick from the ash-tree and strewed both gardens. Mrs. Bromley swept hers up, complaining, but Mrs. Green laughed at hers and said, "Oh, they'll blow away in time."

Then Mrs. Bromley's son, Charlie, was called up and she was left alone in her well-provisioned, carefully darkened house. The days were very long, the nights were longer. She began to look wistfully over the hedge for sights of Mrs. Green, still gay, still singing, still doing her housework, not according to routine but when she felt like it, still bicycling before breakfast, though in a woollen jumper and a tweed skirt now.

The vans no longer came with supplies to the lane, because of the shortage of petrol. In consequence Mrs. Green often ran out of things and came to borrow. But, strangely enough, Mrs. Bromley no longer minded. She was glad to see Mrs. Green under any pretext. She was delighted, too, when she could get Mrs. Green and her little boy into her house for tea. They were such a dear young pair, she thought, and so comforting to be with. Mrs. Green's gaiety was undiminished. When Mrs. Bromley saw the posters on the walls, "Your courage, your cheerfulness, your resolution will bring us victory," she thought of Mrs. Green. It was Mrs. Green's courage and cheerfulness; not hers. Left to herself, she felt she had not much of either. She had to draw on Mrs. Green's.

And so it came about that the following dialogue—astonishing when one remembers Mrs. Bromley's attitude in the summer—the following dialogue took place over the hedge one bright cold morning in late autumn :

"Mrs. Bromley! Mrs. Bromley!" called Mrs. Green in her clear voice, standing on the stone she had placed permanently beside the hedge to facilitate borrowing. "Mrs. Bromley, darling," she said, lowering her voice when Mrs. Bromley ran out to her. "Could you lend me just one egg? For John's lunch. Have you had a letter from Charlie this morning? Is he all right? Will you read bits to me later? One egg, just for John's lunch, is what I wanted. And if you could lend me one teeny-weeny bit of butter for Jim's supper to-night, I'd be so grateful. We've eaten all ours already and we've no petrol to go for more, even if they'd give us any at the shop."

"I tell you what," said Mrs. Bromley. "You three come in and have supper with me. I'll make a nice one. I've plenty of stuff."

"Oh, we couldn't do that," said Mrs. Green. "With things as they are. It wouldn't be fair."

"Oh, yes it would," contradicted Mrs. Bromley. "I laid everything in. I've got the food, but I haven't got the company. Good company like yours. I couldn't lay up a store of that, it seems. You can't provide what I've got, it's true, but then I can't provide what you've got. So we're quits. You know what they say : 'Exchange is no robbery.'"

"Right you are," cried Mrs. Green gaily. "If you look at it like that, we'll come."

LORD MOTTISTONE

LORD MOTTISTONE—better known still to the men of 1914 as Jack Seely—has had a distinguished record in war and peace, in politics, and in public life. By far the best loved of his writings is " My Horse Warrior," and Warrior is still with him—and with us—in 1939.

TELL THEM, WARRIOR

" SO, there's another war on," said Warrior to me yesterday as he turned his beautiful clear eyes to mine in that look of recognition which I have seen and loved for more than thirty years past.

" How do you know? "

" I heard the shooting out at sea. It was not target practice, because it was the wrong time of day. Also, I have noticed that all the young fellows have gone, except the farm chaps, just the same as it was twenty-five years ago. I've been wondering what it is all about, and if we are fighting the Germans again."

" Yes," I said, " we are fighting the Germans again. The war was about Poland when it began, but now the Germans and the Russians have taken Poland."

" Ah, I see," said Warrior, " the same as the Germans took most of Belgium when you and I were there first; and we are fighting to prevent them taking the rest of the world."

" Yes," I replied, " I suppose that is it."

" Well," said Warrior, " are you going to France, the same as you did the last time? If you do, you will take me, won't you? "

" Oh yes, certainly I will; but there are two difficulties. They say we are both too old."

" What nonsense! " said Warrior. " My eyes are as clear, my back is as straight, my legs are as clean as when we started together, twenty-five years ago—and as for you, you seem to throw your leg over a horse a bit better now than you did then. Oh, I think we had better go! "

I told him that the other difficulty is that they say that horses are not wanted.

" That's a good one! " said Warrior. " That's what they told us the last time—but it didn't prevent you and me galloping right up to the Germans and through and beyond them three times over! That's the same sort of nonsense as they talked when they said the war was going to end war. I knew that wasn't true. Still, I hope it will be ended. You will forgive me if I talk to you quite frankly about the other creatures besides you humans. I wish you would make up your quarrels and let us have a happier time. Now, take the case of dogs. War is terribly hard on dogs. They tell me so as they come walking by. **As** time goes on, there is never enough for them to eat; then their masters go away and leave them behind—and if, as often happens, they never come back, a good dog is never happy again. As for us horses, well, you remember what it was like in the retreat which started the war! I was one of the lucky ones. But during those weeks, I must have seen thousands of French and English horses killed or dying of exhaustion. But that was nothing to those long winters when all the lorries and tractors got stuck in the mud, and we poor horses had to do the work. Do you remember the Somme Battle, and how nearly I was finished off when I fell through the ice crust on top of the soft white mud, with you on my back? I often think that was the narrowest escape I had, though my other horse friends were more concerned about the shells and the machine guns. But even all that was just a happy party compared to Passchendaele in the following year. Do you remember how I went in up to my ears in a mixture of mud and water, between Ypres and St. Julien? Oh, it's a cruel game for horses, is this war! Still, it's a great deal better to be with your friend at the war than to be left behind and see him go off by himself or with another horse. I couldn't bear that! No, if you are going, I must come too!"

"It is very good of you, Warrior, to offer to go to the war again, for what with the bullets, the shells, the air bombs, and the gas, you did have rather a hard time during the four years and three months that you spent on the Western Front. We were always together for three and a half years, but during the retreat from Mons I saw you only occasionally. Tell me about that."

"It was a trying time for horses as well as men. The Germans swept through Belgium in the same way as, in this war, they have swept through Poland. They tell me that the burning farms and villages that we remember so well all the way from Mons to near Paris were just the same in Poland the other day."

"Tell me, Warrior, when did you first come under fire?"

"Well, I will tell you all I can remember; and, mind you, we horses have better memories than men. All the rest of the war, you can talk about just the same as myself, because, as you say, we were together by day and night. But in that retreat at the start, you were off all the time in a motor-car, going to the French front and the British front, doing a hundred miles or more every day, while I was left at G.H.Q. all the time with the British Army. Freddy Guest rode me constantly. He was a good friend and a fearless fellow. That makes a great difference to a horse. When the guns begin to shoot, a horse wants to keep moving; he can't bear to stand still. And, of course, once he begins to gallop away, it is very hard to stop. I believe men find the same thing. But if you can only remember that it is safer to gallop towards the guns than away from them, you have a happier time and you are much less likely to be hit. The gunner does not expect you to gallop towards him, so you really have a much better chance. I have heard you say that it was I who took you towards the enemy on many an occasion. Well, that is quite true. I knew it was the better plan.

"A few shells fell around me near St. Quentin, but already I was beginning to understand about shells. It is not a bit of good trying to get out of their way unless you see a whole lot of them bursting in a line, and then it is just as well to get a hundred yards away if you can; but always, as I have just told you, nearer the enemy if possible.

" That was a wonderful gallop I had with you and my good friend Bend-or —Bend-or Westminster, as you called him. The Germans had come on so fast that we were less than thirty miles from Paris, with the Germans still approaching; but I heard you say to Bend-or that they were fifteen miles away and advancing slowly, so there was plenty of time to gallop off and see his friend, the Baron. You said that we could see how things were going on the left flank, at the same time. I suppose it was rather a mad thing to do, but you both said you were sick of motor-cars, and wasn't it just fun to be galloping on horses again?

" As we approached the little village where the Baron lived, we saw shells dropping—but quite four miles away, so there ought to be plenty of time. The Baron was standing in the doorway of his little château, and invited us in. I and Bend-or's horse stood outside, being held by a very old gardener. I heard your voices through the window. It seemed that Bend-or and the Baron had had a row some time and were making it up, because when you came out, the Baron was saying, ' Well then, we are friends for ever. We make friends to the sound of the guns.' Just at that moment, there was a frightful bang—the loudest I had ever heard up till then—and the little lodge gatehouse fifty yards away was blown high into the air.

" We got accustomed to these big shells later on, but that was the first I had seen. There was a heavy column of black smoke as high as a big house, with the flames from the little house shooting up into the blackness. Bend-or said, ' Well, good-bye, Baron, we must be getting on.' When we got to the gate, I really couldn't face it. The smoke was so black, and there was a big hole in the road. However, you made me go round the edge of the hole, as I was to do so many hundreds of times later on, and we started to ride back to Headquarters. Three more shells dropped in the neighbourhood, and one of them set the Baron's house on fire. Bend-or told you afterwards that the Baron himself escaped injury.

" When we got back to Headquarters, we found most of the people and horses gone. You sent me on with the last Headquarters lorry and faithful old Smith in your motor, while you and Bend-or stayed behind.

" Now, what I am wondering is, whether this war that is now going on will be just the same."

" Well, of course, if either side breaks through, it will be just the same: the same burning houses and villages, because ordinary big shells set houses on fire, even if they are not of the kind they call incendiary. But they do tell me that it will be very difficult for either side to break through."

" What about tanks? " says Warrior. " You remember that gallop we had behind a tank at the first battle of Cambrai on November 20th, 1917. We got along fine then; in fact, we went a good four miles together, you and me and the tank, until it finally fell into the canal. Why shouldn't the tanks break through? "

" Oh, there's a new thing since the last war. They've invented what they call an anti-tank defence, which keeps off the tanks in the same way that really good barbed wire keeps off men. No, I don't think the tanks can break through, from all I have heard. Well, you and I must just go and see. After all, when we have survived nearly four years of war, there is no need for us to be worried about this one. But tell me some more about what happened to you in the early stages."

"Well, you rode me once, you remember, during what they called the Battle of the Marne. Then you went off somewhere—I think to Antwerp—and John French used to ride me very often—first on the Aisne, then up near Ypres. I was in a stable at Bailleul. But sometimes I went to Poperinghe or Ypres. John French was constantly riding amongst the troops and going up into those horrid muddy trenches. He used to cheer the men up no end. They were very hard times for us horses, but I felt I was doing some good.

"Then, you remember the happy day when you met me at Boulogne and marched me along the ordinary gangway on to the boat. It was a crowded boat and pitch-dark, but you sat with me most of the time. From Folkestone, you sent me to the Isle of Wight, and from there to Salisbury Plain, where you joined me and I found myself the first charger of the General commanding the Canadian Cavalry Brigade. It was quite a business finding them on Salisbury Plain, the mud was so deep; but wonderful men they were, with some wonderful horses. My greatest friend amongst the horses was called Casey. He could do all kinds of tricks like a dog; lie down and jump up when you said ' God Save the King.' I pretended to think these tricks undignified, but it was partly because I found them so extremely difficult. Casey belonged to a man who commanded the Royal North-West Mounted Police: Lord Strathcona's Horse Royal Canadians, or ' Strathconas ' for short. He was a wonderful man; understood horses as well as he understood men, and that is saying a lot. He was very good to me all through those hard times in France and Belgium. The time he pleased me most was when he said to me, ' You have taught Casey how to behave under shell-fire.' Horses do talk to each other a lot, and I had told Casey a good many things which were useful to him when we went into battle, which we did very soon after we returned to France. When I was on French's staff, I always had some kind of a stable, or at least good shelter, but when I found myself in the battle, the only shelter I had was a haystack, into which the bullets were constantly thudding. Casey came and sheltered under the same haystack, and it was then I told him all about modern war.

"Strathconas loved Casey, and I believe they loved me too. They were extraordinary people. As I told you, they were never allowed either to grumble or to swear—at least, not what they called swearing—and nothing frightened them or their horses. We tried to act as cavalry in the Somme Battle, but it didn't come off. I was lame on the first day, so you will remember you rode a big black horse and got him shot. I was sorry for him, but glad to be alive myself. However, when the Germans retired we had two grand gallops after their rearguards. You rode me both times, and, my word, wasn't it fun to get through what seemed a hail of bullets and be none the worse? I don't believe anything of this sort would have happened but for my great friend—your only rival in my affections—Geoffrey Brooke. He was the most perfect rider that ever sat on my back, and he had a wonderful idea of defeating the enemy by swift movement. Your plans came off both days at Equancourt and Guyencourt, but you won't mind my saying that you could never have made them without Geoffrey Brooke.

"The second day, at Guyencourt, when Harvey got his V.C., was the second-best thing I ever saw. You will remember we were galloping close to Harvey when you told him to take his troop and get round the back of the village while we galloped straight on. There was thick wire which we hadn't seen, at the back of the village, so Harvey, nothing daunted, galloped as hard as he could towards the northern entrance. There were twenty or thirty Germans in a trench, shooting very wildly. Harvey galloped straight at them and then saw the wire in front of the trench. You remember, he jumped off at full gallop—he was a great athlete—and jumped over the wire as his horse stopped, shot the machine gunner with his revolver as he leaped into the trench, and then turned the gun on the remainder. Many of them were killed and the rest surrendered. Not bad, for one man, was it? He was a beautiful rider and, they did tell me, a wonderful footballer. The two things do not often go together, I have found. I'm glad you never took to football.

"Then there was the day when I did a thing which I never would have believed possible. You recollect we had seen a tank rumbling through the village of Flers in the first part of the Somme Battle. I never thought much of the things, but I was wrong. For a year later I cantered along behind one of these things on the Western Front in almost perfect security, the enemy defenders being killed in hundreds instead of us attacking people. Up till then I had always seen the attackers losing their hundreds or more. However, at Cambrai it came off fine but for the canal into which the tank fell—and don't you remember how nearly we fell in after it?

"You will recall how we lived in the village of Masnières on the borders of the canal. Bullets used to spatter against the walls all night. It was then, you remember, that Strachan got his V.C. We saw him galloping over the field and sabreing the German gunner with his sword. Then you remember we were relieved and told to have a month's rest and refit. So, of course, the very next morning you were on my back galloping to a rendezvous where we were told that the Germans had come back on us and captured many thousand prisoners and ever so many machine guns. Don't you remember how you told the Divisional Commander, McAndrew (he was a fine rider, but a bit rough with his horses), ' So you would like us to blow into the battle,' and he said, ' That's the sort of idea '? We got surrounded and I lived in the bottom of an old German trench. You had another horse shot that time instead of myself. If I remember right, you had a great number of horses shot. However, now we come to the time when you lost two in one day. You rode me on the thirtieth of March, 1918, when we galloped straight through our own lines, through the German lines, and planted your little triangular red flag on its lance at the corner of Moreuil Wood. Half of our little party of horses were killed on the way. We had been retiring for nine days without a stop, and the Germans I saw, though pleased with their success, seemed dazed and very tired. Their shooting was bad, but when the whole lot of us charged and got right into the middle of the main body, the Germans were terribly brave. Of course, it was very brave of our horses and men to go at them like this. I see them now as I talk to you—Royal Canadian Dragoons, Fort Garrys, and, of course, Strathconas—all charging along. But then we were desperate. We knew there was nothing else for it. But the Germans would not give in. Don't you remember that man with a little beard who put his rifle against the side of my head and pulled the trigger, just missing your left ear? I remember the hot blast on my neck even now. He was already badly wounded, but he wouldn't give in. The French on our right fought like tigers that day, but, of course, neither they nor the Germans had horses, so we

172

had all the best of it. You remember that was the day when, as in the case of Harvey, we came galloping along with young Flowerdew of Strathconas, and you told him to gallop round the outside of the wood while we charged into it. He got a V.C. too. My word, he earned it! But for him, we should all have been killed, as he was, poor lad! So I shall never forget Flowerdew, the bravest man I ever knew.

" Well, we have had a great talk about the past war, and looking back at it all it does seem a pity that these three brave sets of chaps—the French, the Germans, and ourselves—cannot make it up, and so give us horses a quieter and a happier time. It's all very well to say that the war brings out the fine qualities, and I'm sure that's very true. As I have been saying, with my own horse's eyes I have seen three Victoria Crosses won quite near to me, and indeed they were earned. But what about us horses! In that last attack that I have been telling you about, I got through by some miracle, but eight hundred of my Canadian horse friends were killed on that one day, most of them in the few minutes of that wild gallop which you have often told me saved the fortunes of the day. We horses had no share in making the quarrel; it seems hard that we should suffer so dreadfully—for be sure that, as war goes on, the machines give out and it is all left to us horses to do the cruellest and the hardest work. Still, if they can't make it up, I can only repeat, you and I had better go to the war together again and see if we can't finish it off with a victory, the same as before."

173

L. A. G. STRONG

It is as a novelist that MR. L. A. G. STRONG has made his most characteristic contribution to English literature, though he is outstanding, too, as a critic and journalist. Every story he has published breaks new ground, and, above all, his studies of childhood and adolescence will always be remembered. It is only in championing the cause of different books that the camp is divided; all are agreed on their quality.

A GIFT FROM CHRISTY KEOGH

WELL—said my friend Lukey Mangan—I never had but the one Christmas present off of Christy Keogh, and I hope I won't get another.

Christy Keogh is the bookie whom I and some hundreds of other deluded poor divils subscribe to keep in affluence, owing to the weakness of our nature and the fallibility of our prophetic intuitions. One evening before Christmas, I ran into him coming out of Lanigan's pub.

" Ah, my sound man! " says he, very cordial, clapping me on the back. " Is it yourself? Come back with me now, and take a glass."

I thought I might as well, seeing how many glasses, or the price of them, he'd had off of me. So I hid my surprise, and went in with him.

" Listen to me now," says he. " You're a man I like, and a man is always a pleasure to do business with. That being so, I'd like to signalise it by making ye a little bit of a present, with my best wishes and the compliments of the season. Tell me now—would ye fancy a dog? I have a grand little dog I'm after getting sent up from the country," says he, " and I'm wishful to find a good home for him. And, just as I was castin' about in me mind, thinkin' who could I entrust with him, sure, I run into yourself. Now that's Providence," says he. " That's the workin' o' Providence, for there's no man better able nor better fitted to give Rover a home than yourself. What do ye say? "

Now it so happened I was wanting a dog, for poor little Mick was after being killed by a lorry in the month of October—him, that had the run o' the streets for six years, and must have dodged ten thousand lorries in his time— and we hadn't the heart to go seeking another. But the wound was healed, as you might say, and, though I'll always miss him, I felt, the moment Christy put the words to me, that we'd be glad of another. Besides, thinks I to myself, here is Christy, the decent man, overcome with the sentiments of the season, and wishful furthermore to make some return to me for all the cash he's had off of me this autumn.

So I thanked him very cordial, and said I'd be glad to take the dog, and give him as good a home as I was able.

"That's grand," says he, and takes out a piece of paper from his pocket, and writes on it with the stub of a pencil. "If you call over to Westland Row, and give them in this note, they'll hand the pup over to ye."

We said good-bye then, and off I started. It was about 5 p.m., and sheets of rain, and the coldest wind that ever blew. There was lights in the shop windows, and they were all decorated, but the few people in the streets were hurrying by for dear life and paying no heed at all. I put my head down and turned up my collar, and eventually I got to the address in Westland Row. I gave a man there the note, a seedy-looking thin fellow with a red moustache, and he eyed me in a furtive manner I didn't care for. Then, as he turned away, I caught sight of him smiling in a way I didn't fancy either.

He told me the pup was in a livery stables off of Merrion Square, and that he would accompany me there. I asked him about the pup, but he was evasive in his replies.

At last he stopped at a tall, stiff, rickety door that wouldn't give way till he kicked it, and we found ourselves in a dark cave of a place, all echoes.

"Have you a match?" says he. "Mine is all wet on me."

I searched and found mine, but with my cold, numb, wet fingers it wasn't till the third one that I got a light. He took it from me, and lit an old stable lantern, with which a glimpse of high concrete walls shining and sweating with water. He led the way on, and opened another door, and then, bedad, we were in another world altogether, walking down a warm, long, straw-littered dormitory with a number of stalls on each side. Indignant-looking horses stared at us over the half-doors of their stalls, their eyes rolling in the lantern light, and one fellow lashed out like mad in his stall.

Down near the end there were more stalls and more fierce-looking horses, and it was there I heard a deep bass growl like a jaguar or a polar bear.

"Are there hounds here?" I asked the man.

He looked at me oddly, sideways.

"Not that I know of," said he.

At the very far end was an old tumbledown, derelict sort of a stall, with no horse in it. The man opened the door, and in we went. Well—I don't want to be exaggerative to you, but, honest, the biggest dog in the world was in there, and he was furiously angry into the bargain. He growled and growled and showed his teeth, and his eyes were as black as prunes.

The man with the red moustache didn't seem afraid of him, anyway. He undid the end of the chain, and gravely handed it to me, and the animal on the end of it. I took it like a man in a dream, and we walked quickly back along between the horses, with the dog snuffling and tugging and growling. A minute, and we were out in the street. I gave the man a shilling for my trouble, and he faded away from me like a ghost; and there was I, all alone in the pelting rain, in a dark alleyway, with a crazy great dog on the end of an entirely inadequate chain.

I feigned a confidence I didn't have. "Come on, Rover," says I to the dog.

I led him into the main street, and wandered down it, wondering how the deuce I was going to get rid of him. I couldn't see what kind of a dog he was, but he was big and strong, with a hide on him like a doormat, and he smelt like a poulterer's shop on a hot day.

175

An idea came to me at last. I made for the quays, and, as soon as I got there, I slipped the chain and let the huge beast go. I was wringing wet by now, and horribly unhappy, with no tea, and miles from home.

The dog's delight at getting off the chain was awe-inspiring. He charged like mad after other dogs, scattering them and sending them yelping. He barked at the trams, his bark reverberating up and down the quays and rattling all the windows. He had a terrific bark, a deep, mad, booming, sonorous kind of a bark. And after each one of his lunatic charges, he would rush back in gratitude to me, the author of his freedom, jump up on me in his joy, and beslaver me all over with saliva, mud, and adoration.

There was no getting rid of him, that was clear. A shiver ran down my back, and my head began to throb with cold where the rain had soaked through the brim of my hat. I heard a rattle on the cobbles, looked up, and saw one of Eason's the stationer's vans coming along. I recognised the driver, stopped him, and implored him for the love of God to bring us up the quays.

He did, with amazed ejaculations at the size of Rover, who thought it was a game when I tried to hoist him up on the van. Only when I gave it up, and climbed in, did he give a great clumsy lep and barge in after me.

So we rattled along, the cobbles sending jags and splinters of fire through my head; but anything was better than the rain. Then what does that infernal animal do but imagine he smelt a rat under the piles of Christmas numbers and such that were in the van. Before we realised, he had a few hundred magazines and illustrated weeklies scattered about and destroyed with mud.

The driver stopped the van, and him and myself—it's lucky he knew me, or I'd be in jail yet—him and myself tried to tie Rover up; but he snapped at us, and lay sulking and quivering down at the far end. We drove on so, I watching him and holding my aching head in my hands and bawling at him whenever he tried to move.

Having gone as far as I wanted, I got down, thanked the driver, and gave him half a crown, which he took with an air of despair.

"Here," he said, "don't be leaving him here on me."

I called, and bedam, the demented animal lepped out at once, nearly knocking the driver off his seat, and proceeded to gambol around me as if I was the best friend he had in the world. He ran away then, with the chain trailing and clanking behind him, and next minute I saw two little dogs skelping off down Bridgefoot for their lives with my Christmas treasure after them. There was a look about his shadow turned me cold. He looked like the Hound of the Baskervilles.

I never will know where that dog was born or reared, but he knew the locality as well as I know the back of my hand, and he met me on the canal bank with every appearance of love and affection. He was all over mud, with streams of water pouring off him: I suppose he'd been in the canal looking for eels. He jumped up on me in such transports that he knocked my hat off. I shoved him away as best I was able, and then, as I stopped to get my hat, he grabbed it up and capered off with it.

"Rover!" I yelled at him. "Give it here."

And, do you know, he came to me at once, and dropped it at my feet,

IN THE WILDERNESS: FROM THE ORIGINAL BY REX WHISTLER

" As I was in my youth, when the secret of God was upon my tabernacle "

wagging his tail humbly and ecstatically at me. I put the hat on firmly—it couldn't be much worse than it was already—and started off again.

The next thing I knew, the canal bank was full of men from the brewery coming off a work shift, and soon there was a confused roaring and shouting amongst them. A shower of rocks and stones came my way, and a second after came the dog, carrying in his mouth what I thought first was a man's cap, and then saw with horror was a large piece of cloth. He dropped it at my feet, gave a bark like a bell-buoy, and rushed to the canal, where he drank about four quarts of water.

I made tracks. It was a dark night, and maybe some of them lads coming off the shift had seen him follow me with the bit of cloth. But the divil was in that dog. The more I tried to disown him, the closer he followed me, taking pains under every lamp to gambol close and look up at me, his blood-shot eyes gleaming in the lamplight.

By this time I was in a condition of broken-hearted imbecility. Sounds of uproar and confusion still came from behind me, muffled by the splutter of the rain and the howling of the wind over the canal. Then I heard running steps.

" Ey, misther! "—and a great fellow about eight feet high came towering over me.

" Ey, misther! " he roars. " What about me breeches ? "

I didn't know, but I could make a very good guess.

" Take a look at this, misther," says the man, raising his right leg, and, sure enough, I saw there was a bit about a foot long off the bottom of his trousers. Meanwhile the dog stood just behind me, growling in the most awesome manner.

" I'm sorry for your misfortune," says I, " but I don't own the dog. He's——"

I broke off, staggering to save my balance, as Rover, to show how he appreciated the point, bounded up on me and tried to lick my face. Foiled in this, he lay down, and grinned at the man from between my legs.

" I don't own him," I protested. " He's been following me for the last hour, persecuting the life out of me. I never saw him till this afternoon."

The man lowered suspiciously, first at me, and then at Rover.

" Well, if yous don't own the dog," says he, " I'll soon find out who does. Will ye look at the destruction ? Me new pair o' breeches, that I'm only after putting on me this morning." He looked at Rover again. " Is there a name on his collar ? "

I caught hold of the collar to look, but the animal bounded up and rushed off, pulling me after him. I cried out something to the man, and the last I saw was a glimpse of him over my shoulder, standing and looking after us like an angry bull in a field.

Well, all things have an end, and at last I got home, followed and accompanied still by this accursed animal.

" Glory be! " Mary calls out as I came in. " What is it you have ? "

Then, in the gaslight of the kitchen, I first had a proper look at him. I never seen the like. He was about six years old, futurist in colour scheme, and the size of a calf, with great staring mad eyes, and of no known breed on earth or off it.

As we were staring at him, he put his colossal forepaws on the table, and stood up, hanging his tongue out at us. Mary indignantly shooed him off, and he lurched sideways, bringing down the cloth and all the tea things with it. Before we could do a thing, he golloped down a half-pound of the best butter and was lapping up the spilt milk.

"Out!" screams Mary, grabbing up the broom, but he bared his teeth at her.

"Easy, Mary," said I. "He'd murder you at a bite."

She put down the broom, and I went to pick up the mess, the dog coming over in the middle of the operation to lick the top of my head.

"Coax him a bit," says I to Mary.

"How shall I?" she says, standing there helpless, gazing at the awful apparition of a dog that was after coming in on her.

"What have you you don't want?" says I.

"Nothing," says she. "Oh yes, I have. There's a couple of rashers is after going off," she says. "I must complain about them to Cooney's first thing tomorrow morning." She was like a woman in a trance.

"Never mind about Cooney's," said I. "Try can you entice him away with them."

"I daren't move," says she.

"That's all right," I said. "Here, Rover. Here, boy."

Then, of course, the brute wouldn't budge. But Mary took up courage, and went by him, skipping the last step as he let a growl at her, but didn't rise.

She came back with the rashers.

"Here," she says, dangling one at him. "Good boy."

Bedad, he was up then all right, and swallowed it at a gulp, and stood wagging his tail expectantly for the next.

"Here," she says, backing away into the hall. He followed her, and I heard her open the front door, and then slam and bolt it.

She came back white and shaken, and I thought she was going to faint, but she pulled round. Before she could curse at me, I told her the story, and went off to change my clothes.

Well, for a couple of hours after that we had peace. It seems Rover went exploring the neighbourhood, and struck up a friendship with Madigan's Sealyham out of Haroldville Terrace, leading him into all kinds of wrong-doing; but about ten o'clock he came back, and howled outside the hall door at intervals for the balance of the night.

When we went down in the morning, there he was, large and enthusiastic and ravenous, having scraped all the paint off the bottom of the door in his efforts to get in.

We had to feed him, and there wasn't enough in the house to do it. After that, he just lay down on the floor, eyeing us with unbounded affection, and wouldn't go. He was as fond of Mary by this time as of myself, and when she went down the town for her morning's shopping, he followed her. On the way, he invaded a butcher's shop and stole an awful conglomeration of hearts and brains and long red things with yards of wind-pipe dangling out of them. He followed her all down George's Street with this thing dragging in the mud, and a crowd gathered.

"Is that the way ye do your shopping, ma'am?" someone calls out.

"Faith," says another. "It's a cheap way so. How much will ye take for the lend of him, ma'am?"

Mary poked the brute in the ribs with her brolly, and he went out on to the tram track, laid down the liver, etcetera, and cried at the top of his voice. She ran down the next street, and presently, peeping round the corner, she saw a line of eleven trams held up and the dog still in the middle of the track, chawing up his stuff, surrounded by five other dogs, all in a state of complacent approval.

The poor woman sneaked off home by Harcourt Street, and, as she was passing Wellington Barracks, she saw the dog digging a hole in a geranium bed in the front garden of a smart house, with the lights and liver beside the hole. There was a lady inside, tapping at the window in a distressed and agitated manner.

Mary ducked her head and hurried by, but, bedad, the dog spotted her. He hurriedly got hold of his luggage and ran after her, trotting a yard or so behind her all the way, covered in mud and blood and filth, disgracing her for ever.

Meantime I had gone off to interview my kind friend Christy Keogh. He wasn't at home, but I ran him to earth in Lanigan's, where I told him a number of things about his birth and his parents, and how I hoped he'd enjoy the eleven summonses that were bound to come from all quarters. He laughed at me, and so did everyone else in the bar. Tears rolled down their faces. The worst of it all was, after a few minutes of telling them my story, I began to see the ridiculous side of it, and laughed too.

I laughed the other side of my gob when I got home. The dog was locked in the back-yard, howling like a lost soul, and the windows were all open for perches round with women at them, saying " SSShhh," and messengers kept knocking at the front door with notes from their mothers.

Mary was deathly pale. She would hardly give me a kiss.

" I'm going out," says she.

" Where? " I asked.

" Pictures, Father, Mollie, anywhere," she said. " Luke, if you only knew what I have suffered this day! "

But I could guess.

Well, of course, we were all on to get rid of the dog, but Eileen, who was aged four at the time, took a great liking for the brute. That meant a softening of Mary's heart towards him, though her speech was as fierce as ever: and so, with threats every day, the days wore into weeks, and the brute was a permanence. Eileen was the only one who could boss him around. He'd lie on the floor and let the child do any blessed thing to him, from tying tin cans on to his tail to plaiting the long hairs of his ears. He didn't improve in appearance: a more blasted-looking cur I never saw in my life.

The day came, however, when he accidentally knocked Eileen into the grate. Mary changed her mind very quick then, and issued an ultimatum.

I brought Rover out to Rathfarnham the next day, which was a Sunday. I lost him in the Pine Forest, and when I got home, tired but relieved, the first thing I saw was him sitting on Madigan's doorstep whispering something into the Sealyham's ear and glancing at me sideways.

But I'd done better than I thought, for he went off to Crumlin after that with the Sealyham, and a dreadful life they led, terrorising the inhabitants of that peaceful hamlet. They joined forces with a beagle, authentically the last of the disbanded Crumlin Harriers, and debauched and led into their evil company a real beauty of a brown spaniel.

For months this wretched beagle, the spaniel, Rover, and Madigan's dog played hell all around the districts of Crumlin and Dolphin's Barn. Madigan's dog became a hopeless case—he'll tell you so himself. The brown spaniel went to blazes altogether, and crowned a life of crime by biting a woman selling scapulars at the Mission. The beagle came to be a tramp, and as for Rover, the Lord knows what he did.

Then, after at least six months, he had the nerve to turn up again. I came home one afternoon and found Mary petting him and calling him a faithful old thing and giving him bread and milk. He had cuts all over him, one of his front teeth was gone, and he was absolutely stinking.

Between us we gave him some sort of disinfectant bath, but sure, it was no good. The beagle used to call for him, and sometimes they'd fight like Red Indians all up and down the road, and complaints came pouring in from the neighbours till I thought we'd have to quit. So, in sheer despair, I went out one morning, got arsenic from O'Brien's the chemist, and gave it to the brute in his porridge.

I never saw a dog so much improved as Rover was after that. He put on weight, his coat grew richer, he was set up every way. Every way except his conduct, that is. There was no improvement in that. In fact, he sinned with greater gusto than ever.

We had him till August, when we went to Bray for our holidays. I locked him out as I was going. I had no compunction. That brute could fend for himself any place, and make a living. The last I saw of my kind friend Christy Keogh's Christmas gift was on Harcourt Street Station platform, with his head buried in an old woman's basket which she had momentarily laid down.

I haven't had the nerve to start a new dog since, and I doubt I will. But if I do, I'll choose him myself, and it won't be near the Christmas season either. And the next time Christy Keogh or any other bookie shows a sign of being benevolent, I'll leave town till he's himself again.

WALTER DE LA MARE

*MR. WALTER DE LA MARE has written " The
Listeners," and many another volume of verse for our delight.
He gives us here two examples of the shorter form of verse
which is perhaps his favourite mode.*

AND SO TO BED

"NIGHT-NIGHT, my Precious"; "*Sweet* dreams, Sweet";
"Heaven bless you, Love"; the sheeplike grown-ups said.
Two eyes gazed mutely back that none could meet,
Then turned to face Night's terrors overhead.

JOY

THIS little smiling Boy
Stretched out his hands to me,
Saying his name was Joy;
Saying all things that seem
Beautiful wise and true
Never need fade while he
Drenches them through and through
With witchery;
Told me that Love's clear eyes
Pools were without the sky,
Earth without Paradise,
Were he not nigh;
Even that Sorrow is
Him in a dark disguise;
And tears light-bright because
Sprung from his eyes.

Then went he singing on
Just like a child, and Oh,
All his sweet converse done,
Where could I go?
What could I do
But seek him up and down—
Thicket and thorn and fell—
Till night in gloom came on
Unpierceable?
And lo, unmoved, pale, calm,
Stepped from the dark to me,
Voiced like the nightingale,
Masked, weeping, He.

DENIS MACKAIL

*MR. DENIS MACKAIL wrote " Greenery Street " in 1925,
and from the publication of that most human and happy novel of
early married life he has been acclaimed a champion of young
people in love. He is essentially a London novelist—witness
" The Square Circle " and " The Wedding "—and he is one of
the few living writers who are equally at home in the technique
of the full-length novel and of the short story, of which he here
contributes a very typical example.*

IT'S THE THOUGHT THAT COUNTS[1]

HULLO, girls and boys! Isn't it about time you heard the story of Wilfred
Whaplode? We think so, anyhow. Here it is.

A very conscientious chap. Extremely regular in his daily habits.
Always anxious to do the right thing. Scrupulous in his devotion to duty.
Yet actually rather a good fellow—especially if you agree with us that there's
no harm, so long as you're not self-conscious, in being a little shy.

Aged about twenty-seven or so.

And occupying—when he wasn't working dashed hard at his office in
Hannibal House—a bachelor flat in Buff Street. Early to bed and early to
rise there. Breakfast, in fact—after some more very systematic customs—
at eight-thirty. Thus reaching the neighbouring tube-station at nine sharp.

By this time he had also read his private correspondence, if any, and the
main news-items and a couple of leading articles in his more than respectable
morning paper. In the tube itself he mopped up the rest of the matter,
glancing at practically everything except the crossword puzzle, which he found
a bit frivolous. And thus it was, at about 9.14 a.m. on the eighth of April,
somewhere in the bowels of the earth, that in skimming a column called
" Forthcoming Marriages " he was suddenly struck by a statement which
made him blink.

" Mr. R. P. Clitheroe," he read, " and Miss C. Gumley." Also a short
though expensive paragraph in which it was made clearer still that this couple
had not only plighted their mutual troth, but were intending to have themselves officially turned into one. " Very shortly," said the forecast. So Wilfred tucked the paper under his arm and pulled out his little pocket-diary.

He wrote in it. " Get present for Charlotte Gumley." He stowed it
away again. He went on with his reading. At the usual and appropriate
station he alighted—or at any rate was shot out of the carriage with a lot of
other toilers of the deep—and six minutes later he entered his business sanctum
and sat down at a large desk. Punctual, once more and as ever, to the tick.

[1] *Author's note.*—This story doesn't seem to have very much to do with the war. But why should it?

No sign, you see, that the blink had betokened a broken heart. If that's what you suspected, you're quite wrong. This trifling reflex had merely been occasioned by the fact that, although Mr. R. P. Clitheroe was totally unknown to him, he had been acquainted with Miss Gumley for quite a number of years.

Not exactly intimately. But ever since they had been children and neighbours in St. John's Wood. Naturally, therefore, both their early homes had long since been pulled down, to make room for an enormous block of flats. Yet somehow the slight link had never been entirely sundered, and of course Wilfred Whaplode was the last character to shirk a conventional liability. What's more, he could very well afford it.

"Hullo!" he had thought. "Getting married, is she? Well, well, how time flies! But I'm sure I hope she'll be happy, and of course I must send her something."

Out came the pocket-diary. Down went the reminder. Some of us, it must be admitted, having done this much, might easily have forgotten the whole thing. Not Wilfred. That pocket-diary, in his case, was no mere method for absolving the conscience. He studied it constantly, and at about 10.27 he examined it again.

"Oh!" he said, addressing his secretary. "There's just one other letter, Miss Halfpenny—if you don't mind. On my private note-paper, please." Procrastination was never one of his qualities.

Miss Halfpenny sat down again. Whether she minded or not, stenography was her livelihood. Moreover, though her employer seldom if ever looked her straight in the face, it was impossible to criticise his consideration or invariable courtesy.

She poised her neatly sharpened pencil.

"Hrrm," said Wilfred. "'My dear Charlotte.'" He paused, thought for a moment, and went on again. "'Allow me,'" he said, "'to offer you my sincerest congratulations on the announcement which I have just read. I have not the pleasure of knowing your fiancé, but I am sure he is very fortunate indeed. I hope you will have many years of happiness together, and as a slight token of our long-standing friendship, if I may call it that, I am sending you——'"

He stopped. He looked slightly at a loss.

"'I am sending you,'" said Miss Halfpenny helpfully.

"Yes, yes," said Wilfred. "But that's just it. What *am* I sending her?"

"You haven't said yet, Mr. Whaplode."

"I know. I know. Rather a problem, isn't it, Miss Halfpenny? I wonder—— Well, have *you* anything to suggest?"

His secretary, with perhaps even more justification, looked rather at a loss, too.

"Do you mean for a wedding-present, Mr. Whaplode?" she asked.

"Yes. That's right. Can you think of anything?"

"Well," said Miss Halfpenny, as obligingly as ever, "I don't know that I can, Mr. Whaplode. But of course," she added, "they always say it's the thought that really counts."

"Do they?" said Wilfred. The phrase pleased him. But of course it was no real answer to his little difficulty. He gazed round his somewhat simple and ascetic apartment, as if for inspiration. But a filing-cabinet wouldn't be much use. Nor a calendar. Nor a bent-wood hat-and-coat rack. He drummed rather desperately on his blotting-pad.

"Look here," he said, though he still didn't look at his secretary. "Can't you help me, Miss Halfpenny? Can't you think of something—well, something *useful*? Or—well, what *do* women like?"

"Stockings?" said Miss Halfpenny, truthfully, no doubt, but rather surprisingly.

"Oh, no, no, no," said Wilfred. "Hardly suitable in this case, I think. Rather too—ah—intimate, Miss Halfpenny. No, what I want is—— Look here!"

It seemed that he'd had an inspiration, after all.

"Listen, Miss Halfpenny. Cash this cheque, will you?" He scribbled rapidly. "Go out after lunch—take as long as you like—and choose something. Will you? Here's the name and address." He dictated again. "Just fill in whatever it is you settle on at the end of that letter. Put ' Kind regards. Yours sincerely.' And—well, that's all, I think; except that if I'm not back from this meeting, you're pretty good at my signature, aren't you? I mean, the sooner, the better—what? That's the idea. Thanks awfully, Miss Halfpenny. Well, now, *that's* off my mind."

He then instantly turned to a telephone which was ringing, and his admirable secretary slipped away. If he had happened to look at her, if he hadn't, for many months now, treated her—though always civilly—as little more than a piece of office mechanism, he might possibly have noticed two things.

First, that she was remarkably pretty. Secondly, that the glance she gave him, just as she left the room, contained several rather mysterious ingredients, amongst which something like pity and something like irritation should certainly be included. Yet even if, in some respects, there were grounds for these feelings, she was the very last sort of secretary to point out that shopping wasn't part of her job.

She shopped, in fact. She selected a tasteful lamp and lamp-shade, both of excellent quality, paid for them, gave orders for their immediate dispatch, returned to the office, completed her work there, and finally—since Wilfred still hadn't returned—forged his signature, and posted his private letter.

Efficiency personified; even if her employer still didn't know what actual gift had enshrined his good wishes. But of course Miss Gumley knew, by the time the letter had followed the parcel. This was the first result of the announcement, and though there was a slight drawback about it, she seems to have been rather touched. She missed him on the telephone at Buff Street, but caught him within a few moments of his arrival at Hannibal House.

"Hullo?" she said. "Wilfred? This is Charlotte. I say, I *must* thank you for your *marvellous* present. It *was* kind of you! And your *charming* letter!"

Mr. Whaplode blinked again. He was just a little taken aback or by surprise.

"Oh!" he said. "Not at all. I—ah——" He remembered that invaluable expression. "Of course," he said, " it's the thought that really counts, you know."

With his free hand he rang urgently for Miss Halfpenny; but of course Miss Gumley could hardly be expected to realise or wait for that.

"Oh, Wilfred," she was saying, "what a *very* nice way to put it! And do you know it's the first present I've had? In fact, the only rather tiresome thing is—— Well, I was just wondering——"

Here Miss Halfpenny came in. Wilfred made a feverish but extremely enigmatic signal at her, and tried to pick up the conversation at the same time.

"Yes?" he said. "Wondering what?"

"Well, you see, Roddie and I—by the way, you *must* come and meet him, will you?"

"Delighted," said Wilfred, looking distinctly harassed.

"Oh, good! Well, you see, as a matter of fact, his leave's just ending and we're going practically straight out to his job in the Soudan. And of course there's no electricity there, so——"

"Oh, I *am* sorry," said Wilfred. He certainly sounded it, too, though he still didn't know whether he had given her a radio or a refrigerator. "How dreadful!" he said. "I say, what an awful thing! But of course——"

"Oh, Wilfred, you can't really mind as much as all that!"

Sometimes, it seems, when these girls get engaged, it sets their minds running on a rather extraordinary track. To round the thing off, they have even been known—and particularly, for some reason, when rather plain—to seek almost eagerly for signs of heartache elsewhere. And there's no doubt, just at the moment, that Mr. Whaplode was in a bit of a stew.

"Eh?" he said. He laughed nervously. He also glanced frantically towards his secretary; but with all her merits the girl was no mind-reader.

"Oh, well," he said—and, dash it, he hadn't even opened his letters yet —"of *course* I'm upset about it. But do please let me know what——"

"Oh, Wilfred! Do you really think you ought to?"

"Yes, of course. I mean, what else can I——"

"Oh, very well—if you're sure it'll be all right. This evening? For a cocktail? Of course Roddie'll be here—and I warn you, he's terribly jealous—but yes, do do that!"

Mr. Whaplode was in a slight state of confusion. Somehow, it seemed, that attempt to conceal his ignorance had landed him in a curious misunderstanding. But he was still unable to consult Miss Halfpenny. And, of course, he wanted to get this business of the present put straight.

"Oh," he said. "Thanks awfully, Charlotte. Certainly. I'll be there."

As he replaced the receiver, he sighed rather heavily. His secretary waited for a moment, and then spoke to him.

"Did you want me, Mr. Whaplode?" she asked.

"Eh?" He pulled himself together. "Oh, yes, Miss Halfpenny. I— that was Miss Gumley just now. I—ah——" But, of course, he mustn't complain, when the girl had obviously done her best. At this point, also, he suddenly saw that there was a note on his desk. A brief but adequate description of the gift and what it had cost. Dash! As if he oughtn't to have known it would be there. She had even put a little pile of change on it.

"Is—is anything wrong, Mr. Whaplode?" she was asking, sympathetically.

"What? Oh, no. No. Nothing at all." Anyhow, it was all his own fault. He couldn't possibly appear to blame her, when she had taken so

185

much trouble. As for the lamp and lamp-shade, well, perhaps he could use them himself, or keep them for another occasion. Quite all right. Take something else along with him this evening. Fetch 'em away at the same time. Phew!

"Nothing at all," he repeated. "Very much obliged to you, Miss Halfpenny. Have you got your book there? Well, let's get on, shall we?"

Peace at last, or at any rate for the time being. Wilfred dictated. Miss Halfpenny took down his words. But he still didn't look at her, though she was just as pretty as ever.

Just before closing-time he shot into the gift department at a large store, and on the advice of the salesman purchased and came out with a somewhat costly cigarette-box. Perhaps it was also a little feminine and flashy. He certainly wouldn't have wanted it himself. But then it wasn't for himself, and even if it had to be transported on a camel, it would take up very little space. In fact, he was distinctly pleased with this second choice.

He sped on in a taxi, and rang Miss Gumley's bell. At another flat, rather further out than his own. A maid, whose mouth seemed more or less permanently open, admitted him, and conducted him to the little sitting-room.

"Wilfred!" cried Miss Gumley, darting forward and seizing his hand. "How *very* nice this is of you!" She seemed to be winking or something. "And here," she added, in a curiously confidential tone, "is my Roddie."

"Eh?" said Wilfred. "Oh, how do you do?"

Mr. R. P. Clitheroe was large, red-faced, and slightly lacking in the usual development of the upper part of the skull. His own greeting, however, was quite friendly. He evinced no sign of jealousy, or, if it comes to that, of any other particular emotion. He addressed the visitor as "old boy," and Wilfred rather liked him, though he couldn't imagine anybody wanting to marry him. Well, if it came to that——

He collected his thoughts, and immediately offered his little parcel.

"Really!" cried his old acquaintance. "My *dear* Wilfred—you *should* have made them change that other *lovely* present!" She fluttered her eyelashes—quite a new trick, this—and wrenched at the string. "So *very* generous!"

"Oh, nonsense," said Wilfred modestly. "I—I told you, it's much more the thought that really—Hullo! Is anything the matter? It's not broken, is it?"

"No, no." She tittered, again in rather an unusual manner. "It's *wonderful*, Wilfred! But—well, you see, I've never smoked, and Roddie always sticks to his pipe. So would you mind *dreadfully* if——"

"Not at all," said the courteous Wilfred. "Here, give it me. Of course I'll find you something else. *Please* let me!"

Miss Gumley simpered again. For heaven's sake don't let's say that love turns all young women into dangerous pests. Yet in certain cases even a chap like R. P. Clitheroe (now calmly demonstrating his pipe in a mephitic mist) seems capable of affecting their intelligence.

"Oh, well," she said, "of course I must have *something*—well, something rather special, don't you think?—to remember you by."

R. P. Clitheroe didn't turn a hair. It was Wilfred who looked a little anxious and startled, for honestly he'd never thought he was such a particular friend. But he was polite. " Certainly," he said. " Oh, rather. I hope you will."

Miss Gumley emitted a piercing and mystical laugh. She repeated it so frequently during the rest of his distinctly uncomfortable visit, that perhaps this explains why, on finally taking his leave, he went off without either present. He was a bit bewildered, you see.

But, of course, he still had a memory and a conscience. He realised his omission only a few minutes later, and as soon as he got back to Buff Street, he rang up.

The love-birds had flown. To the pictures, said the maid's voice; but after that she became much less helpful. Took Mr. Whaplode's name, that's to say, but in spite of having seen him barely an hour ago, seemed definitely obstructive and suspicious about the parcels.

A fault in the right direction? Well, after all, London was full of confidence tricksters and he couldn't really have taken much more action to-night. That original pledge in his pocket-diary—and it seemed almost impossible that he had entered it less than thirty-six hours ago—was still, of course, unfulfilled. No chance of drawing a neat line through it yet. But perhaps, with more help from Miss Halfpenny . . .

Rather a soothing thought, you know. A very reliable girl, despite her purely innocent and accidental mistake about the lamp and lamp-shade. She never laughed loudly. She never tried to be confidential or arch. He made an effort to recall her features, but somehow they eluded him. Well, well; it didn't matter. But in the morning he'd certainly have a word with her, and get some of this business cleared up.

It was annoying, though, that he had unaccountably mislaid the receipt for the cigarette-box.

Dinner. Bed. Breakfast. Tube. Back in the office. Dictating industriously. Glancing again at his personal memoranda, and giving a slight start.

" Oh—Miss Halfpenny! "

" Yes, Mr. Whaplode? "

" Look here—I—I wonder if I could trouble you about a private matter again. I——"

Dash! His telephone was ringing. " Just a moment," he muttered. Snatched at the receiver. " Hullo? "

" Oh, Wilfred! My dear—it's Charlotte! "

" Oh, good morning. I was just——"

" Were you? Well, of course, I found your message last night. But really, you know, it might have been terribly awkward. Supposing Roddie'd come in with me. How *could* I have explained? My dear, you *should* be more careful! "

" Eh? But I was only——"

" I know. Of course *I* understand. My dear, of course *I* realise. But he's so simple and trusting. We *mustn't* do anything to hurt him."

What the blazes was she talking about? Why the dickens did she keep saying " my dear " like that?

" I haven't the slightest wish," said Wilfred, with some emphasis, " to hurt anybody. I——"

" Ah, but, my dear, it isn't always what one *wishes*. He's just a big child, you know. I'm everything to him. Just *everything*."

187

"Quite," said Wilfred, as pleasantly as he could. "But——"

"No, don't make it harder, *please*. After all, we'll be leaving so very soon, and I should hate to think I'd hurt anyone, either. You must be brave, Wilfred. Listen—where are you lunching to-morrow?"

"Nowhere," said Wilfred, thankful to have partially understood something at last. "But I say—Charlotte—about a present for you. Well, and, look here, about those ones I——"

"Not now," said Miss Gumley. "I can't talk to you now. He'll be round here any minute. But he's got this business lunch to-morrow; so shall we say Belloni's? Do you know it? In Jermyn Street? One-fifteen. I'll be there. Perhaps I can help you, Wilfred. Who knows?"

She then rang off, having probably enjoyed herself a good deal. Once more we should hesitate to say that all young women go crackers when they get engaged. That isn't our philosophy at all. Yet sometimes, if they reach the age of twenty-six before capturing the heart of an admirable dullard, or if—on the eve of departure for the edge of beyond—they yearn wildly for still further proof of their destructive charm, they can most positively become a little imaginative and alarming.

Mr. Whaplode, at any rate, though far from gathering what was up, now looked so baffled and heaved such a terrific sigh as to cause his secretary to extend her hand; almost, for an instant, as if she would have given him a bracing slap on the back or a gentle pat on the head. For she certainly appreciated many of his sterling qualities.

He turned, though. He never saw her blushing or hastily dropping her arm. A cloud—almost like that from Mr. R. P. Clitheroe's pipe—seemed momentarily to have hidden everything.

"That," he said, heavily and half to himself, "was Miss Gumley again."

"Yes, Mr. Whaplode?"

He gave another start. The cloud vanished. We have mentioned that he was an extremely conscientious worker.

"That's all, thank you," he said. "Just get on with those letters, will you, please?"

For the thought or impulse which the telephone had interrupted no longer seemed nearly so practical. A strange instinct informed him that even Miss Halfpenny, greatly as he valued her intelligence and assistance, couldn't help him out of a mess unless he explained it. And as he couldn't explain it to himself, how could he hope to explain it to her?

He groaned, we're sorry to say. Somehow, it appeared, he had now promised to give his almost unrecognisable old playmate lunch to-morrow. Presumably, for he could think of no other reason, so that he might offer her yet a third gift. Not counting the lunch.

But to lay such a situation, or even part of it, before a sensible, straightforward girl like his secretary was considerably more than he cared to contemplate. In fact—this was one of the few sensible, straightforward thoughts of his own—his plain duty was to extricate himself from whatever was happening without dragging anybody else into it at all.

Good lad. He felt calmer again, as we think he deserved. He went on working as hard as anyone in the whole office.

But Miss Halfpenny, though she certainly typed his letters as accurately as ever, could hardly be unconscious of his entanglement. She'd heard him bleating so miserably on the telephone. She'd both seen and heard him sigh. At one soul-stirring moment he had asked if he could trouble her about his private affairs. Her heart had leapt—for however guilty or reckless his passion, wasn't anything better than worshipping someone and never being treated as a human being at all?

Yes; it was out now; or at any rate she could no longer conceal it from herself. She loved him. She knew now that she had loved him for months. Furthermore, she was under the impression—common, perhaps, in these circumstances, but by no means necessarily false—that she would go on loving him so long as she was anchored to her exceedingly shapely frame.

So that poor Miss Halfpenny became slightly pink-eyed as she pounded the typewriter in her own little room. And if, she thought, by striking the space-bar with unusual violence she could blow Miss Gumley—so cruel and cunning—into a thousand fragments, why, nothing would give her greater pleasure and satisfaction than to do so.

Meanwhile—and that, by the way, is a notion which can come to even the sweetest and gentlest of young women—she hadn't even the slight solace of knowing about the bungalow in the Soudan.

Wilfred, on the other hand, thought of it constantly. It represented—and more than ever after that perplexing and exhausting lunch—a species of Eldorado. Not for himself, of course. But as a haven to which, in only a few more days now, his persecutress would be taking herself for—thank Heaven—the best part of three years. If only, he prayed, she could manage it even sooner.

Not that he was the least troubled either by or on behalf of Mr. R. P. Clitheroe. This character—having obligingly dropped the lamp, lamp-shade, and cigarette-box at Buff Street—seemed to have passed altogether out of his life. But Charlotte hadn't; and what she wanted, apart from a fourth wedding-present—for the expensive hand-bag which he had offered her at Belloni's had unfortunately just been anticipated by an aunt—he was still wholly unable to make out.

Something, apparently. Her hints were as incessant as they were obscure. So were her words on the telephone. So were his own, if it comes to that, for can you imagine anyone so punctilious failing to ring up whenever he found a request?

" Oh, hullo—I say, this is Wilfred. They told me you'd——"

" Oh. Just a moment." Rum noises. Thumps. Footsteps. Rustling sounds. " Oh, my dear, I can't speak to you now, I'm afraid. You see what I mean, don't you?"

" Well, but I thought——"

" No, no. Please!"

" Eh? But don't you——"

" Oh, Wilfred, I'm *trying* to make it all easier for you."

" Oh. Are you? Well, listen; I've been thinking again. Would you like me to——"

" No, no. You *mustn't* ask me that!"

" Yes, but, dash it, Charlotte, there must be *something* I can——"

189

" Oh, not now. My dear, I *do* understand. You needn't think I don't. But you *must* remember Roddie! "

" Eh ? Why ? Look here, surely——"

" No, Wilfred. I'll let you know. If I possibly can. You *mustn't* make it more difficult for me."

" Yes, but, Charlotte—— Hi!——"

She'd gone again. No doubt she was having grand fun. No doubt it was much more interesting and amusing from her end. To have all the security of a bloke like R. P. Clitheroe, and all the sport of keeping another fellow—as she seems to have imagined—twittering at her beck and call.

In a sense, besides, this was no fancy. The shop which had supplied the hand-bag dealt in nothing else, so that there was no possibility of exchanging it. With three handsome wedding-presents in his sitting-room at Buff Street, no conscientious chap like Wilfred could conceivably forget the task which was still incomplete. The sands were running out. Why on earth couldn't he put a plain question ? Why in thunder couldn't she answer it ?

More irritation and bewilderment. More sighs. Miss Halfpenny heard them, and many of his thwarted ejaculations on the telephone as well. All this was absolutely no sort of fun for Miss Halfpenny. And still, constantly as she strained to serve him in every way, he never even looked at her.

Poor child. She was so very well worth looking at.

That's how it went, as the days lumbered by. Somewhat reversing the ordinary procedure—but with every regard, one may be certain, for the proprieties—Mr. R. P. Clitheroe was to accompany his beloved to Paris (where it appeared that his aged mother hung out) and only to marry her when they got there. Then to Brindisi, Alexandria, and the Soudan. This much even Wilfred had discovered.

On the final evening, therefore—still having achieved nothing better—he dashed round to Miss Gumley's flat, and this time with a choice of no less than three presents. A dressing-case, an expanding and contracting suit-case, and a luxurious hat-box. He'd travelled himself. Surely *anybody* who was going on a journey like that could do with another bit of luggage.

The porter helped him to take them up in the lift. The same rather stupid-looking maid opened the door. She fell back with an air of suspicious amazement.

" It's all right," said Wilfred pleasantly. " I haven't come to stay here. If I could just see Miss Gumley——"

" She's out, sir."

" Eh ? Oh. When's she coming in ? "

" I couldn't say, sir, I'm sure. There's no dinner been ordered, sir."

" Oh," said Wilfred, slightly checked. Yet perhaps it was natural that she and R. P. Clitheroe should celebrate their last evening in London. " I see," he said. " Well, look here, would you tell her . . ."

He explained. Miss Gumley was to keep whichever article she preferred, and he'd call or send for the others. He said this three times. He also apologised for some reason, though it's not quite clear for what. He then left, and if ever a gentleman believed that he had solved a particularly awkward and ticklish knot, his name, at that moment, was Wilfred Whaplode.

It was true, of course, that having no account at the trunk-shop, he had had to pay for the whole lot. But no doubt that could be adjusted. It was a detail, anyhow, compared with the feeling that he had at last done his duty and brought the whole problem to an end. He slept well, for a change. He looked several years younger as he swept breezily into his office on the following morning.

He glanced at his correspondence. He whistled. At this moment, he was thinking, Charlotte and R. P. Clitheroe were in all probability already on their way to Victoria or Croydon. He wished them well. He liked the thought that he had contributed to the convenience of their long trip. He hoped sincerely that no mischance would hasten their return. He smiled kind-heartedly. He was on the point of ringing for Miss Halfpenny, when Huggins, the commissionaire, entered instead.

" Mr. Clitheroe, sir," he said.

" Good heavens! " said Wilfred, and shot up.

" Hullo," said R. P. Clitheroe. " Sorry to butt in like this. I thought Charlotte was here."

" Good gracious! " said Wilfred. " Why ? "

" Wanted to see you," said R. P. Clitheroe. " Bit of a state this morning, poor girl. By the way, jolly decent of you to send those boxes, old boy, but—— Well, mind you, *I'm* not saying this."

" Eh ? What aren't you saying ? "

" Well, old boy, I'm afraid she thought three of 'em rather too much of a good thing. And as a matter of fact, old boy——"

" Yes, but I never——"

" That's all right, old boy. *I* know you're fond of her. Very natural. Wonderful little woman. But there it is. We're all packed up, anyhow—just off, in fact—so she made me take 'em round to your flat. You'll find 'em there, old boy."

" But, dash it——"

" There, there. Steady, old son. She'll be along any minute."

" What, here ? "

" That's right, old chap. Insisted on it. Said she knew you wanted her to have *something*. So she thought if you could take her out shopping—what ? Well, you've still got an hour, old man, and *I* shan't interfere. Point is, though, I've just discovered we've got each other's passports, so I won't keep her a minute, but——"

" Excuse me," said Wilfred, making hastily for the door. Evidence of R. P. Clitheroe's jealousy still seemed strikingly inconspicuous, but if he or that confounded harpy thought they could treat him like this—well, they were plumb wrong and he'd had just about enough. Escape, he thought. Before it all started again. Never mind about his debt of honour or anything else now.

He dashed into the passage.

He stopped, even more abruptly. She'd arrived! He could hear her asking for him. If she came round that corner——

He grabbed the nearest door-handle and burst breathlessly into Miss Halfpenny's little cell.

" I'm out! " he gasped. " I won't see anyone! I'll stay here! "

Miss Halfpenny stared at him with her hand on her pretty throat.

"Mr. Whaplode!" she said. "What *is* the matter?"

"There's a madwoman out there," said Wilfred. "Miss Gumley. She's after me again. I loathe her! I only tried to give her a wedding-present, and now I'm landed with six of 'em, and she's still trying to drive me clean off my—— *Sh!* Tell the Sergeant I've been taken frightfully ill. Say I'm in hospital! Anything you like, as long as she thinks I've gone!"

Never had Miss Halfpenny sped more gaily on an errand. She was back almost immediately. Never had she been more efficient. Her employer looked at her with such deep gratitude on his pallid features that——

But no. That isn't the point. She loved him already, and more than ever when he came running to her for help in distress. The point is that he *did* look at her. And whether it was the contrast between her sweet face and Miss Gumley's; or the cumulative effect of nearly a whole year during which he had come to rely on her as on no other creature on earth; or simply the illuminating result of powerful emotion on a gentleman who hitherto had always put duty and dictation first, the fact remains that he gave a sudden loud gulp and seized her hand.

"Miss Halfpenny!" he cried, urgently. "Quickly! What's your Christian name?"

And of course you couldn't exactly call that a proposal of marriage in itself. Yet if, at the same time, two characters should fall madly and rapturously into each other's arms, and if one of them was not only very comfortably off, but able to provide a lamp, lamp-shade, cigarette-box, hand-bag, and all the luggage for an early honeymoon—well, of course, it's the thought that counts.

AUGUST 1939
The Evacuation of School Children was
carried out with complete success.

FROM THE ORIGINAL BY MABEL LUCIE ATTWELL

GRACIE FIELDS

The fame of MISS GRACIE FIELDS is universal. Her personality and her art have contributed equally to make her a public figure, and it is the most natural thing in the world that a Cabinet Minister should be cheered in the House of Commons when announcing her war-time return to the B.B.C. Her recent illness was a matter of general anxiety, and she could have chosen no subject more pleasing to us all than that of "getting better."

ON GETTING BETTER

COME to think of it, it's almost worth while being ill on account of the pleasure it gives you to feel yourself getting better. Not that it's easy, mark you. For weeks you've lain in bed saying " nowt about 'owt " with a collection of red-hot pincers sticking into you.

Folks have sent flowers. You enjoy looking at them and having them about, but there are times when you wonder whether the next lot won't be lilies. And you're so limp that you wouldn't much mind if they were.

Then the doctors get busy again, and one day you wake up with the pincers cooling off a bit and things seem more rosy: at least not so lilyish. You begin to sit up and take notice of those flowers. Some are from old friends, others from new ones, and a whole lot from people you never knew existed. But they do, bless 'em!

Presently the day comes when you get out of bed. Eh—but you do feel daft! For one thing, your legs have gone back on you. Maybe they weren't worth insuring at best. Still, they did work. They held you up and went where you wanted them to. But not now. Oh no. Nothing like that! You haven't got any legs. While you were unconscious the doctors were mucking about more than you suspected. They've fitted you out with a couple of gormless serpents which sink down in coils on the ground and go to sleep, until pins and needles wake them up with a jerk.

One thing's quite certain. You'll never be able to walk again. And to think there was a time when you sang, " Walter, Walter, take me to the altar! " and enjoyed it. But that's finished. " Eric—Eric—lift me with a derrick! " is all you could manage to sing now. No, not sing, croak.

After that, nothing happens at all. The days go by. They rout you out of bed every now and then to prevent you going rusty, and tell you you're getting on like a house on fire. A spent match in a black-out is what they really mean. You hobble around and clutch hold of bits of furniture which look friendly and reliable. But they're not. Not a bit of it! They slither away and sneer at you when you collapse on the floor. All the same, you're getting better. Everybody tells you so. You tell yourself so. But you don't believe it. That's just one of the rules of the game you're all playing.

A few weeks back you didn't think at all. You couldn't. It's different now. You think too much, and it's the same thought that crops up all the time. It bobs up in as many different ways as you can see lights in Blackpool, but it all boils down to the same thing. You're finished. You won't go your own old road any more. It's no good fighting against it. You're too tired. Best maake oop your mind to't, lass, an' have done with it.

But it's not true. Maybe you found that out for yourself. I didn't. It took the Bishop of Blackburn to do it for me. He put fresh heart into me, by taking me out of myself and showing me there was still a job of work waiting for me—the best kind of job, trying to cheer folk up, and cheering yourself up most of all by getting on with it.

I learned a lot from him. Thinking it over, it *was* almost worth while being ill.

It is quite impossible for me to praise too highly the wonderful doctors and sisters and nurses of the Chelsea Women's Hospital. God bless them all!

C. H. MIDDLETON

MR. C. H. MIDDLETON already had a great reputation as an expert in every branch of the literature of gardening when he sprang into the widest popular fame with his inimitable Broadcast Talks at the B.B.C. on Sunday afternoons. His name is somewhere near the top of the list in any ballot of Broadcasting popularity.

KEEP THAT GARDEN GOING

I BELIEVE all English people are gardeners at heart, although they may not know it, and by " English " I mean, of course, all the people of the British Isles, never forgetting that many of the finest gardens, even in southern England, are cultivated by Scotsmen.   We do not all find a particular thrill in wielding a spade or pushing barrowloads of manure, but we all love flowers, and we know and appreciate the quiet peace and restfulness of a garden, even though it be but a small one, tucked away in some corner of a London suburb. The soft green turf of the lawn, the scent of roses and lavender, the cool shade of the apple tree, and the song of the birds : all these have become an essential part of our homes, and life would be dull without them.

I was talking to a globe-trotter recently, who has travelled the world over, and he told me that he always feels a sense of restfulness on returning to an English summer, because the whole country, in comparison with many others, seems to be one great garden, and he thinks there are no flowers in the world like the English flowers. That may be something of a paradox, because, strange though it may sound, the majority of the favourite flowers of our gardens are not English at all.   This climate of ours, about which we make so many rude remarks, is a mixture of all the climates of the world, and in it we grow all the choicest flowers of the world. How did they get here ? The answer to that question gives me an opportunity to pay tribute to that—shall I say despised ? no! perhaps neglected would be a better word—that neglected race of toilers of the soil known as gardeners, who are taken very much for granted in peace-time, but who rise to the surface in war-time to become a very essential and much-appreciated section of the community.

Gardeners are often depicted by cartoonists and comedians as frowsy old men with abundant whiskers and dirty necks, but very little intelligence. Fortunately some of us know them better than that, and we realise the enormous debt of gratitude we owe them for having made our beloved gardens possible. Gardeners of the past have penetrated the jungles, the lone mountains, and all the wild forbidding corners of the earth, often at the risk, and even loss, of life, in search of floral treasures to enrich our English gardens; they have tamed and cultivated the wild flowers of the world and developed their fullest beauty. By cross-breeding and selection they have multiplied their colours and forms and gradually produced the multitude of glorious blossoms which beautify our homes, and build up such great national floral festivals as the Chelsea Show.

Think of the rose as an example. Nearly every temperate country of the world has its wild roses, just as ours has; modest little flowers in themselves, but by being brought together and intermarrying, what a magnificent family they have produced. The gorgeous, many-coloured roses which we grow and gather so freely have but little resemblance to their ancestors, and it seems almost unbelievable that the roses of today could have been developed from such small beginnings, but they have, thanks to the skill, the patience, and the perseverance of gardeners. Gardeners, too, have taken the wild weeds of the hills and hedgerows and civilised them, and from them have bred and developed the popular vegetables of today—no mean task. Compare, if you will, the great fleshy root of a modern parsnip, with its wild ancestor which still flourishes on the chalky hills, and read the story there. Or think of celery: the wild celery is a poisonous narcotic which lives in filthy bogs and swamps. Whatever induced a gardener to bring such a plant into cultivation has always been a mystery to me; but somebody did, and improved it out of all recognition, until a plant was produced which is among the most wholesome and palatable of all our vegetables.

It is interesting to note, too, looking back over the ages, that as the population has increased gardeners have discovered and developed new sources of food supply to feed it. As far as I am able to trace, back in Tudor days vegetables seem to have been little known, or at least they played a very small part in the daily diet. Even as recently as the days of Charles Dickens we find little evidence that these natural foods found favour in the kitchens or gardens of the country. I am a great reader of Dickens, but although he wrote much about food, he rarely included vegetables in it, except to refer rather contemptuously to someone as possessing a pimply vegetable-diet sort of complexion. What a difference today, when vegetables and fruit form an important part of our everyday food supply! The development of the potato, the tomato, and others, around which a great industry has grown, is due to the work of gardeners, and doubtless, when further supplies are needed, they will rise to the occasion and produce them; perhaps we shall live to see the lawless roots of the thistle and the dock civilised and developed into palatable vegetables.

Let us then pay tribute to the gardeners; their rewards are small, they pass on unhonoured and unsung, acquiring lumbago rather than wealth; but they love their work, and they have given us a great heritage which will be always ours—the love of flowers and trees, and the sweetening influence of a garden. The influence of a garden is something very real, it penetrates to the soul, and has a wholesome effect on the character. I always say that gardeners and garden-lovers are the nicest people in the world; they never enjoy the fruits of their labours unless they can share them with others. A sort of happy brotherhood exists among them. They share each other's plants and seeds, lawnmowers, syringes, and rollers—at least my neighbours do. They discuss their triumphs and failures, their sorrows and problems, and the remedies thereof, with the greatest freedom. I believe there are but two classes of people like this—gardeners and invalids. At least I never saw butchers giving each other chunks of liver, or sausages !

And what an increase there has been lately in the popularity of gardening! I can remember the time when the average city gentleman would have thought it rather effeminate on his part to have shown any special interest in flowers: but not today; now you will see him nosing round the flower shows, discussing the different varieties of dahlias or roses with all the knowledge of an expert; indeed, he feels rather out of it if he cannot do so. A butler remarked recently that he didn't know what things were coming to. "At one time," he said, "if you kept your ears open at a dinner party you could pick up a useful racing tip now and then; but all you hear nowadays is about the latest rhododendron or something, and the best manure to give it." I remember once I got into a train at Surbiton and there were four Cabinet Ministers in the compartment—at least they looked like Cabinet Ministers, but you can't always judge by appearances. They discussed various topics of the day, and then one of them solemnly drew from his pocket a particularly fine specimen of a runner bean, and they talked runner beans all the way to Waterloo. I dare say that man got quite a kick out of growing beans, and prided himself on growing them a little better than his neighbours. The spirit of competition is very keen among gardeners, they love to outshine each other. I remember one case of a man who had an oil barrel standing on end close to his garden fence, cunningly concealed by bushes. On the barrel was a tub of rich soil, and growing in the soil a hollyhock, which towered heavenwards. When somebody asked him what the big idea was, he whispered, "It's for the benefit of the chap next door; he beat me by a foot last year." Which just goes to show to what lengths this competitive spirit will lead one unless there is an outlet for it in the form of a local flower show. I like flower shows ; there is tremendous satisfaction in winning a five-shilling prize with your sweet peas or tomatoes, even if it *does* cost you thirty shillings to do it, and I believe it makes good sportsmen of us. I remember seeing an old gardener standing in front of his vegetable exhibit which was marked " Third Prize." His friends were gathered round, and, said one, " Rotten bit o' judgin', Sam; you ought to have had first." " Maybe I did," replied Sam; " but, y' know, I've often had first when I ought to have had third, and I didn't grumble then." A fine spirit that! I wish we could see a little more of it about today—outside gardening, I mean.

Another thing which interests me is the way many amateur gardeners seem to dote on one particular kind of flower or vegetable : with one, roses are the only things that matter; with another it may be apples, or potatoes, and nothing else seems worth growing. I know a man in the Midlands, a man in very comfortable circumstances, whose one great hobby is growing onions; he spends all his leisure hours with them, and tries to grow them as big as his head. All the pot-hunters for miles around come to borrow them for their local shows, but he never exhibits them himself, and I doubt if he ever eats one.

But perhaps the strangest case I knew was of a man whose one great love was growing outsize sunflowers; he got them to an enormous size, and one year he planted half a dozen all in a row just outside his front garden fence, for the benefit of passers by. Each one grew with a stem 8 feet high with one enormous flower at the top, at least a foot across, and he loved to stand at the gate and talk sunflowers to anyone who was weak enough to pause and admire; till one day a short-sighted motorist pulled up and asked for two gallons of petrol, which was rather embarrassing.

But I'm afraid I wander from the point. I was saying that we gardeners are noble people, and that we can rise to the occasion when called upon to do so and deliver the goods. Very well, the nation is at war, the occasion has arisen, and we must respond to the call. We must adapt our gardening methods to the changed circumstances, and, to a certain extent, convert our lovely gardens into munition factories, for potatoes and beans are munitions of war as truly as bullets are. It may seem that our small individual efforts cannot amount to much; that our hundredweight of potatoes or bushel of brussels sprouts can make but little difference; but, believe me, it can. If every garden produced what it could in the way of vegetables, without straining itself in any way, the addition to the nation's food supply would be enormous: it would amount to thousands of tons—thousands of tons less to be purchased elsewhere; thousands of tons less to be carted about by our already over-taxed transport system. And the food produced from the home garden is valuable food; fresh vegetables contain all sorts of vitamins and things which help to keep us fit and cheerful. Salad vegetables are particularly good. I heard a doctor say once that if we ate a salad of some kind with every meal, we should rarely need doctors at all, and I'm sure you will admit that fresh lettuces and tomatoes are much more agreeable to the human system than pills and potions. When you consider that a rabbit or a sheep lives almost entirely on the natural herbage as it grows, and quickly develops into a strong, healthy animal, it does look as though there must be a considerable amount of nourishment in it. I am not going to suggest that we should all emulate Nebuchadnezzar and turn out to grass, but I do suggest that we should eat far more of Nature's ready-made foods, and that we should produce them at home.

How, then, shall we set about this war-time task of food production? To the over-zealous patriot, perhaps the first impulse is to sally forth with the spade and root up all the rose bushes and herbaceous plants and make a bonfire of them. That is not the way to do it; there is no need for panic measures. We must keep our enthusiasm within reasonable limits and guide it along common-sense lines, or it may run away with us. There is no need to destroy all our flowers; we shall need them more than ever. In every garden there are borders, banks, and corners which are not suitable for vegetable growing : small front gardens are of little use for the purpose, and there is no need to dismantle the rockery. To attempt to grow vegetables in unsuitable soils and places is a waste of time, labour, and substance.

On the other hand, most gardens possess an available space of good soil which could be cleared and used for growing food crops. It may mean sacrifice; war always does. Perhaps we shall find it necessary to sacrifice part of the lawn, or lay bare one of the flower borders; if so, let us concentrate in the reduced space all the cream of our erstwhile floral beauty. I would like to see the smaller borders, the rockery, and the little front gardens gayer and more colourful than ever next year, and our living-rooms kept cheerful with cut flowers. We shall probably have to cut down our annual expenditure on flowers, but we need not be unduly drastic. With the ever-increasing popularity of gardening a great industry has grown up to cater for it. The nursery, seed, and bulb trades have served us well in the past, and they cannot live without our continued support. They will doubtless turn their attention to food production now, but it is very much in our interest that the floral side of their business should be kept alive. We shall need them again. Even in war-time, flowers are still desirable, or even necessary; perhaps more so than ever, both in our gardens and in our homes. In these hectic times, when the marvels of science and invention seem almost beyond our comprehension, we are apt to overlook the still greater wonders of Nature; for there is surely nothing more wonderful in the world than life itself, as seen in the growth and development of a beautiful flower. Flowers, sometimes without our knowing it, have a soothing and sweetening influence on our lives; they form the visible link which binds this unhallowed earth to heaven, and for those who have eyes to see and souls to receive, flowers bring a message from the Great Architect who designs them: a message of comfort and quiet optimism, and a reminder of the better things in life which even war cannot take from us.

No, do not let us discard our flowers entirely; rather let us think and plan carefully to retain them wherever possible, at the same time devoting the most suitable part of the garden to the essential need of the moment—food production. If we all did that, there would be no shortage.

Having decided on our vegetable plot, the first operation will be to dig it. Now, digging is really a very simple business, but it can be turned into hard labour and a painful ordeal. Digging has broken many a weak spirit, and has nearly broken many a weak back; but there is no reason why it should, if it is taken, like medicine, in reasonable doses. Perhaps I ought to remind you of the sad story of Uncle Walter, who became the tenant of a war-time allot-ment. His schemes were many and ambitious, and he felt very patriotic as he set forth, twirling the spade round his fingers like a drum major.

" What about a spot of digging, me lads ? " he burbled, between snatches of song; " keep you as fit as a fiddle, me lads; shake your liver up." Presently the earth began to fly, as Uncle Walter excavated furiously, rather like a terrier digging a rat out of its hole. Soon he shed his coat, and then his waistcoat, as he warmed to his task. A week later grievous groans and naughty words could be heard coming from the front bedroom as Uncle Walter, fettered with mustard plasters and liniment, called a spade a great deal more than a spade, and the allotment remained uncultivated. No! gentle reader, if you contemplate digging for the first time, take advice from one who has suffered, and " hasten slowly." Don't get excited over it, do a little at a time, and retire before the pains come on. Gradually you will get used to it, and be able to endure considerable spells without fatigue; you may even come to enjoy it, and then it will do you good.

There are several methods of digging, but the principle is the same—it merely means breaking up the ground as deeply as possible, without bringing the lower subsoil to the surface, or burying the top soil down below, at the same time burying all the turf and rubbish a good spade's depth below ground. Beginners sometimes find this a rather difficult manœuvre, but a little thought and practice and the maintenance of a wide trench and a clean spade soon bring experience, and the mastery of initial setbacks.

Then there is the vexed question of manuring, which is so often discussed in abstruse and complicated language. I am not going into details here; there is abundant information on the subject just now, available to all who seek it. To put it in very simple language, it is something like this: if we took nothing from the soil, we shouldn't need to manure it; but the plants we grow are rather exaggerated specimens, much bigger and fatter than their wild relations, and we crowd them together far more than Nature does. This means that, to grow to maturity, they take a good deal out of the soil in the way of plant food, and absorb it into their own systems. This wouldn't matter much if they were left there undisturbed; the soil would in turn absorb them as they decayed, and the plant foods would still be there. But in the garden the plants are not left there—we take them away for food. Therefore we must return to the soil as nearly as possible the equivalent of what we have taken from it; not only in the chemical sense, but in bulk too. Simple, isn't it? Or is it? At any rate, it is not an insoluble problem; but rather too long a story for me to do justice to in these pages.

Having prepared the ground, we must then decide which of the vegetable crops are the most valuable from a diet point of view, or the most suitable for our own individual requirements. These are decisions which must be left to the individual judgment of those concerned. There is no point, for example, in slavishly following someone else's advice to grow parsnips and artichokes if we do not like them and never eat them. All the same, I think it is worth while to learn something of the dietary value of the different vegetables—an interesting study for a winter evening, after calling at a bookseller's shop or the local public library. Doubtless the main staple foods of our daily life will be supplied from sources other than the garden, but these can be rendered much more palatable and health-giving by the addition of the simple products of Nature. The green leafy kinds of vegetables, in particular, supply valuable mineral salts often lacking or less abundant in the more solid foods.

Above all, the aim in planning a vegetable garden should be to keep up a steady supply: to cater for all the seasons, avoiding gluts at one time and scarcity at another. A well-cropped allotment or vegetable garden should be able to produce a fresh green vegetable for every week of the year, but how many do? More often we find generous neighbours ready to give of their abundance during the late summer and autumn, but not so in the late winter and early spring. It requires experience to spread the supply fairly over the whole year, and in small gardens it is hardly possible. In such cases I would suggest that the months of March, April, and May be the first consideration.

These are the difficult months; the rest of the year is usually well supplied. In the seed catalogues the alluring pictures of such succulent dishes as green peas, beans, and tomatoes are inclined to outshine the less attractive vegetables, such as purple-sprouting broccoli, the kales, leeks, and spring cabbages; but these are all-important, because they turn in after a hard winter, at a time when fresh vegetables are scarce and expensive.

Careful thought must be given to this question, and quantities worked out to prevent waste. It is so easy to sow or plant too much of one kind at a time, and then be unable to use it while it is at its best. The cabbage, or brassica family, is perhaps one of the most important groups in the kitchen garden. With a little careful manœuvring, this family alone can keep us going in " greens " all the year round. Cauliflowers and cabbage supply the summer and autumn. As winter draws near the brussels sprouts arrive, and keep us going till well into the new year. These can be fol- lowed by the savoy cabbage, to my mind one of the neglected, or misused vegetables, because it is usually sown too early, and gets mixed up with the brussels sprout season, when it is not appreciated. To get the full value from savoys, a late variety should be selected, and the seed sown in May; then the plants will wait until the sprouts are all used up, and fill a difficult gap. After the savoys the purple broccoli and the kales will see us through the early spring until the spring cabbages are ready, which, in turn, will last until the summer is with us again. In addition to these, experienced gardeners can keep the winter and spring supplied with delicious white heads of broccoli, or winter cauli- flower, but these often prove a little too difficult for the beginner.

All these are matters which lend themselves well to what I call arm-chair gardening. With the aid of pencil and paper, a good catalogue, and the Ministry of Agriculture's threepenny war bulletin, called *Food from the Garden*, many a winter evening can be profitably employed in working out schemes which save time in the busy season, prevent mistakes, and ensure that in due course each crop will fit nicely into its allotted place. Especially is it wise to work out a detailed scheme of cropping, which will allow for rotation of the crops, so that at least two years elapse before a crop occupies the same piece of ground again. For you may take it from me that once you know the joys of growing and eating your own vegetables, you will not lightly give it up, war or no war.

No single method of cropping is suitable for all gardens—there are several in existence, but they all need adapting to individual circumstances. One of the simplest methods of cropping is to divide the plot into three sections, and group the vegetables according to their season of use: early kinds on one plot, mid-season on the next, and late varieties on the third. The groups then follow each other round automatically year after year, and not only ensure a perfect system of rotation, but allow for thorough cultivation of the ground with a minimum of labour and expense. It needs thinking out carefully, of course, but it provides a nice little relaxation for a winter evening, and a profitable one, too.

I am afraid I am getting dry and technical, as is my wont. To me, garden- ing is a joy—provided I can get someone else to do the hard work—and, strange though it may seem, I can find just as much pleasure and interest in growing vegetables as in growing flowers, and so will you, I am sure, when you get over the initial difficulties. There is beauty in a cabbage which you may never have noticed; your war-time gardening will reveal it to you. Let us get down to it, then, and wield the spade and the hoe with a will and a smile, and show the world that the gardeners of Britain can mobilise their resources and deliver the goods when duty calls, without sacrificing the peace and beauty of the garden. Let us break down the barriers of exclusiveness and self-restraint, be neighbourly, and share our pleasures and difficulties with others, and when the nightmare is over and the morning breaks, the flowers will be there to greet us, and roses and lavender, and onions and turnips, shall all hold high festival together, and once again we will repeat the gardeners' prayer:

Little gods of little things,
Look upon our little labours;
Make our little gardens just
A little better than our neighbours'.

202

GEORGETTE HEYER

MISS GEORGETTE HEYER enjoys a double reputation as an historical novelist and as the author of some first-rate stories of detection. Both the discerning admirers of " Regency Buck " and the C.I.D. fans who appreciate the brilliance of a book like " Behold, Here's Poison," will enjoy the short story she has contributed on this occasion.

PURSUIT

THE curricle, which was built on sporting lines, was drawn by a team of four magnificent greys, and the ribbons were being handled by one of the most noted whips of his day: a member of the Four Horse Club, of the Bensington, the winner of above a dozen races—in short, by the Earl of Shane, as anyone but the most complete country bumpkin, catching only the most fleeting glimpse of his handsome profile, with its bar of black brow, and masterful, aquiline nose, would have known immediately. Happily, however, for his companion's peace of mind, the only persons encountered on the road were country bumpkins, the curricle having passed the Islington toll-gate, and entered upon the long, lonely stretch of road leading to the village of Highgate.

The Earl's companion was a governess, a lady, moreover, who would very soon have attained her thirtieth year, and who was seated bolt-upright beside him, dressed in a sober round gown of French cambric under a green pelisse, and a bonnet of moss-straw tied over her smooth brown ringlets. Her hands, in serviceable gloves of York tan, were clasped on the crook of a plaid parasol, and she appeared to be suffering from a strong sense of injury. Her eyes, which were a fine grey, and generally held a good deal of humour, stared stonily at the road ahead, and her mouth (too generous for beauty) was firmly compressed. For several miles she had seemed to be totally oblivious of the Earl's presence, and except for shuddering in a marked fashion whenever he sprang his horses, she paid not the smallest heed to the really remarkable driving skill he was displaying. Though he feather-edged his corners to perfection, put his horses beautifully together, cleared all obstacles, including a huge accommodation-coach which took up nearly all the road, in the most nonchalant style, and handled his long whip with the veriest flick of the wrist, he might as well, for all the admiration he evoked, have been a stage-coachman.

To do him justice, he had neither the expectation nor the desire of being admired. The excellence of his driving was a matter of course; he was, besides, in a very bad temper. He had been interrupted in the middle of his breakfast by the arrival on his doorstep of his ward's governess, who had travelled up to London from his house in Sussex to inform him, in the coolest fashion, that her charge had eloped with a lieutenant of a line regiment.

203

He considered her attitude to have been little short of brazen. Instead of evincing the contrition proper in a lady who had so grossly failed in the execution of her duty, she had said in her calm way that it served him right for not having given his consent to the marriage six months before. You would have thought from her manner that she had positively sped the young couple on their way to the Border (though that she swore she had not); and she had actually had the effrontery to advise him to make the best of it.

But the Earl, who had enjoyed his own way ever since he could remember, was not one who acquiesced readily in the oversetting of his will, and instead of accepting Miss Fairfax's advice he had ordered out his curricle and greys, had commanded Miss Fairfax to mount up on to the seat beside him, turning a deaf ear to her protests, and had driven off at a spanking rate, with the express intention of overtaking the runaways, and of bringing the recalcitrant Miss Gellibrand back to town under the escort of her governess.

Since he was driving an unrivalled team over the first stage of the journey, and could afford to change horses as often as he chose, Miss Fairfax could place little dependence on the eloping couple's contriving to outstrip pursuit. They had, indeed, several hours' law, but she guessed that Mr. Edmund Monksley, living upon his pay, would have to be content to travel with a pair of horses only harnessed to his post-chaise. The hire of post-horses was heavy, the journey to Gretna Green long, and the Earl's method of driving too swift for any job-chaise and pair to outdistance.

The bare expanse of Finchley Common being reached, a faint hope of being held up by highwaymen sustained Miss Fairfax's spirits for some way, but when the equipage arrived at the Whetstone gate without incident, she relapsed again into melancholy.

Her silence seemed to irritate the Earl. He said in a sardonic voice, " We have a good many miles to cover, I dare say, so you may as well come out of your sulks, ma'am. I should be interested to learn what right you imagine *you* have to indulge in this air of outraged virtue! "

" I have told you, sir, until I am quite tired of it, that I had nothing to do with Lucilla's flight," said Miss Fairfax coldly.

" No! You merely encouraged the fellow to visit my ward whenever he chose, and in spite of my prohibition—which you were perfectly well aware of! "

" I didn't encourage him at all. He never set foot inside your house, sir."

" Then where the devil did they meet ? " demanded his lordship.

" In the orchard," replied Miss Fairfax.

" Very romantic! " said the Earl, with a snort of disgust. " And pray what were you about, ma'am ? "

" Looking the other way," said Miss Fairfax unblushingly.

" I wonder you dare to sit there and tell me so! It only remains for you to say that this damnable elopement has your approval! "

" Well, it has not," she replied. " I should have preferred a pretty wedding for them, but since you were so extremely disagreeable, and Mr. Monksley's regiment has been ordered to the Peninsula, I really do not know what else they could have done, poor things! "

" Do you realise, ma'am," demanded the Earl, " that you have helped my ward to throw herself away, at the age of seventeen, upon a penniless

204

nobody, wholly dependent for his advancement upon the hazards of war ?—since I am very certain he will never be able to afford to buy his promotion ! "

" No, I fear not," she agreed. " I do not know, of course, the extent of Lucilla's fortune."

" Negligible ! "

" Then I expect you will be obliged to purchase a company for him," said Miss Fairfax.

" I ? " he ejaculated, looking thunderstruck.

" You are so wealthy a few hundred pounds can't signify to you, after all."

" Upon my word, ma'am ! I shall do nothing of the kind ! "

" Very well," said Miss Fairfax, " if you are determined on being disobliging, I dare say Lucilla won't care a button. She is a soldier's daughter, and not in the least likely to turn into a fashionable young lady. I feel sure she and Mr. Monksley will deal extremely together."

" Are you aware, ma'am, that it is my intention to marry Lucilla myself ? "

There was a slight pause. Miss Fairfax said rather carefully, " I was aware of it, sir, but I have always been at a loss to know why. You must be quite sixteen years her senior, nor have you, during the three years I have been in charge of Lucilla, shown the least partiality for her society. In fact, you have kept her secluded in the country, and have only visited her at the most infrequent intervals."

" If you mean that I am not in love with her, no, certainly I am not ! " responded the Earl stiffly. " The match was the wish of both our fathers."

" How elevating it is to encounter such filial piety in these days ! " observed Miss Fairfax soulfully.

The Earl dropped his hands, and let his team shoot, nearly unseating Miss Fairfax.

Silence reigned once more. At Barnet, which marked the end of the first stage, the greys were still going well, a circumstance which induced the Earl to sweep past the Red Lion, with its yellow-jacketed postboys and its twenty-six pairs of good horses, and press on for another nine miles to Hatfield. Miss Fairfax, who had never driven so fast in her life, began to fear that at any moment they must overtake the fugitives. She ventured presently to ask the Earl when he expected to catch up with them.

" I have no means of knowing. Before nightfall, I trust."

" Indeed, I trust so too ! " said Miss Fairfax, with a good deal of feeling. " But if you do not ? "

" Then, ma'am, we shall put up at an inn for the night, and continue our journey in the morning."

Miss Fairfax appeared to struggle with herself, saying presently in a voice of strong emotion, " I shall pass over the impropriety of such a scheme, my lord, but I desire to point out to you that all the baggage I have with me is this reticule ! "

He shrugged his shoulders. " I regret the inconvenience, but it can't be helped."

This was too much for her. " Let me tell you, sir, that it can be helped very easily, by your abandoning this chase, and returning, like a sensible man, to London ! "

" I shall return when I have caught my ward, and not before."

205

"Well," said Miss Fairfax, controlling herself with an obvious effort, "it all goes to show how mistaken one may be in a person's character. I was used to think you, sir, for all your faults, perfectly amiable and gentlemanly."

"For all my faults!" he repeated, surprised into looking round at her. "And pray what are these faults of mine?"

"Temper, pride, reserve, obstinacy, stupidity, and the most overbearing manners!" she replied, without hesitation.

There was just the suggestion of a quiver at the corners of his mouth. "You are frank, ma'am! I, on the other hand, thought you, until this morning, the perfect governess."

Miss Fairfax did not appear to derive any extraordinary degree of gratification from this tribute, but turned a little pale, and said unsteadily, "I beg your pardon. I should not have spoken so. I am aware that in your eyes I have acted wrongly."

He glanced quickly down at her, a softer expression on his face, but he said nothing for a few minutes, being fully engaged in quartering the road, to avoid a succession of deep pits in it. After a time, however, he said in a gentler tone, "Come! we gain nothing by bickering, after all. I never thought to find myself quarrelling with you, Mary Fairfax!"

"Didn't you, sir?"

"Why, no!" he said, slightly smiling. "You have always seemed to me the most restful of women, ma'am."

"I suppose you mean unobtrusive," said Miss Fairfax crossly.

It was many hours later, and the last grey light was fading from the sky, when the curricle entered Grantham, a distance of over a hundred miles from London. Miss Fairfax, by this time resigned to her fate, was enveloped in his lordship's many-caped driving-coat of drab cloth, and his lordship himself was in a mood of dangerous exasperation.

All had gone smoothly during the first part of the journey. The greys had held up until Hatfield was reached, and there the Earl had been fortunate enough to secure a team of strengthy, quick-actioned beasts to carry him to the next stage. But a little beyond Biggleswade they had encountered a whisky, driven by a very down-the-road-looking man, who came sweeping round a bend on the wrong side, and collided with the curricle. Thanks to the Earl's presence of mind in swerving aside almost into the ditch, there was not much damage done, but a necessary repair to one of the off-side wheels had to be effected at the next town they came to. This meant a delay of nearly an hour, but the Earl's temper was not seriously impaired until much later, when, crossing Witham Common, one of the wheelers of the team put-to at Stamford went dead lame. To be reduced at the end of a long day to running pick-axe set the seal to his lordship's exasperation. There was nothing for it but to drive slowly on to the next posting-house. The Earl, mounting the box again, after an inspection of the wheeler's leg, told Miss Fairfax bitterly that the whole business, from start to finish, might be laid at her door, an accusation which she received in weary silence.

Conversation thereafter was of a desultory nature. In Grantham, the Angel and Royal showed welcoming lights glowing in its oriel windows; and as the curricle passed under the Gothic stone arch into the courtyard, Miss

Fairfax was conscious, not of any desire to return to London, but of a profound inclination towards dinner, and a well-aired bed.

The Earl handed her down from the curricle. She was so stiff that to move was quite painful, but she managed to discard the voluminous driving-coat, to straighten her bonnet, and to walk with a very fair assumption of dignity into the inn. She fancied that the maidservant who escorted her to a bedchamber looked at her curiously, but she felt too tired to enter upon any extempore explanation of her baggage-less condition.

The Earl had engaged a private parlour, and, although it was early summer, had caused a fire to be kindled in the grate. He looked to be in a better humour when Miss Fairfax presently entered the room. He was engaged in snuffing one of the candles in a branch on the table, and said in his abrupt way: " I hope you are hungry. The cooking is good here."

" I am hungry," she replied. " But mostly I am quite in a worry to know how to account to the chambermaid for my lack of baggage. It must present the oddest appearance! "

" You need not regard it. I am known here."

This careless response did not seem to Miss Fairfax to offer the least explanation of her plight, but she refrained from pointing this out to his lordship. As she moved towards the fire, he said, " When we changed horses at Stilton, I made certain enquiries. From what I was able to ascertain, we should by now have caught up with the runaways, had it not been for those unfortunate mishaps. They certainly stopped at Stilton, not many hours before we did. They are travelling with a single pair of post-horses. Since there is no moon, I fancy they will be putting up at Newark, or thereabouts, for the night."

A suspicion that the couple might be in Grantham crossed Miss Fairfax's mind. As though he had read her thought, the Earl said, " I cannot discover that they stopped in this town. Nothing has been seen of them here, or at the George. It seems odd, but it is possible, of course, that they changed horses at Greetham. I wish now that I had enquired for them there. However, they will scarcely go beyond Newark tonight. I shall drive there when we have dined."

" Nothing," said Miss Fairfax, with resolution, " would induce me to travel another mile this day! "

" It will be quite unnecessary for you to do so. I shall bring Lucilla back with me."

" If you would only let them be married! " sighed Miss Fairfax.

He ignored this remark, and, upon a servant's coming in to lay the covers, merely invited Miss Fairfax to sit down at the table. She obeyed him, but although she had fancied herself to have been hungry, and was now confronted with a very handsome dinner, she found that she was too tired to partake of anything but the lightest of repasts. The Earl pressed her in vain to salmon, lamb, green goose, and apricot tartlets: she would take nothing but some soup and a glass of wine. " To tell you the truth," she said candidly, " I feel a trifle sick."

" This, I collect, is a reproach to me for having obliged you to come with me! " said his lordship, in a goaded voice.

" Oh, no! " she murmured.

He went on eating his dinner, a heavy frown on his face. Miss Fairfax was wondering whether she would be permitted to go to bed before the Earl's return from Newark, with (or without) his ward, when one of the servants came into the room with the intelligence that a lady and gentleman had that instant arrived at the inn, and were demanding to see his lordship.

" A lady and gentleman ? " repeated the Earl. " Demanding to see *me* ? " He looked towards Miss Fairfax in the liveliest astonishment. " This is certainly unexpected ! " he said. " Can it be that Lucilla has thought better of her rashness ? "

Miss Fairfax, who had risen from the table and gone back to the fireside, did not feel equal to hazarding any conjecture. She agreed that it was indeed unexpected.

It turned out to be more unexpected than the Earl had bargained for. Instead of Miss Gellibrand and her swain, a matron with a face not unlike a parrot's sailed into the parlour, closely followed by an insipid-looking gentleman in a sad-coloured redingote.

The Earl stood staring, his napkin still grasped in one hand, the other lightly holding the back of his chair. The matron, having paused on the threshold, tottered forward, all the plumes in her beehive-bonnet nodding in sympathy with her evident agitation, and pronounced in thrilling accents, " We are in time ! "

" What in the name of heaven does this mean ? " demanded the Earl, looking as black as thunder.

Miss Fairfax, who had recognised the newcomers as the Earl's aunt-in-law and her son, his cousin and heir, blinked at them in considerable surprise.

Lady Wilfrid Drayton paid no heed to her, but said, addressing her nephew, " It means, Charles, that I am in time to stop your doing what you will regret all your life ! "

" Upon my word, ma'am, someone seems to have been busy ! What the— what do you know of the matter, pray ? "

" I know all ! " said the lady comprehensively.

" The devil you do ! Perhaps you will be so obliging as to tell me, ma'am, to which of my servants you are indebted for your information ? "

" It does not signify talking ! " she said, sweeping this home-question aside. " Most solemnly I warn you, Charles, that you are making a terrible mistake ! "

Her son, who had been engaged in sucking the knob of his cane, removed it from his mouth to say, " Knowing it to be a matter closely concerning us——"

" I know nothing of the sort," interrupted the Earl, looking at him with cold contempt. " In fact, I cannot conceive what the devil you mean by thrusting yourself into my affairs ! "

" Your actions are the concern of all your family," announced Lady Wilfrid. " When I learned how you had set off with this woman, and with what disastrous purpose, I saw my duty plain before me ! "

A slight flush rose to the Earl's cheeks. " Be good enough, if you please, to speak of Miss Fairfax with civility, ma'am ! "

" I shall never believe that the whole affair has not been her doing ! "

" That, ma'am, is not a question for you to decide ! "

" You *may* say what you please, but I know better. I knew her for a

designing female the instant I clapped eyes on her, though never did I dream she would have gone to these lengths!"

"Miss Fairfax's conduct," said the Earl surprisingly, "has throughout been unimpeachable!"

"My poor Charles, you have been sadly deceived! As a mother, as your aunt, I most earnestly implore you to give up this project, and return with us to London! Do not allow your own good judgment to be overcome by the wiles of an unprincipled woman!"

"You are labouring under a misapprehension, ma'am," said the Earl, meticulously polite, but with a dangerous sparkle in his eyes. "So far from my having acted upon Miss Fairfax's instigation, she is here wholly against her will!"

The effect of this pronouncement was hardly what he had expected. Lady Wilfrid uttered a shriek, and exclaimed, "Merciful heavens!" while her son turned a pair of goggling eyes upon Miss Fairfax, saying, "Good Gad! You don't say so, cousin! Well, if this does not beat all! 'Pon my soul, I would not have thought it of you, no, damme, I would not!"

"I don't believe it!" said Lady Wilfrid, recovering from her stupefaction. "She meant to entrap you from the start!"

"Oh!" cried Miss Fairfax, raising her hand to a suddenly burning cheek.

The Earl, glancing swiftly from one to the other of his relatives, said, "We are, I believe, at cross-purposes, ma'am. Oblige me by telling me in more precise terms, if you please, why you have followed me to this place."

His aunt bent a look of deep reproach upon him. "Attempt to pass that unprincipled female off with what degree of credit you may, you will not deceive me! Can you deny that you are on your way to Gretna Green?"

"So that's it, is it?" said the Earl. His frown had vanished, but the smile which took its place caused his cousin to remove himself thoughtfully to the other side of the table. "No, my dear Aunt Almeria, I do not deny it!"

The afflicted lady gave a gasp. "A nobody!" she said. "You, a confirmed bachelor (for I don't consider for a moment that nonsensical notion you had once of marrying your ward!), to fall under the sway of a wretched little dab of a governess! You cannot mean it!"

Miss Fairfax, who felt ready to sink, made a movement of protest, but the Earl spoke before she had time to forestall him.

"I never meant anything more in my life," he said deliberately. "You have had your journey for nothing, ma'am: my determination to wed Miss Fairfax is fixed. As for your dismay, I am well aware that my marriage must come as a sad blow to my cousin there, but I have more than once warned him that it is ill waiting for dead men's shoes. I have the honour, ma'am, to wish you a very good evening!"

He strode to the door, and wrenched it open. Before anyone could move, however, his effect was spoiled by the tempestuous entrance of a young lady in a travelling cloak whose hood had fallen back from a head of bright, tumbled curls. Without appearing to notice the other occupants of the room, this damsel cast herself upon his lordship's chest, exclaiming, "Oh, my dear guardian, I'm so thankful you are here! The most dreadful thing! You must come at once!"

The bemused silence which had greeted Miss Gellibrand's dramatic entrance was broken by the voice of Lady Wilfrid, stridently demanding to be told what Lucilla was doing in Grantham. No one enlightened her. The Earl, disengaging the lapels of his coat from his ward's grasp, said, " What has happened ? What has that fellow been doing to you ? "

" Oh, nothing, nothing, you stupid thing ! " said Miss Gellibrand, stamping her foot. " He is in a deep swoon, and I am quite distracted ! "

" In a deep swoon ! " exclaimed the Earl, in tones of considerable surprise. " In God's name, why ? "

" I think his shoulder is broken," said Miss Gellibrand tragically.

" What in the world has he been doing to get his shoulder broken ? And how do you come to be here ? I thought you at Newark ! "

" So we should have been, only that that odious chaise lost a wheel, just as we had passed the Ram Jam, and we were pitched into the ditch. And Edmund, in attempting to save me, was thrown heavily on to the side of the chaise, all amongst the breaking glass ! "

" Oh, my poor child, were you hurt ? " cried Miss Fairfax, moving towards her.

" Oh, is that you, Mary ? No, only the tiniest scratch. And at first I had no notion that Edmund had sustained any serious injury, for he never said anything, and in the scramble I didn't notice that he was not using his left arm. We thought only of proceeding on our journey, knowing that Shane, and very likely you too, would be hard on our heels. Then the thing was, how to come by another chaise ? We thought we should have been able to have hired one at Stretton, and we got on to a cart that was going there, while the postboy rode on to get a wheelwright to fetch the chaise away. Only when we reached Stretton there was no chaise to be had, no suitable conveyance of any sort. There was nothing for it but to come on by the stage to Grantham. And I must say," added Miss Gellibrand buoyantly, " had it not been for my beginning to be in a pucker over Edmund, I should have enjoyed it above all things ! Only fancy, dear sir, we had to sit four a side, and a horrid old man was chewing green onions all the way ! And such an uproar as was made over our not being on the way-bill ! Edmund had actually to bribe the coachman before he would take us up. He said if it was discovered he had *shouldered* us he would very likely be dismissed ! However, that doesn't signify. Though we had lost so much time, we were not unhopeful of out-stripping pursuit, and my spirits at least were mounting when they were utterly overpowered by the sight of you, sir, driving past the stage ! I thought all was lost, not knowing then how glad I should be to see you ! For when we reached this town, we were set down at the most vulgar-looking inn, and I discovered that Edmund was suffering the greatest anguish, hardly able to stand ! There was no staying at that horrid tavern, so we came to the Angel, Edmund leaning upon my arm, and myself, as you may suppose, in the greatest alarm imaginable. And then, to crown all, they tried to turn us away from here, saying it was a posting-house, and they could not admit stage-passengers ! I do not know what would have become of us had not Edmund sunk suddenly into a swoon ! Everything was bustle and confusion then, but I caught sight of your curricle being wheeled into a coachhouse, my dear sir, and staying only to see my sainted Edmund carried into the house, I ran upstairs to find you. Please, please come to Edmund at once, and explain everything to that odious landlord!"

Lady Wilfrid, who had listened to this tumultuous recital in astonished silence, turned towards Miss Fairfax, as the Earl left the room in the wake of his volatile ward, and said in a stunned voice, "It is Lucilla who is eloping?"

"Yes," said Miss Fairfax.

Lady Wilfrid eyed her suspiciously. "Am I to understand, then, that you are not about to marry my nephew?"

"No, indeed," said Miss Fairfax, rather forlornly. "I accompanied Lord Shane merely to take Lucilla home again."

"Well, I don't understand!" suddenly announced Mr. Drayton. "He said he was about to be married to you!"

"I think," said Miss Fairfax diffidently, "that you made him lose his temper, and he said it to make you angry."

"He was always a disagreeable creature," said Lady Wilfrid. "I collect that he has set his face against Lucilla's marriage, I dare say for no other reasons than pride and self-will."

"Indeed, ma'am, I believe Mr. Edmund Monksley to be a most unexceptionable young man," replied Miss Fairfax, perceiving that in Lady Wilfrid Lucilla would find an eager ally. "The only objections are Lucilla's youth and Mr. Monksley's lack of fortune."

Lady Wilfrid fixed her with a singularly calculating gaze. "My nephew had never the least disposition to sympathise with the Pangs of Love," she uttered. "With me, it is otherwise. I have the tender heart of a parent, and such vulgar considerations as poverty, or inequality of birth, weigh with me not at all. Nothing could be more affecting than Lucilla's story! But then I am all sensibility, quite unlike Shane, who has a heart of stone! I shall tell him that he has no right to forbid this marriage."

The Honourable Frederick, who had apparently been pondering the situation, once more ceased sucking the knob of his cane to say in a tone of great relief, "Well, this is famous! If he does not wed the governess, and we can prevail upon him to consent to Lucilla's marriage to this swooning-fellow, I do not at all despair of a happy issue."

"Excuse me," said Miss Fairfax, conscious of her reddening cheeks. "I think I should go downstairs to assist in restoring Mr. Monksley."

By the time Miss Fairfax reached his side, Mr. Monksley, a fresh-faced young man, with very blue eyes and a decided chin, had recovered consciousness. Finding himself looking straight up into the countenance of his Lucilla's guardian, he at once embarked on a speech, which would no doubt have become extremely impassioned had not the Earl cut it short by saying, "Yes, you may tell me all that later, but you had better be still now until the surgeon has attended to your shoulder."

Tenderly clasping one of Mr. Monksley's hands, Miss Gellibrand said in resolute accents, "Nothing you can say, Shane, will prevent my going to Gretna as soon as Edmund is well enough!"

"Nonsense!" said his lordship. "These Gretna weddings are not at all the thing, and you had better put such romantic fustian out of your head at once."

"Believe me, my lord," said Mr. Monksley faintly, "nothing but the sternest necessity could have prevailed upon me to propose so clandestine a union to one for whom I entertain feelings of the deepest respect!"

"I wish you will not talk to me like a play-actor!" said his lordship irritably. "If you must marry my ward, let it at least be in a respectable fashion!"

"Angel!" cried Miss Gellibrand, lifting a glowing face.

His lordship regarded her with the utmost disfavour. "If it is angelic to be more than willing to rid myself of a most tiresome charge, I am certainly an angel," he said witheringly.

The arrival of a surgeon, carrying an ominous black bag, created a timely diversion. Mr. Monksley's broken shoulder was set and securely bound; two of the serving-men carried him upstairs to a bedchamber; and it was not until he had been comfortably disposed between sheets, and was being fed with spoonfuls of broth by his adoring Lucilla, that Miss Fairfax had leisure to go in search of her employer. She found him in the parlour belowstairs, giving some directions to the landlord. When he saw her, he smiled, and held out his hand, a gesture which made her feel very much inclined to burst into tears. The landlord having bowed himself out of the room, she said, however, in as prosaic a tone as she was able to command, "Mr. Monksley is feeling much easier now. You have been so very kind, sir!"

"Oh, the devil take Monksley, and Lucilla too!" said his lordship. "We have more important things to consider. What in thunder are we to do, Mary Fairfax? I told that abominable old woman that we were going to be married at Gretna Green. But no consideration on earth would prevail upon me to behave in such a preposterous fashion! Besides, I cannot possibly take you to Gretna without another rag to your back than what you stand up in."

"My dear sir, there is no need for you to trouble your head about it," said Miss Fairfax, trying to smile. "I told Lady Wilfrid there was no question of our going to Gretna."

"You did, did you?" said the Earl, looking at her rather keenly.

"Yes, of course, sir. Where—where is Lady Wilfrid?"

"Gone to put up at the George, where I heartily hope she may find the sheets damp!"

"But—but why?" stammered Miss Fairfax.

"Because," said the Earl, "I told her that we were going to be married just as soon as I can procure a licence!"

Miss Fairfax had the oddest sensation of turning first hot and then cold. "You are being absurd!" she said, in a voice which did not seem to belong to her.

"Mary," said his lordship, taking her hands in his, and holding them fast, "have those shocking faults of mine given you a disgust of me?"

"No," said Miss Fairfax weakly. "Oh, no!"

"I don't know how I came to be such a fool (but you said I was stupid), yet—would you believe it?—it was not until my aunt accused me of it that I knew I had been in love with you for years!"

Miss Fairfax trembled. "But you can't! Marry to disoblige your family? Oh, no, no!"

" My family be damned! " said the Earl. " I wish you will look at me, Mary! "

" Well, I won't," said Miss Fairfax, making a feeble attempt to free her hands. " I did think that you regarded me sometimes with—with a certain partiality, but I know, if you do not, how shocking such a match would be, and I won't marry you. I shall look for another eligible situation."

" No one will employ you without a testimonial, and I shan't give you one."

" I think you are extremely disagreeable, besides being mad! " said Miss Fairfax, in a scolding tone.

" Yes," said the Earl, taking her in his arms. " And I have also the most overbearing manners, so you may as well stop arguing with me, and kiss me instead."

Miss Fairfax, apparently much struck by this advice, abandoned her half-hearted struggles, said, " Oh, my dearest! " in a wavering voice, and subsided meekly into his embrace.

EDITH EVANS

*MISS EDITH EVANS seems to have been associated in some
way with almost every theatre in London and to have delighted
us in the whole gamut of female parts, from Shakespeare to
Shaw, from Restoration to modern comedy.*

THE PATRIOTISM OF SHAKESPEARE

THE ordinary simple definition of patriotism is love of country. But the
trouble with definitions is that they are apt to be either too un-
yielding or too woolly.

Still, I suppose that love of country is, to begin with, a cherishing of it in
our hearts. Exaggeration of this feeling may well lead to a shouting, flag-
wagging kind of patriotism, which is easily provoked to angry argument and to
an offensive assumption of superiority. There are people who indulge in this
arrogant, exclusive patriotism. Shakespeare himself, one might argue, is guilty
of it, the proof lying in that colourful passage of *Henry V* (Act III, Sc. I),
beginning: "Once more unto the breach, dear friends," and ending as
follows :

> "And you, good yeomen,
> Whose limbs were made in England, show us here
> The mettle of your pasture: let us swear
> That you are worth your breeding: which I doubt not;
> For there is none of you so mean and base
> That hath not noble lustre in your eyes.
> I see you stand like greyhounds in the slips,
> Straining upon the start. The game's afoot:
> Follow your spirit: and, upon this charge
> Cry ' God for Harry! England and Saint George! ' "

The whole speech is a fine bit of rhetoric. But it would be a great mistake to
deduce from it that Shakespeare was a blatant, jingoistic patriot. To take this
view is to overlook the fundamental fact that a playwright is a man who creates
characters and puts into their mouths the words that people, endowed with the
thoughts and emotions he has given them, would most fittingly use.

Shakespeare was a poet and a genius. But he was also a working dramatist
and a player who well knew that such an effective swash-buckling passage as
King Henry's speech before the walls of Harfleur, lines which have been the
goal and downfall of many an aspiring actor, was calculated to bring the house
down. In other words, it does not follow at all that the speech represented
Shakespeare's attitude towards war.

Certainly he had no illusions about the horrors of war, especially for

214

the under-dog. This is amply shown in the little scene in *Henry V* (Act IV, Sc. I) when the soldiers are talking to the disguised king the night before the Battle of Agincourt. Though Henry makes a plausible defence of his campaign, he is yet also on the defensive with one of his lowliest subjects.

Then there is that other famous speech of John of Gaunt in *Richard II* (Act II, Sc. I). In those memorable lines there is no arrogance, but a gentle love of country, of the soil, and of the people.

Living in a robust full-blooded age, Shakespeare had often in his plays to strike a martial note. Even so this speech is not like King Henry's blazing piece of rhetoric. John of Gaunt speaks as a man of great position mourning what he holds to be the humiliation of England. But he is not only a states-man. He is a man voicing his abiding love for his land, an emotion that finds expression in line after line of vivid, affectionate phrases filled with a warm, yet homely love. " This blessed plot," " this happy breed of men," " this nurse," " this land of such dear souls "—these are not mere ornaments of speech, but the outcome of deep-rooted feeling.

It would, of course, be absurd to claim that Henry's harangue before Harfleur was simply a magnificent chance for an actor, whereas John of Gaunt's speech reflected Shakespeare's own feelings. We cannot pick out some part of his work which happens to support a contention and conveniently ignore other passages that contradict it. In any case, both speeches are en-tirely in keeping with the characters of the two who utter them. For all that, there *is* much of Shakespeare's own love of country in the lines he gives to John of Gaunt. And it is not difficult to back the assertion.

In 1588, when Shakespeare was twenty-four years old, there occurred one of the greatest crises in all our eventful history—the arrival off our coasts of the Spanish Armada. That was something more than equivalent to the present constant threat of air-raids. The power of Spain was the most dreaded in Europe. The minds of all men must have been centred upon the menace. Conversation everywhere in court, inn, house, and street must have turned almost wholly, as it does among us today, upon the course and outcome of the war.

Shakespeare, we know, had an alert and receptive ear. There are references in his work to people and events of his time: to Marlowe, " the dead shepherd," in *As You Like It*, to Elizabeth and Leicester in *A Midsummer-Night's Dream*, to Essex by name in one of the choruses of *Henry V*, and by implication to the trial of Dr. Lopez, the Portuguese Jew, in *The Merchant of Venice*. *Love's Labour's Lost*, a very early play, bristles with topical allusions, or so I believe, for these deep mysteries are not for me. But the point I am making is that Shakespeare was clearly wide awake to what was going on around him. Many passages in Spenser's *Faerie Queene* deal unmistakably with the critical days of the Spanish Armada. But nowhere in the whole of Shakespeare's work is there a single line that refers directly to that terrific event. Evidently, as an artist, he was not stirred thereby to write patriotically. Had he been so, he would have produced some inflammable masterpiece that would at any rate have given the other young men of the time something to think about.

It was not the notion of military glory or conquest that for him meant love of country. But it was, I feel sure, a deep and passionate love of the people and

215

of the countryside. Here and there we can, so to speak, steal upon him and take him off his guard. In these lines, for instance:

> " This guest of summer,
> The temple-haunting martlet, does approve
> By his loved mansionry, that the heaven's breath
> Smells wooingly here: no jutty, frieze,
> Buttress, nor coign of vantage, but this bird
> Hath made his pendent bed and procreant cradle:
> Where they most breed and haunt, I have observ'd
> The air is delicate."

Part of the purpose behind those verses was, we know, to show Duncan and Banquo admiring the peace and tranquillity of the surroundings of Macbeth's castle where, all unknown to them, death already awaits the king. It is a fine piece of dramatic irony. It is also, I think, Shakespeare's own love of the country coming out. Where he writes as a poet freed, as in *Venus and Adonis*, from the constraints that the playwright must put upon himself, this feeling for the countryside is still more plain.

I am not trying to make out that Shakespeare was a vigorous opponent of cruelty to animals. I imagine he was not. His ideas in many respects were those of the teeming, vigorous age in which he lived. My point is simply that he knew the sights and sounds and smells of the country as a native of that Stratford which lies in the very heart of England.

And, as he knew and loved the country, so he knew and loved the people in it. Bottom and his fellows are only supposed to live in Athens. They are really Warwickshire rustics and English to the core. And so was Shakespeare. Whether he wrote of Verona as in *Romeo and Juliet* or of Rome in *Julius Cæsar*, he was essentially English, and Juliet's nurse is no product of Italy, but of the earth, earthy, and the most English earth at that.

It was a broad land that he loved, and his outlook, so far as the necessity for writing in character allowed, was equally broad. He never preached. He did not sentimentalise over people, but he remained compassionate. He was tolerant and generous. We do not see Hamlet or Cleopatra as thin-lipped, tight-souled people. It was narrowness that he condemned: it is the narrow people mostly who come to a fall in his work. Perhaps he hated ugliness more than bad conduct, and hated it because it was ugly. And, now I think of it, while he praised the heroism called forth by war, he did not praise the thing itself, and that because it is ugly. That is a view of patriotism we hold today.

There is another point, too, that brings him into line with what we are feeling at the present time. Shakespeare is continually on the side of individual liberty. He was by no means, to use that unmelodious word, a totalitarian. In *Julius Cæsar* (Act II, Sc. I) his sympathies are with Brutus, and not with Cæsar, because Brutus, free from any personal malice, sees individual liberty in danger:

> " It must be by his death," says Brutus, " And, for my part,
> I know no personal cause to spurn at him.
> But for the general. He would be crown'd.
> How that might change his nature, there's the question:

216

> It is the bright day that brings forth the adder:
> And that craves wary walking. Crown him?—that!
> And then, I grant, we put a sting in him.
> That at his will he may do danger with.

Shakespeare was not opposed to order. Far from it, and I think that through the mouth of Ulysses in *Troilus and Cressida* he expressed his own ideals of order.

> " Take but degree away, untune that string,
> And, hark! what discord follows: each thing meets
> In mere oppugnancy: the bounded waters
> Should lift their bosoms higher than the shores,
> And make a sop of all this solid globe:
>
> .   .   .   .   .
>
> Force should be right: or, rather, right and wrong—
> Between whose endless jar justice resides—
> Should lose their names, and so should justice too."

Surely it is clear that Shakespeare believed in order as fully as he did in individual liberty and tolerance. Perhaps his tragedies are tragedies mainly because the chief characters in them transgress against the few broad rules to which even freedom-loving men must submit. Macbeth fell through ambition; Lear through pride; whilst a friend of mine, far more acute than myself, holds the view that Hamlet, loving those same ideals of liberty, order, and tolerance, could not reconcile them with the world he saw about him. The times for him were " out of joint," and the attempt to set them right forced him into crime. That may be so.

But to sum up these random reflections. It seems to me that Shakespeare's patriotism was in no way a military eagerness to down his country's enemies. It was rather a feeling that England's love of order, its sense of humour and toleration, its dislike of strutting arrogance, were things worth striving to preserve. "The oppressor's wrong," "the insolence of office," "the proud man's contumely," are revealing phrases.

Yet his was not a narrow patriotism. Shakespeare has penetrated into every corner of the world, but his has been a peaceful penetration. It is impossible for people of many lands to love Shakespeare without in some measure loving the land that bred him. He is, as I have said, essentially English, but I do not mean by this that we must hold him to any particular spot or selfishly claim him exclusively for our own.

By his " Englishness " I mean that he comprises all the best qualities of his race, not least among them those qualities which project and send us forth to adventure. Born in the heart of England, it is the heart of England that he takes with him as an ambassador wherever he goes. His understanding of men and scenes, particularly of country scenes, causes him to be understood by people all over the world. He is English, but he is also universal, and folk in foreign lands reading him or seeing his plays gain an insight into this country while recognising through his lines the best of their own. Most at home in England, he is a stranger nowhere.

217

H. C. BAILEY

MR. H. C. BAILEY is the author of many novels and short stories. His best-known literary creation is Mr. Reggie Fortune, that dreamy, bland personage who combines the qualities of surgeon, gourmet, and detective. " The Thistle Down " is a new Mr. Fortune story.

THE THISTLE DOWN

"THIS is Max Tollis speaking," said the telephone angrily, " Sir Max Tollis."

" I am sorry," the parlourmaid answered, " Mr. Fortune has a consultation."

" Put me through to him," the telephone commanded. " It's a matter of life and death."

Mr. Fortune was building a theatre of his own design for the small girl whom he liked best. He set up the proscenium arch before he listened to this appeal. Then he asked, " Whose life? Whose death? " For Sir Max Tollis, though known to and knowing everybody, was immensely uninteresting to him.

" Bob Dale has been shot," Tollis responded with vehemence. " My secretary, Fortune, a dear boy. God knows how it happened. I can't believe it was suicide. I have the police here, but they're all at sea. I'd give my soul to get the truth clear. Would you come down, like a good fellow? If there's a man alive can work the thing out, it's you, Fortune. Bob never killed himself."

" When the police want me, they'll tell me so," said Reggie.

" Damn the police! I'm thinking of the boy's good name. I was fond of him."

" Where is he? " Reggie asked.

" What? He was found here, my little place, Frith House, just beyond King's Walton. It's only fifteen miles."

" In an hour," said Reggie, and rang off.

He took much less, for, curdling the blood of his chauffeur, he drove himself through London. When he swung round the last curves of the drive which led to the white concrete lump of Frith House a man came out of the door and stopped to wait for him and met him with a puzzled smile.

" Good morning, Mr. Fortune."

" Well, well! " Reggie sighed satisfaction. " So you're in charge. Splendid."

" The same to you, sir," Inspector Underwood answered. " I know you're quick, but this beats all. I've only just 'phoned to ask the Yard for you."

"I am wonderful. Yes. But not now. Tollis asked first. Sayin' the police were all at sea."

"They haven't had much time to make land. Tollis is taking it very hard. I don't blame him."

Tollis came bustling from the house, a large, imposing, florid person. "Fortune, I'm deeply grateful to you." He shook hands impressively. "You know Inspector Underwood? Perhaps you will explain to him——"

"I have. Yes. Anything been moved?"

"No, sir," said Underwood. "The body and the car are still as they were when the local police got here at ten o'clock."

"And nothing done!" Tollis cried. "Now, Fortune, will you come and examine the poor fellow?"

"One moment. Where was the dead man previous to bein' dead?"

"God knows," Tollis answered. "This is the position. My wife and I spend practically all our time here. But yesterday we were both at our flat in town for the Derwent wedding and the Charities Ball. After that was over we drove straight down here and arrived about four in the morning. Bob's car was in the garage then, the chauffeur says, but, of course, it didn't occur to him to look inside. When he opened the garage again after breakfast he saw Bob lying in the back of his car dead and cold. There was a wound in his head and a pistol on the car floor. We got the doctor and the police, and they said he'd been shot. That's all they could say!"

"Not bein' magicians," Reggie murmured. "Nor am I, Tollis. However. Anything known of the movements of the dead man yesterday?"

"I wish there was," said Tollis.

"And there is," said Underwood. "A footman here took a telephone message for him at three o'clock from a Mrs. Meryon—just to tell Mr. Dale 'Same place. Same time.' He did tell Mr. Dale and after that nobody saw Dale again. The servants didn't think anything of his being out to dinner— he often went off when Sir Max wasn't here."

"It's the first I've heard of this," Tollis exclaimed.

"You haven't been in much of a state to ask things, sir," said Underwood.

"I suppose I'm not." Tollis looked from one man to the other. "Mrs. Meryon—and Bob. I don't understand."

"Lady known to you?" Reggie asked.

"My wife calls. The Meryons are new-comers; they've taken a cottage for the summer. I believe Mrs. Meryon was on the stage, a striking figure of a woman. It's news to me Bob was on any terms with her."

"We'll work that out," said Underwood.

"Whatever you want to do, do it." Tollis was impatient. "But you'd better show Mr. Fortune everything here."

"I will," said Underwood, and Reggie took a case from his car and went with them to the garage, which was concealed from the house by a bank of rhododendrons.

Two cars stood in it, a resplendent limousine and a much-used ten which had shed some oil on the floor. Underwood opened the off-side back door of the smaller car.

Reggie saw a body slumped down in a heap as if he had slid from the back seat, the body of a young and dapper man. His face had been rather too

219

pretty for manhood before the mouth sagged loose, before blood clotted across his cheek. The blood came down from a wound which darkened the fair wavy hair above his right ear.

"Photograph and finger-prints and all that?" Reggie asked, and Underwood nodded. "What did the doctor say?"

"Time of death uncertain, but not less than twelve hours ago. Cause of death, shot from a weapon held close to his ear, which might have been that pistol by his legs on the mat. And taking all things together, it was quite possibly suicide."

"Nonsense," Tollis exploded. "I'll never believe that. I knew Bob. He was the last man in the world to kill himself. He never had a grouse. He didn't know what worry was. He enjoyed every minute he lived."

"And then—this." Reggie waved a hand at the huddled body. "Well, well." He picked up the pistol. "Webley self-loading. About ·455." He looked at the wound. "It could be."

"You say suicide, Fortune?" Tollis demanded. "Damn it, man, you haven't examined him yet. You can't jump at suicide, like the local doctor, because you find a pistol with him."

"I never jump," said Reggie.

"I don't believe Bob ever had a pistol—or knew one end from the other," Tollis retorted. "He wasn't that kind of fellow."

"Don't look it. No. However." Reggie put the pistol in his pocket. "We will now have a nearer view. Give me a hand, Underwood." They lifted the stiff body from the car and Reggie knelt down and opened his case. . . . He pored over the wound and his round face was plaintive. "Well, well," he sighed and smiled awry. With a pair of tiny forceps he detached from the congealed blood something filmy, fluffy, and put it into a metal box.

"What the devil's that?" Tollis cried.

Reggie did not answer. He was extracting another feathery tuft and another. He picked yet more from the dead man's hair, but those he put in a second box.

Then he rose and displayed them to Tollis. "There you are."

"What is the stuff?" Tollis asked angrily.

"You don't know it? Fruit of carlina vulgaris. The common thistle."

"Thistle down!" Tollis muttered.

"As you say."

"Are you sure?"

Reggie laughed. "Oh yes, yes," as Underwood gave him a questioning stare.

"Thistle down on him," Tollis cried, "in the wound! Why, then, he couldn't have been shot here in the garage!"

"But where thistle down was blowin' about. Yes. That is the natural inference. That bein' thus, go along with Underwood and see if any of your servants can tell him the places Dale frequented when he went off in your absence. And I'll take another look at the wound."

After they had gone, his attention was transferred from the wound to the pistol. Years old, he decided, seen a lot of service, fired recently, one cartridge gone from the magazine. He pocketed the pistol again and proceeded to search the car. "Case of cartridge not here," he murmured with a crooked

220

smile, but he went on hands and knees to pore over the mats again. He found tufts of thistle down upon the mat at the back, flattened out by the pressure of a foot which had left spots of damp dust. Beside them was a smeared blood-stain.

Having taken Dale's keys, he locked the car doors, then wandered about the garage, peering into every corner. " No cartridge case," he purred, and went back to the house. A butler of irritated visage answered the bell. " Inspector Underwood engaged with Sir Max? " Reggie enquired. " All right, I'll carry on." He crossed the hall and shut himself into the telephone box. . . .

When he came out the butler, hovering by another door, turned with a start. " In there, are they? " Reggie smiled.

" If you please, sir," the butler ushered him into a room half-study more than half-lounge.

Tollis and Underwood sat there with a woman standing before them.

" Just telephoned 'em to take the body away," said Reggie. " Well? "

" This is Miss Benn," said Underwood, " Lady Tollis's maid. She tells me she's seen Dale's car on Longley Common more than once and him round about there with Mrs. Meryon."

" Oh." Reggie surveyed the woman. " As if they were—friends? "
She pursed her prim lips. " They looked like it."

" Thank you. That's all." He dismissed her. " You didn't know that, Tollis? "

" She'd never told me."

" Nor your wife? "

Tollis flushed. " Of course not. She's a decent woman. My wife loathes scandal."

" I hope Lady Tollis hasn't been too much distressed by Dale's death."

" Naturally she's upset. She was fond of the boy. We both were. This story of Mrs. Meryon is staggering. I should never have thought Dale would care for a woman of her type, and a married woman too."

" You believe the story? "

" I believe what Benn said, absolutely. She's no scandalmonger."

" I had to drag it out of her," said Underwood, " and it fits with the 'phone message from Mrs. Meryon telling Dale to come to the same place, same time."

" That is so," Reggie agreed. " Yes. By the way, did you find a cartridge case? "

" No, sir." Underwood's sagacious eyes watched him steadily like a dog's. " I couldn't see one in the car or in the garage."

" What's that? " Tollis broke in. " Dale was shot, wasn't he? "

" Oh yes. Yes. But the pistol found with him would eject a cartridge when fired. It was fired. And the cartridge isn't there."

" Why, then," Tollis cried—" then Dale didn't commit suicide."

" That is the obvious inference," Reggie murmured.

" That's what you meant when you showed me the thistle down in the wound. He was killed somewhere else and brought back with the pistol to get the murder taken for suicide. You're marvellous, Fortune."

" Not me. No. Only see what there is. And believe evidence. We haven't finished. Murderer not yet found. Nor the place of murder. Where do thistles grow round here, Tollis? "

Tollis looked at a loss. " Nowhere near that I know of. Beyond my grounds there's woodland. Frith Wood. My God, the common, though—Longley Common, a cursed lot of thistles there! "

" Well, well. Longley Common. Where Dale has been seen with Mrs. Meryon. Who wanted him same place yesterday. Place where thistles grow. Where there might be a cartridge case of a Webley ·455. I wonder. Get your wife's maid, Tollis. Want her to show us where she saw Dale and Mrs. Meryon companying together."

" Very well." Tollis rose. " What a ghastly business! "

" Not nice, no. The sooner it's over the sooner to sleep. We'll see Mrs. Meryon on return. Have your chaps fetch her here, Underwood."

Reggie's car, with the maid beside the chauffeur, conveyed them some two miles of a winding green tunnel of a road through beechwood before it came out on a common which spread, dim in haze beneath a sultry sky, wide spaces of coarse grass studded with thistles.

" You'd better stop now," said the maid as they passed a rough track through the grass. " It's along there I've seen Mr. Dale."

Reggie jumped out of the car and contemplated the track and the common. " Lots of thistles," he murmured plaintively.

" The devil of a lot," said Tollis. " Do you mean Mr. Dale was here by the road, Benn? "

" Oh no, sir," she answered. " He took his car along the track up to those clumps of trees. But I thought this gentleman's was too big."

" Shall we walk then, Fortune? " Tollis asked.

" Yes," Reggie sighed. " Do the painful right. Go ahead," and Tollis went up the track with the maid.

" There has been a car along here," said Underwood to Reggie's ear. " Worn Dunlop tyres. And so are Dale's."

" As you say," Reggie answered. But he was not looking at the tyre marks; he surveyed the thistles on either side, the misty expanse of the common, and turned with a dreamy smile to Underwood. " My dear chap! " he murmured.

Underwood stared about him. But Reggie's pensive attention had concentrated on picking a way along the sandy ruts. The long grass about them was wet from the haze.

The maid stopped, pointing at a tongue of open ground dividing two copses of birch and crab-apple. " That's where Mr. Dale put his car," she said, " and Mrs. Meryon and him among the trees."

" Thanks very much." Reggie came up to her. " Stand fast. Now we'll see what we can see, Underwood."

On the dank way from the track to the copses the tussocks of grass were disturbed and some thistles had been broken down. " Thistles enough about," said Tollis.

" Oh yes. Yes. Plenty and fruity." Reggie stopped to collect some tufts of down.

" My God, she's right! " Tollis cried. " There has been a car here; come and look at this."

" What? " Reggie was putting the thistle down in a box with affectionate care and Underwood watching him. He stooped to pluck some grass. "Go to it, Underwood."

Underwood strode on to Tollis and was shown the traces of a car starting and turning by the trees. "Yes, there's been a car here several times," he pronounced, "and once quite lately. A small car and tyres like Mr. Dale's."

Reggie strolled up to inspect and agree. "That is so. Place where the car was. Place where thistle down is. If you find the cartridge case also, you might prove where the murder was."

"The cartridge?" Tollis repeated. "Oh, yes, of course; that would clinch things absolutely." He looked about him. "But it's almost like hunting for a needle in a haystack."

"You think so? Should be near where his car last rested, what?"

"There is that," Tollis said slowly. "My God, you are keen, Fortune!"

Underwood went delicately over the crushed grass and Reggie joined the search. It was not long before Underwood plucked his arm and showed him a gleam of brass in the dank tufts. Reggie picked it up with forceps and held it to the light. "Yes, I think so," he murmured—"from a self-loader ·455. Easy to prove it came from pistol." He put the cartridge away and over his round face came a small benign smile. "Now we'll go talk to Mrs. Meryon." . . .

When they reached Tollis's house again a detective met them and told Underwood that the sergeant had Mrs. Meryon there and Mr. Meryon with her. He pointed to the study.

"You'd better come too, Tollis," said Reggie.

"If you say so—it's a foul business," Tollis answered. "Anything you want."

They went into the study, and Meryon, a swarthy, lean man, started up and limped towards them demanding which of them was Inspector Underwood and why his wife was brought to that house.

Underwood told him to sit down. "I am investigating a case of murder, the murder of Mr. Dale, the secretary of Sir Max Tollis here."

"You're Tollis, are you?" Meryon scowled at Reggie.

"Not me, no. My name's Fortune." Reggie contemplated the woman, while Meryon transferred his scowl to Tollis. She had not moved; she sat erect, lithe and tense, the rich, dark colours of her face set in stern calm.

"How do you do, Sir Max?" She spoke with contempt, and Tollis bowed.

"I have to ask you some questions, Mrs. Meryon," Underwood went on. "When did you last meet Mr. Dale?"

"Some days ago. I don't remember which day."

"Was that on Longley Common?"

"Possibly. I walk there sometimes."

"And he used to drive out there to meet you?"

"What do you mean?" Meryon roared.

"I have to put these things to Mrs. Meryon, sir," Underwood told him. "Were you aware of her meetings with Mr. Dale?"

"Yes. I knew all about them. We were both sorry for him."

"Why?" Reggie murmured.

"He was a nice boy in a rotten job."

" Dale never told you that," Tollis cried.

" Didn't he? " Mrs. Meryon raised her black eyebrows.

" What was rotten about his job? " Reggie asked.

" Sir Max can tell you. I never knew just what Mr. Dale meant."

Tollis laughed. " That's the story! It won't do, ma'am. Dale was with me for years before you came here."

" Yes, he told me that too. I don't know when he began to be afraid of you."

" Not very clever," Tollis sneered. " It's no use pretending Dale wasn't happy with me. The whole place knows he was. But I had better leave the lady to you, Inspector." He rose.

" If you please," said Underwood. " Now, Mrs. Meryon, how often did you go alone to meet Dale on the common? "

" I never went to meet him. He sometimes met me."

" But not with your husband there? "

" That's a scandalous question." Meryon started up. " I'll report you for it."

" Been in the Army, Meryon? " Reggie asked.

" What? I'm not a regular. I was through the last war."

" I thought so. Ever carry a pistol? "

" Why? " Meryon scowled.

" We want to know."

" Was Dale shot? "

" We're askin' the questions."

" I had one on service, of course."

" What sort? "

" Webley automatic. Lots of fellows had 'em."

" I know. Have you kept yours? "

" Good Lord, no."

" When did you get rid of it? "

" Years ago."

" Well, well." Reggie turned to Underwood. " Don't forget the message."

" I hadn't." Underwood was aggrieved. " I was coming to that before."

" My dear chap! Sorry. My error." Reggie looked at his watch. " Too bad." He pushed back his chair and wandered away to the window.

" Now, Mrs. Meryon," Underwood said again, " why did you telephone Dale yesterday to——? "

" I didn't," she interrupted.

" A 'phone message from you to Dale was taken by the footman here after lunch yesterday saying to meet you ' same place, same time.' "

" It wasn't from me," she said quietly.

" We shall be able to trace the call, Mrs. Meryon."

" Why haven't you? " she asked.

Reggie strolled across the room and went out.

" Having received that message," Underwood continued, " Dale left this house, and I have evidence he proceeded to Longley Common, where he had been in the habit of meeting you, and he was shot there. Do——"

" Trace the call," said Mrs. Meryon. " I went up to town yesterday morning with Douglas. We did a matinée and——"

224

The door was opened and a booming voice called: " Sir Max Tollis! This way, sir, if you please."

Tollis bustled out. The door was shut behind him. He found himself confronting a solid man with two others at his elbows and Reggie in the background.

"I am Superintendent Bell," the central man announced. " Sir Max Tollis, I have to send you to the police-station, where you will be detained. You may be charged with a grave crime. I warn you that anything you say will be taken down and may be used in evidence."

" What charge? " Tollis gasped.

" The crime I am dealing with is the murder of Robert Dale."

" Fortune! " Tollis cried. " You know I sent for you."

" Oh yes," Reggie murmured, " to prove Dale didn't kill himself. I have. You told me you'd give your soul to get the truth clear. I've got it, Tollis."

Tollis lurched forward, babbling incoherent panic. " Take him away," said Bell.

Reggie went back to the study.

" Sorry you've been troubled," he apologised to the Meryons, who were looking dazed. " Couldn't do without your side of it. As you see."

" I don't," Mrs. Meryon answered sharply.

" My dear lady! You said Dale hated his job and was afraid of Tollis."

" So he was, but he never told me why. He only moaned."

" Look at it the other way round. Tollis was afraid he would tell you why. That's what you gave us. Motive for murder. Motive for putting it on you and Meryon. You've been very inconvenient to Tollis. Thanks very much."

Mrs. Meryon spoke loud enough for Reggie to hear what she said to her husband as she went out. " The man's as bland as a cat." But he was gratified. He likes cats.

Bell stood aside to let her pass and then came in. " Well, young fellow " —he clapped Underwood on the shoulder—" you've done a good job of work this time. Tollis is an old fox. That thistle down was the smartest touch I remember. And yet it's going to hang him."

" The thistle down? " Underwood looked stupefaction.

" Oh yes," Reggie assured him, " you spotted the flaw. Thistle down in the wound, thistle down in hair and car, proof Dale was not shot in the garage, but out in the open. Only the thistle down was damp. Which gave the game away. That thistle down never took the air. It never blew on to Dale. It was put. Cunning fellow, Tollis. Falls down on detail. Well, he had his engagements in town yesterday for an alibi. He knew the Meryons were not at home. So he sent a 'phone message in her name telling Dale to meet her on Longley Common and went there and collected thistle down. When Dale went to the garage and started his engine Tollis shot him, using the sort of pistol Meryon had in the war. Then planted the thistle down on the body and collected the cartridge case from the floor and went to town. Bold bad fellow. Called me in this morning to prove how fond he was of Dale and make sure the death wouldn't pass as suicide, but murder by Meryon out of jealousy. Produced the maid's evidence of meetings with Mrs. Meryon and so got us to the thistles on the common. Which were still damp, as when he picked the down yesterday. Havin' led us to the place Mrs. Meryon and Dale met,

P

he left us to find the cartridge there. You noticed how well he managed that, said it was huntin' for a needle in a haystack. Devilish clever, as he said of me, confound his impudence. But he was weak on detail again. Smear of car oil round the cartridge rim. No oil on the common. But oil on the garage floor. Which is where it fell when ejected. I told Tollis if we found the cartridge we might prove where the murder was. He missed the point."

"I didn't get the hang of the thistle down, sir," said the honest Underwood. "I just thought there was something queer about it."

"My dear chap! You did," Reggie chuckled. "Your work."

"I suppose it makes a case." Underwood looked at Bell.

"There's more than that thistle down, my lad," Bell answered. "Mr. Fortune 'phoned me about it being wet and asked me to have a look at the clothes Tollis wore yesterday. When we tried his flat, we found a lounge suit packed up to send to the cleaners. In the turn-up of the trousers some damp grass seed, in one of the jacket pockets bits of thistle down, and on the cuff of a sleeve a blood-stain. That's the case. And it'll hang Max Tollis."

"Yes, I think so," Reggie murmured.

"It's strong enough," Underwood frowned. "But why? I mean to say, what's the motive?"

"My Underwood! You heard Mrs. Meryon. Fear. Fear she had hold of Dale, he'd tell her why his job was nasty, why he was afraid of Tollis. Tollis had to wipe him out and the Meryons with him."

"But Tollis is a public man and all that," Underwood objected. "I don't see how his secretary could have anything on him to risk murder for."

"Ah! Wait till we've gone through Tollis's papers, my boy," Bell answered.

"My guess is blackmail," said Reggie dreamily. "The higher rate, big-game blackmail. Always thought Tollis knew too much."

C. DAY LEWIS

A decade ago, a young schoolmaster just down from Oxford was beginning to find a place on the lists of discerning critics as a poet who was going to be important. MR. CECIL DAY LEWIS has now won fame, not only as a poet, but also as a novelist, anthologist, critic, and (as Nicholas Blake) detective-story writer too. His contribution here is an extract from a new translation of the " Georgics," upon which he is working.

ORPHEUS AND EURYDICE

(Translated from the Fourth Book of Virgil's "Georgics.")

NOT without sanction divine is the anger that hunts you down.
Great is the crime you pay for.   Piteous Orpheus calls
This punishment on you.   Well you deserve it.   If Destiny
So wills it.   Bitter his anguish for the wife was taken from him.
Headlong beside that river she fled you.   She never saw,
Poor girl, her death there, deep in the grass before her feet—
The watcher on the river bank, the savage watersnake.
     The band of wood-nymphs, her companions, filled with their crying
The hill-tops: wailed the peaks of Rhodope: high Pangaea,
The warlike land of Rhesus,
The Getae lamented, and Hebrus, and Attic Orithyia.
Orpheus, sick to the heart, sought comfort of his hollow lyre:
You, sweet wife, he sang alone on the lonely shore,
You at the dawn of day he sang, at day's decline you.
The gorge of Taenarus even, deep gate of the underworld,
He entered, and that grove where fear hangs like a black fog:
Approached the ghostly people, approached the King of Terrors
And the hearts that know not how to be touched by human prayer.
But, by his song aroused from Hell's nethermost basements,
Flocked out the flimsy shades, the phantoms lost to light,
In number like to the millions of birds that hide in the leaves
When evening or winter rain from the hills has driven them—
Mothers and men, the dead
Bodies of great-heart heroes, boys and unmarried maidens,
Young men laid on the pyre before their parents' eyes—
And about them lay the black ooze, the crooked reeds of Cocytus,
Bleak the marsh that barred them in with its stagnant water,
And the Styx coiling nine times around corralled them there.
Why, Death's very home and holy of holies was shaken

To hear that song, and the Furies with steel-blue snakes entwined
In their tresses; the watch-dog Cerberus gaped open his triple mouth;
Ixion's wheel stopped dead from whirling in the wind.
    And now he'd avoided every pitfall of the homeward path,
And Eurydice, regained, was nearing the upper air
Close behind him (for this condition had Proserpine made),
When a lunatic impulse took her lover off his guard—
Pardonable, you'd say, but Death can never pardon.
He halted. Eurydice, his own, was now on the lip of
Daylight. Alas! He forgot. His purpose broke. He looked back.
His labour was lost, and the pact he had made with the merciless King
Annulled. Three times did thunder peal over the pools of Avernus.
"Who," she cried, "has doomed me to misery? Who has doomed us?
What madness beyond measure? Once more a cruel fate
Drags me away, and my swimming eyes are drowned in darkness.
Goodbye. I am borne away. A limitless night is about me
And over the strengthless hands I stretch to you, yours no longer."
Thus she spoke: and at once from his sight, like a wisp of smoke,
Thinned into air, was gone.
Wildly he grasped at shadows, wanting to say much more,
But she did not see him: nor would the ferryman of the Inferno
Let him again cross the fen that lay between them.
    What could he do, where go, his wife twice taken from him?
What lament would move Death now? What deities hear his song?
Cold she was voyaging now over the Stygian stream.
Month after month, they say, for seven months alone
He wept beneath a crag high up by the lonely waters
Of Strymon, and under the ice-cold stars poured out his dirge
That charmed the tigers and made the oak-trees follow him.
As a nightingale he sang that sorrowing under a poplar's
Shade laments the young she has lost, whom a heartless ploughman
Has noticed and dragged from the nest unfledged: and the nightingale
Weeps all night, on a branch repeating the piteous song,
Loading the acres around with the burden of her lament.
    No love, no marriage could turn his mind away from grief.
Alone through Arctic ice, through the snows of Tanais, over
Frost-bound Riphaean plateaux
He strayed, bewailing his lost Eurydice and the wasted
Bounty of Death. In the end Thracian Bacchantes, flouted
By his neglect, one night in the midst of their Master's revels
Tore him limb from limb and scattered him over the land.
But even then that head, plucked from the marble-pale
Neck, and rolling down mid-stream on the river Hebrus—
That voice, that cold cold tongue cried out " Eurydice! "
Cried " Poor Eurydice! " as the soul of the singer fled,
And the banks of the river echoed, echoed " Eurydice! "

RUBY FERGUSON

RUBY FERGUSON is a novelist with command of two widely different fields. On the one hand, as R. C. Ashby, she has written first-class mystery; on the other, she is a romantic writer. The whimsical and charming " Lady Rose and Mrs. Memmary " was her most successful contribution to this kind of fiction—and here is the lovable Mrs. Memmary again.

MRS. MEMMARY'S VISITORS

EVERY time Lady Rose heard the front-door bell peal and echo through the empty halls of Keepsfield her heart gave a jump, thinking that something beautiful might be coming to her after all these bleak years. Then she would remember that she wasn't Lady Rose any more, much less the Countess of Lochlule, but only Mrs. Memmary the caretaker, whose business was to let the house.

Every day she would sweep and dust and polish the great rooms, the glittering parquets, the marble stairs and the gallery above, the mural paintings and the carving and the embroidered chairs that were left behind from the days of Keepsfield's pride.

In that still autumn weather when her work was done and the sun-filled hours had run to dusk, she would walk out on the west terrace and pretend that the last fifty years were just a dream. The park at least was hardly changed, with its blue-green vistas, equestrian statues, and armies of embowered trees melting, melting into the lavender-tinted sky. She never crossed the park now, for though she could not believe she was nearly eighty years old, her body knew it and failed her spirit; but she remembered that beyond the park were the sand-dunes, and there ran the fresh tides of the Firth of Forth, blue waves white-capped, as on the day she ran away from her governess to play on the shore, and met a man called Mr. Charles Kingsley who gave her a book called *The Water Babies*. She was then a little girl used to gifts and adulation.

It was the house which worried her now; the huge white mansion with its colonnades and classic pediments filled with sculptured figures, the glory of a bygone age, as she watched it crumble under that slow, grey disease which attacks derelict mansions. Keepsfield had been the finest house in Scotland; it had sheltered kings; the last earl had lived in a state of splendour which far outshone that of his monarch and friend, the old Queen at Balmoral. When Lady Rose was a child, life at Keepsfield had moved with a tremendous dignity; witness the cordon of liveried servants bowing the Earl to his carriage, or the procession of footmen who bore aloft the silver dishes when the nobility of Scotland sat down to dine a hundred strong.

And now all that was left of ancient glory was summed up by a board in the park which announced to passers-by that the house was to let, partly furnished; and all that was left of the old family was—well, she had long since ceased to think of herself as Lady Rose, much less the Countess, for she was just a white-haired, blue-eyed, spare old woman in a straight black dress— Mrs. Memmary, the caretaker who showed people round.

Often in an afternoon the bell would be ringing; it was ringing now. Perhaps this time it might be someone from the old life, someone to talk to. Or perhaps a person sympathetic and kind, who would be silent before the beauty of the house, silent enough to hear the walls speak of their recollections and to feel the soft weight of all the dreams which lay folded under the painted ceilings.

Mrs. Memmary opened the door. Arrogantly at the foot of the steps stood a long, gleaming Lagonda. Two women faced her, mother and daughter; the elder with pearls and coils of grey fox fur, the younger bare-headed and soignée, wearing expensive sports clothes.

" We've come to look over the house. Mrs. Copp and Miss Copp."

" Will you come in ? " Mrs. Memmary softly closed the door as they entered, chins high, curiously gazing. They stood in the marble entrance hall; a shaft of sunshine fell from the central dome, and the marble bloomed like the heart of an Ophelia rose.

" So this is the famous hall! " said Mrs. Copp; " I wonder why they had all this marble dyed pink."

" All the rose-marble was brought from Greece," said Mrs. Memmary meekly; " it is the natural colour, I assure you."

" Ah ! " Mrs. Copp considered. " Do you care for it, Salomé ? "

" The staircase ? Oh, not too bad, Mummy."

" Well, you should know, darling. You've got such taste."

" My daughter," she explained benignly to the caretaker, " has perfect taste. She was educated on the Continent, and she *knows*. One can be so taken in with antiques. Are those large chairs genuine ? "

" *Genuine*, madam ? "

" Now don't misunderstand me. Half the stuff in these places is brought in to sell."

" One of the chairs, madam, belonged to Mary, Queen of Scots. She chose this purple velvet for the upholstery. All these others were worked in *gros point* at least one hundred years ago by the women of the Targenet family."

" *Gros point*," put in Miss Copp, " has rather gone out, Mummy."

" There ! " said Mrs. Copp. " It just shows the chairs would be useless to me, and I might not have known it. What are you looking at now, dear ? "

" I'm just thinking, Mummy, this carpet is almost threadbare."

" So it is. But, of course, they'd have to allow for that, wouldn't they ? We couldn't have the place looking like a second-hand shop." She suddenly remembered her guide, and said, " You have a ballroom here, haven't you ? How many people could I entertain at once, I mean if I decided to take the place ? "

Mrs. Memmary put the tips of her fingers together and smiled.

" I have known five hundred entertained here to a ball."

(Five hundred ! Satin skirts and jewels and tartan sashes; chieftains' kilts and velvet coats and dirks in stockings; laughter and violins and the marching-in of the pipers; candelabra with flames like crocus-flowers and each dropping a thousand lustres; waltz and schottische and cotillon and eightsome reel; dark Highlander, blonde Lowlander; Macdonald, MacGillivray, Campbell, Fraser, MacBeth; silver dishes and crystal goblets and ruby Venetian glass for the ladies; English footmen with white silk stockings and black silk backs; light on the ceiling, light on the parquet, light on faces and lips and shoes and rings; lovely voices, tall men, beautiful eyes; Mackenzie, Douglas, Kennedy, Grant.)

"Oh," said Mrs. Copp, "you've been here some time?"

"I was here as a child."

"Brought up on the estate, I suppose. I once had a maid for fourteen years; she thought she owned me. I expect the kitchen arrangements are antiquated?"

"I'm afraid you would think so, madam."

"And the dining-room as dark as a vault! Well, lead on; we'll follow, though I don't hope for much."

Along the main corridor Mrs. Memmary led the way on that dutiful round which she made daily.

"This is the dining-room. The panelling is intact, and you have the original mahogany table and twenty chairs. If, under modern conditions, you thought this room too far from the kitchens, there is a smaller room that could be adapted."

"Oh, definitely," said Mrs. Copp; "I should put a couple of billiard-tables in here. What is that little place, opening out?"

"Just a butler's serving-room; the carving was done there."

"How amusing. Why is the ceiling so dark?"

"Because they used to keep such huge log fires. The ceiling ought to be restored; it is painted with life-sized deer galloping over a park——"

"But you've got central heating now, of course," interrupted Miss Copp.

"Well, no—but it could be——"

"I ask you, Mummy! What is the use of a place without central heating?"

"Don't be impatient; we could see to all that." Mrs. Copp gave a slight shiver, either at the prospect of no central heating or from general dis-favour. "I don't like these long windows. I suppose one could substitute leaded casements."

"Hardly, in a house of the eighteenth-century classic type," ventured Mrs. Memmary in mild protest.

"Oh, rubbish!" cried Miss Copp. "Why, the hotel we stayed at last night had a Tudor room, and a Venetian room, and the ballroom was Moorish. Why not?"

(Why not? After all, what did it matter—a little thing like that—when the traditions of a lifetime were swept away, and beauty crumbling could find no place for rebirth. It was too late now to fight, much less weep over the relics.)

The Copps were pleased with the drawing-rooms, but disagreed violently over plans for their future decoration. Mrs. Memmary, tired of standing, escaped from their wrangling voices into a world of recollection which seemed daily nearer and more ready to receive her. In every room of the house a little scene could be re-enacted; old voices heard again, young and fresh; old frocks reworn, bright and new.

The modern voices crashed in and shattered her dreams.

"I wish the house were in a better district," Mrs. Copp was saying plaintively; "I do like Braemar. After all, there isn't anything in Scotland except the shooting."

"And the golf, Mummy."

"Yes, dear; but the people one *encounters* on a golf course! I suppose we ought to see the bedrooms. Show us the best; we'll take the rest for granted."

They ascended to the high, dim corridors of the second floor, past doors closed on emptiness. At last Mrs. Memmary turned a handle.

"This," she said quietly, "was the late Countess's room."

It was a gracious room, twenty feet square; on the walls the remains of an ice-blue satin-striped wallpaper, patterned with faded sprays of lilac. To one who sought it there still hung on the air a delicate perfume. Beyond the two tall windows the Bronze Avenue of copper beeches ran out of sight, making a sun-dappled glade. Empty and silent was this room. Who could fill it with pictures of the past ?—Mamma seated at her dressing-table in a green satin robe with white fur mules on her toes, laughing and squirting her perfume over the nose of the kitten held by protesting Rose. . . .

The old caretaker kept her eyes downcast on the ground.

"This might do for me," said Mrs. Copp, "but there's only one man who could decorate it, and he'd charge the earth to come here from London. And *how* I hate a bedroom with a high ceiling! What do you think, Salomé ? "

"Not too bad, Mummy; only the plumbing would cost thousands."

"Plumbing ? " said Mrs. Copp, drawing a finger disdainfully over the cracked paint of the window-frame.

"I expect the bathrooms aren't fit for a dog."

"Oh dear, I never thought of that. Are there any portraits, oil-paintings, you know, of ancestors and so on? I didn't notice any." She looked enquiringly at the caretaker.

"There are a few portraits," said Mrs. Memmary. "They hang in the little gallery that you didn't care to see."

"Oh, that dark hole." Miss Copp laughed lightly. "If they're respectable, we might adopt them; that's what Mummy means."

The Copps walked on, lost in a wordy argument, leaving Mrs. Memmary to follow.

"Now, dear, do you really care for it ? "

"Well, Mummy, it's mouldy but rather gorgeous."

"Yes, and, of course, indescribably filthy——"

"And smells too frightfully musty——"

"But it *is* impressive. I mean, it could be——"

Mrs. Memmary's knuckles whitened as the nails of her clenched fingers bit the palms.

"How much do they want for it ? "

At the sudden question she started; for ten minutes they had forgotten her. "Were you speaking to me ? "

"My good woman, yes. Wake up. How much do they want for the rent of the place ? "

Mrs. Memmary swallowed something hard and sharp at the back of her throat and voiced her fiercest lie.

" Five thousand a year, madam."

" Five thousand! But that's fantastic! " cried the daughter.

" Of course it's fantastic," said Mrs. Copp, importantly; " but if we do decide to take the place, it won't cost us anything like that. You see, we know the owner, the Countess of Lochlule, very well."

(" That startled her! " she murmured to her daughter as she saw the old caretaker's blue eyes shoot wide open with surprise.)

" You know the Countess! "

" Oh, yes. We see a great deal of her in London; she'll want to know about our visit. Such a pity she lost all her money. But I think she'll just love us to have the place at a nominal rent, won't she, darling ? "

" Oh, probably, Mummy; but let's go. We've been here for hours, and I want a drink."

Mrs. Copp smiled indulgently. " Thank you for showing us round, my good woman. Have you got a shilling, Salomé ? . . . Only tenpence ? Well, give her the tenpence, dear; I've only got half a crown."

Miss Copp already had the Lagonda's engine racing with a din that shocked the green stillness of the park. Her mother climbed in more clumsily, fluffing her furs.

Mrs. Memmary shut the door on them and, alone once more in her sacred silence, leaned against the panels with closed eyes. The baneful pennies chinked one by one to the floor. Gradually her furious heart stopped pounding. They were gone . . . gone . . . gone! Those hateful women . . . those vandals. The peace of her house would come back, falling as the soft shaft of primrose light fell from the central dome.

Cr-r-rash-thud!

Far away in the house, and muffled by distance, the sound was sufficient warning to her quick ears. She ran up the stairs and along the main corridor, listened for a second, and flung open the door of the study. As she suspected, she had left the windows open to the terrace and somebody was in the room; a young man, very startled, wearing shorts and an imitation leather cycling jacket, his hair rough, the promontories of his face burnt red by the sun.

His smile was frank and disarming. He broke out, " I'm sorry. I'm very sorry, y'r ladyship. I didn't ought to have come in, but honest I didn't think there was anybody here, and I did want a peep at the carving. Lovely, it is! "

" Yes—but how did you get here ? "

" Well, you see, m'm—your ladyship—I'm on a cycle tour, and I'm riding along the side of the park when I see a notice that it's all to let. So I nip across the park just to have a quick look at the house. Fair took my breath away, if you'll excuse me saying so; it's that beautiful. And then, going along the terrace quiet-like, I saw this window open. Well, I do a bit of wood-carving myself; I couldn't resist. Coming in I knocked the chair over; but I picked it up quite safe."

All this tumbled out with a breathless sincerity. Mrs. Memmary smiled, a smile that began at the corners of her lips and lighted warm sapphire lamps in her eyes.

" Of course you can look at the carvings," she said. " This over-mantel took a craftsman the better part of his life-time. The chair you knocked over

233

belonged to a King of France, Louis whom they called Le Roi Soleil. You can see the gold fleur-de-lis on the leather."

The young man looked awed. "What room is this?"

"It *was* the Earl's study."

"The Earl? Well, earls are a bit out of my line, except in the kiddy fairy-tales. Who does it belong to now?"

"To the Countess of Lochlule."

His eyes widened. "Oh, my! I suppose she's a grand lady." He looked wistful. "Hard up, I expect, if she has to let her ancestral home. Well, it's none of my business—I'm only a working man—but if this was my place I'd . . . I'd go down with it. I'd die before I'd let a stranger set foot in it." He tugged awkwardly at a coat button. "Silly, aren't I?"

Mrs. Memmary looked surprised. "I don't think you're silly. I like what you said . . . but, you see, strangers—rich ones—would pay to have it kept clean and in good order."

"Who wants it clean and in good order?" he burst out, uncontrolled and a little afraid of himself. "I reckon it's seen its glory, and when that's all gone . . . well, if it was mine I'd rot and fall with it. I'd starve, if I could feel it was still mine. . . . Who was she, this Countess?"

Mrs. Memmary looked down, twisting her fingers.

"She was the Earl's only child," she said slowly—"Lady Rose. She spent her childhood here and was very happy. She grew up a beautiful girl, and made a good match—a neighbour, Sir Hector Galowrie—but it wasn't love, you understand. He was a proud, cold man. He died before she was thirty, and left her a young widow with three children and a heavy burden of estates and tradition . . . you'd hardly understand. Her father was dead; Queen Victoria, whose god-child and favourite she was, made her Countess of Lochlule in her own right. But she so far forgot herself—she did a dreadful thing."

"Go on," he urged.

"She married again before her husband was three months dead. She shocked the whole of Scotland, her family, the Queen. You see, she married a young man, *a nobody*, an office clerk whom she met in a public garden in Edinburgh!"

The visitor gave a brief nod of understanding. "I suppose," he said, "people couldn't be high and mighty all the time in a place like this. It was just romance, wasn't it?"

"Yes, it was pure romance. He and she were happy ever after, too. But it ruined her; she had to leave her home, and England. She was ostracised by society. Her children were taken from her and brought up strangers to her. That was fifty years ago; she's old now, and poor, and quite alone. That's just the Countess's story."

"I'm sorry," breathed the young man; and added, "I'll have to go. Thank you, your ladyship; I won't forget this place. I wish my girl could see it, but"—he smiled confidingly—"it might spoil her for a little semi on a housing estate. Thanks for everything."

He nodded an abrupt farewell and stepped out into the sunlight.

Mrs. Memmary took three quick steps forward; something seemed to fly from her heart to him.

"Stop! A minute. . . . Why do you call me—that? You mustn't call me 'your ladyship'; I'm only Mrs. Memmary, the caretaker."

He paused, puzzled. "I don't know. There was something . . . I don't know. But maybe I'll come back again; I'd like to. It's a bit of Scotland's glory. My mother was Scotch—not a lady, you know, just what she called 'a bit Highland lassie.' She used to say that was what started the pipes calling to my heart. . . . Well, I'll be going, m'm. Cheerio, as they say. Chin-chin!"

Mrs. Memmary stood by the window till he was out of sight, bent over his handle-bars, racing; then she closed the casements on the August evening and drew the curtains across. There would be no more visitors to-day.

. . . .

"Oh, look!" cried the girl, scanning her picture-paper; "it says here that that old woman's dead; the one whose grand house you saw in Scotland."

"What? Her!" The boy started up from the grassy bank where he was drowsing. It was a fine Sunday afternoon, and they had just eaten their picnic lunch in a Cheshire lane. "What does it say?"

"It says that Rose, Countess of Lochlule, died at Keepsfield, her Scottish residence. Suddenly, it says. That was the place, wasn't it?"

"Oh, her!" The boy flung himself down again. "I had a fit. I thought you meant the other one; my old lady, the caretaker. Mrs. Memmary, she was called. Look, Lil, we'll go up there next year when we're married. It's lovely; it's like a world of *romance*. It's the pipes calling to your heart, as Mum used to say. Oh, listen to me, talking so soft! But I will say, whatever the real Countess may have been, my old dear was a lady and no mistake. Here's to her, Lil: Mrs. Memmary!"

J. B. MORTON

The name of MR. J. B. MORTON lightly conceals one of the famous pseudonyms of Fleet Street, for this is " Beachcomber," for the past fifteen years columnist of the " Daily Express."

A LOVE SONG

(FOR BAGPIPES AND TWELVE HUNDRED AND FORTY VOICES)

(I)

WHEN love comes to the harbour-master
　　Of a small market-town,
　　It's little he cares for the coastwise craft
Careering up and down,
It's little he cares for freightage rates
　　Or ridiculous harbour dues,
And any old scow can sail in or out,
　　Whenever the skippers choose.

Refrain :
The people who live on harbour dues,
　　They may as well close down,
When love comes to the harbour-master
　　Of a little market-town.

(II)

When love comes to the harbour-master
　　He sits all day and sighs,
Scribbling her name on lading bills;
　　And when the night-winds rise,
And the signals of distress go up,
　　With flash and counter-flash,
He tosses upon his thorny couch,
　　Composing ardent trash.

Refrain :
The people who live on harbour dues
　　Quite rightly feel done down,
When love comes to the harbour-master
　　Of a little market-town.

236

(III)

Who is the harbour-master's love,
  The lode-star of his hope ?
Who takes his mind from his fine peaked hat,
  His whistle and telescope ?
Who but the laundress, Amy Legge,
  That lives in the market-place,
And turns men's hearts clean inside out
  With her great flaming face.

Refrain :

When love came to the harbour-master
  It hit him pretty hard,
And he wandered like a poor lost dog
  About the laundry yard.

(IV)

When love comes to the harbour-master,
  Life cannot be the same,
And men unloading coils of wire
  Will hear him cry her name.
He bids the ships of the world go hang,
  The buoys may rust and rot,
While he ties a piece of tarry rope
  In a true lover's knot.

Refrain :

The people who live on harbour dues,
  They wear a puzzled frown,
When love comes to the harbour-master
  Of a little market-town.

FRANK SMYTHE

MR. FRANK SMYTHE is one of the four men living who have most nearly reached the top of Mount Everest; and his distinction as a mountaineer is enhanced by his writings about travels and adventures in the high places of the earth. This contribution is full of the fascination of climbing as it is expressed in his famous book " The Spirit of the Hills."

THE CRAG

THE south side of the hill, that facing the sea, slopes gently and is heather-clad, except for a few moss-covered boulders that have taken permanent root in the peaty soil, but the north side falls precipitously in a crag. It is as though some giant had taken a knife and slashed a great slice out of a monstrous pudding.

It is six hundred feet high, this crag, and a quarter of a mile in width. Two deeply cut gullies intersect it from base to summit, and between them the grey schistose rock bulges outwards in a supporting buttress. Beneath it, a slope of rock fragments, varying in size from a pebble to a fair-sized house, extends to a small tarn, a dark-green eye that records every wayward light and wandering wind. On the far side of the tarn, heathery slopes rise to a ridge, and beyond this ridge are other ridges, each bluer and more remote, fading into the opalescent hazes of the north.

It is a desolate scene. No tree, no field, no road, no human habitation break the tremendous monotony. There is no movement except for the wind in the heather, the passage of clouds, and the shimmering of the tarn. Sunlight seldom falls on the crag; there is nothing kindly in its shadowed precipice. Water oozing from its cracks and ledges has left long dark stains on the rocks, and it is grimly silent except for thin trickles in its gullies, that fall with a subdued whispering sound over stones and boulders. Yet in May and June, when the sun edges into the north, the rocks dry and the crag glows warmly in the long luminous twilight. At such times the ledges are gay with star-like saxifrages and bilberries ripen on the terraces.

There are days of peace when the distant sea gleams like a silvered pavement, and only the ravens and wailing curlews intrude upon the boundless serenity of earth and atmosphere, and there are days when storms congregate in the west and the wind flings itself furiously from the foam-streaked Atlantic, lashing the hills with salty rain. Then the crag awakens from its slumber. It is magnificent and mysterious; new voices are roused; new vistas made visible. Roaring, whining, whistling, the wind searches every nook and cranny; it pours tempestuously into the gullies; it tramples the rakes and ledges; now approaching with a sound like that of an express train in a tunnel, now breaking like a thunderclap on the crest, now descending on the tarn in a tumult of fury, snatching up sheets of water with careless ease, and flinging them in violent deluges against the cliffs hundreds of feet higher, where wild affrighted mists tear endlessly past, shredding out into twisting curtains of rain.

The crag seems almost to respond to these rude buffetings. Calmly it faces the charging mists like some seasoned warrior confident of his power, now apparently smothered beneath some onrush, then breaking free, hard-faced, stern, triumphant.

There are other times, when the wind veers to the north, and an Arctic breath whitens the fells. The tarn freezes; every drop and trickle of water is stilled, and icicles beard the chockstones in the gullies. Then out of a sky of cruel feline green comes the snow—and a great silence.

For many centuries after the ice had ground and scored the rocks, and hollowed out the bed of the tarn, the ravens had nested undisturbed on the crag, but one warm July day two men came over the opposite hill and descended the heather slopes to the tarn. They were dressed in tweeds, with caps and knee breeches, and they carried knapsacks on their backs. They seated themselves on a boulder by the tarn and gazed long and earnestly at the crag above them.

" A fine bit of rock," said one.

" The left-hand gully looks possible," said the other.

" Right," said the first, " we'll try it."

They rose to their feet and scrambled up the slope of screes to the mouth of the gully. There they halted, and one of them took a coil of rope from his shoulder, undid it, and tied one end to his waist, his companion doing like-wise with the other end. Then they paused and gazed upwards.

The gully was deeply cut and enclosed by two walls of great steepness. One wall was vertical, even overhanging in places, a smooth precipice offering scarce lodgment to a fly. The other wall was a little less steep. It was wet and slimy, and patches of grass, moss, and heather clung to it; it was more broken than the other wall, but infinitely more treacherous to climb.

These things the men noticed. They saw also that the uppermost portion of the gully narrowed, forming a chimney narrow enough for a man to straddle, a fearsome rift with a strip of blue sky discernible through it and the silver-lipped edge of a slow-moving cloud.

Countless rains, frosts, and suns had choked the gully with debris, among it being several huge rocks which had jammed between the walls. In some places there was a clear gap between these chockstones and the silted-up bed of the gully, but in other places the gaps had been filled with fallen debris and it would be necessary to pass the obstacles on the outside.

The two climbers advanced to the attack. They trudged up some more screes, and presently stood beneath the first boulder in a shallow cave between it and the bed of the gully. It was a dismal place. One half of a small stream that poured down the gully found its way over the outside of the boulder, whilst the remaining half seeped through the debris at the back of the boulder, so that the boulder and the walls on either hand were dripping wet and covered here and there with green slippery slime. The boulder overhung, and it was impossible to climb directly over it: the obstacle had to be passed by scaling one or other of the walls between which it was wedged. That on the right was

239

impossible; the smooth wet rock was destitute of holds for hand or foot, and the sole alternative lay to the left up the vegetation-masked rocks.

Leaving his companion standing in the dripping cave, one of the men began to climb. Reaching upwards, he pulled away slaty, insecure masses of rock until firmer material was exposed. The fragments crashed into the bed of the gully, then rolled to rest on the screes; soggy lumps of turf and moss followed.

Ten feet, twenty feet, thirty feet, the leader's progress was slow, but confident and sure.

To the second man standing in the cave this was a dull time. He could not see the leader, but he could hear him, the gritting of his boot-nails, an occasional exclamation, and the rattle and hum of dislodged fragments. The rope ran out slowly through his hands, foot by foot and yard by yard. He looked at it meditatively. It was useless to his companion should he fall, and useful to him only when his turn came to follow. And yet it was valuable to both. It was something more than a mechanical link; there was a potency in it; it transmitted a flow of human force. He could feel his companion through it, his confidence and his strength, and his companion could feel him, his thoughts, whether he was half-hearted or worried, whether he had the " wind up," whether he was calm and assured. In any emergency the rope would serve as a common denominator of emotional force, of resolution, determination, hope, or fear.

Now and again, he glanced outwards away from the crag. The dark walls of the gully framed sunny hills and leisurely cloud shadows; he could see, also, a corner of the tarn, unruffled, and serenely still. Strange, and a little mad, it seemed to be climbing a chill, wet, and possibly dangerous gully when he might be lounging at ease on a sun-warmed boulder. Why was man never satisfied with easy things? Why must he strive to tread where no foot had trodden before? Why must he exchange comfort for discomfort and safety for danger? Perhaps one answer lay in the crag. There was something about it, about a mountain, that brought out the best in you; it tested you and in some mysterious way helped you. Mountains were made for simple men, not knaves and fools. It was good to climb them, to feel mind and body working in perfect unison and accord, and to see beauty. There was health to be found, and a philosophy, a peacefulness of mind and a serenity of spirit. In mountaineering there was a strength of purpose that had its roots in no chase, blood-lust, or suffering, but in something personal and intimate between man and Nature, and through Nature, God.

He was recalled from his thoughts by a sudden shout, " Come on! " The leader was up the first pitch.

He obeyed. His day-dreams were replaced by stern realities. There was nothing speculative or unreal about the slimy rocks or in his chilled finger-tips as they groped for holds.

He joined the leader, and together they progressed up the gully. There were many pitches, some easy, some difficult, some bordering on the impossible. Each problem called for a different solution and each solution took time. It was a longer climb than either had supposed, and the sun was well past its zenith when they came to the foot of the final chimney.

Seen from below, this chimney had looked both steep and difficult, and its appearance did not belie the original estimation. It seemed to overhang the placid waters of the tarn, now many hundreds of feet distant. To climb it meant hard and exacting work, and there was, in addition, a psychological problem to be faced—the fear of the unknown.

As they stood resting for a few moments and eyeing this culminating problem, a raven floated past uttering mocking croaks which echoed hollowly between the walls of the gully.

" I think it will ' go '! " said the leader resolutely.

" Looks all right," replied the second man. " I've got you well held, anyway," he added, as he passed the rope round a spike of rock.

With his back against one wall, and his feet against the other, the leader began to climb the rift. It was hard work, and the second man, anxiously paying out the rope, heard the short, hard gasping of over-taxed lungs.

The chimney gradually splayed out, until the leader was wedged across it almost full length, supporting himself by the pressure of feet and shoulders. The second man seemed very far beneath him; he could see his face staring upwards out of the gloomy depths of the gully. Every muscle now was tuned, every nerve was taut to do battle with the crag's last defence.

Twenty feet alone remained to be climbed, but it was not possible to " chimney up " any longer, the rift was too wide. One or the other of the walls must be climbed. The right-hand wall was impossible, but there were hand-holds and foot-holds in the left-hand wall.

But before going farther he must assure himself that the climb was possible, gauge exactly the strength necessary to mount that twenty feet, and whether, should it prove impossible, he would have a sufficient margin of strength left on which to retreat safely.

Supposing, and the thought would keep recurring, that it *did* prove impossible? Would he be able to re-wedge himself across the chimney, and make his way down to his companion? The possibilities were finely balanced, too finely balanced. Damn it! what was the use of *thinking* any longer? Better get on with the job—it was the sort of job that was better done quickly or not at all. Yes, it would " go "; of course it would " go." There must be no more glances down at the distant blob of white that was the face of the second man, or at the muddle of boulders nearly six hundred feet below at the foot of the crag. It had *got* to " go."

The rocks were dry here—thank God for that. And they were warm to the touch, not cold, slimy, and repellent like those lower down. If only they were not so steep; he was too dependent on his arms and fingers.

He noted the position of the holds, measuring with his eyes their distance apart, planning his upward moves like a chess player—there would be no time or strength for unnecessary delays.

He reached upwards with his hands. His finger-tips crooked on holds that were small but sufficient; and they were firm. He pulled, and at the same moment allowed his feet to come away from the opposite wall of the chimney. For a second, not longer, the whole of his weight came on his fingers, then his feet found holds also, and he could rest his arms. But not for long: the wall was too sheer, some strain must always come on his arms in preventing a backward topple. It was no place on which to linger.

He reached upwards with one hand and secured a fresh hold, a mere finger scrape, but sufficient, then balanced upwards with infinite delicacy on to a higher foot-hold.

Yes, it would " go," but it was very difficult, almost the limit. Hold by hold he progressed. He did not once look down, it were better not; his companion was fully eighty feet below. A fall through space, the rope snapping like cotton; one did not think of these things, but they were always there at the back of the mind on the border of the actively conscious, waiting only for the call-boy Fear to manifest themselves on the stage of endeavour.

Now he was just beneath the crest of the wall. What if the finish were awkward, perhaps a sheer arm pull on to a smooth sloping slab? Holding himself in position with his left hand, he reached up with his right over the edge of the wall. His exploring fingers suddenly engaged, and instinctively curled, round a warm rock edge, a solid, unmoving part of the crag. Great, oh, great! It was worth everything, every doubt, every anxiety, to feel that sun-warmed edge, rough, friendly, and tenacious in his grasp.

He reached up with the other hand. It was easy, too easy, yet the perfect finish of a great climb.

For a moment he paused, almost as though unwilling to complete the climb, and the afternoon sun smiled down on him, warmly and benevolently. Then he pulled, quietly and deliberately pulled, with both hands. Momentarily his muscles bunched and tautened, then slid and rippled like well-oiled machinery. In an instant he was up, as lithe as a panther, up and on to the crest of the crag.

It was late in the afternoon as the two men sat together on the crest of the crag smoking their pipes. The hills were a deep dusky purple, and beyond them the sea was molten bronze. Not a breath of wind stirred the heather and bilberries, and even the old raven had ceased its croakings and had resettled itself on some inaccessible ledge.

It had taken six hours to climb the gully, and they might have walked to the point where they now sat in twenty minutes.

The afternoon lengthened, and shadows grew about the tarn. At last one of the men knocked out his pipe against a rock and rose to his feet.

" Time we were going," he said.

His companion assented, and languidly coiled the rope. Then they were gone, striding down the heathery side of the hill.

Slowly, imperceptibly, the sunlight was transmuted to gold, and the shadows of the hills grew and grew in the hollow where the tarn rested. In the soft luminescent light the crag lost its harsher features as a man does at death. It became vague, tremendous, unearthly.

As the sun set, the long twilight deepened over the hills and the northern sky was filled with colours, with gold and daffodil, with green and blue, with amethyst and opal. There was silence and a great peace.

Very slowly, very gently, night fell.

MARY THOMAS

MRS. MARY THOMAS was, until comparatively recently, Editor of " The Needlewoman," and her books—"Dictionary of Embroidery Stitches," " Mary Thomas's Knitting Book," and " Mary Thomas's Embroidery Book "—although all written during the last five years, are already standard works on the art of the needle.

OUR KNITTING FORCES

MEN have always been great knitters, and hold their own particular ideas on the subject, which differ considerably from the " style " knitting of today.

Most men prefer Round Knitting (4 or 5 needles) to Flat Knitting (2 knitting pins), and dislike knitting from written directions. They are always attracted to Colour Knitting, popularly known as Fair Isle, and delight in creating their own colour patterns.

Sailors have an affection for Bead Knitting, often form their knitting stitches in a different way from women, hold their needles, which they prefer to be of strong steel, flat in both hands and generally knit with the yarn in the left hand! Good knitters are invariably ambidextrous.

Most men prefer creating fabric rather than styling, and they knit, as the Scottish women say, " a good cloth," firm and evenly made.

WHAT TO KNIT

Knitting in war-time automatically conjures up to the vision such articles as Balaclava helmets, socks, sweaters, mittens, comforters, etc., but all these are things which mothers, wives, and sweethearts knit themselves for their own men folk. They always have, and always will do so, and they are always gratefully appreciated.

Man's interest, on the other hand, is to knit something for his women folk, his children, or for the home, and rightly so, as this is where his heart lies, and so affords a happy recreation. The following suggestions show how knitted garments and presents can be made without following long written directions:

STITCHES

The first hint is about stitches.

The usual method of making Knit and Purl stitches is as in Figs. 1 and 2. The needle is inserted from front to back and the yarn cast under the needle for

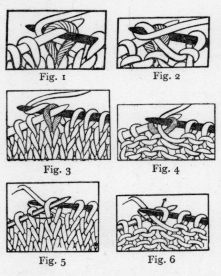

Fig. 1   Fig. 2

Fig. 3   Fig. 4

Fig. 5   Fig. 6

knitting, and inserted again from back to front and yarn over needle for Purl stitch.

Sailors and many who have travelled East will make their Knit and Purl stitches as in Figs. 3 and 4. Insert the needle into the *back* of the stitch and cast the yarn *over* the needle for Knit stitch, and into the back of the stitch and yarn under needle for making the Purl stitch. Some will even take the yarn *under* in making either stitch, as in Figs. 5 and 6, the needle again being inserted into the back of the stitch.

These different techniques get handed down in the Services and remain because they are preferred. They demand less finger play, produce the same fabric, and are more conveniently made when the yarn is held in the left hand. The Knit and Purl of each pair must always be used together. They won't mix, so please, nurse, don't try!

COLOUR KNITTING

As colour is always appreciated, here is the method:

Figs. 7 (*a*), (*b*), and (*c*) show how patterns are designed. The subjects are Christian and known to all European peasants: (*a*) the ancient Christian cypher P.I.X., and (*b*) the Anchor of Faith.

Both designs are of similar sentiment and both contain the same colour schemes—White, Blue, Orange, Yellow, and Green, and variety is obtained, not by change, but by exchange of colour, such as using a motif colour for the background and the background colour for that motif, or by a general exchange all round. The idea is soon understood once knitting has begun.

Any other five colours can be used—those given here are but suggestions.

The third motif (*c*) is

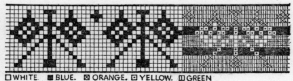

□ WHITE. ■ BLUE. ⊠ ORANGE. ⊡ YELLOW. ⊞ GREEN

Fig. 7 (*a*)

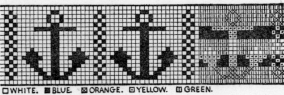

□ WHITE. ■ BLUE. ⊠ ORANGE. ⊡ YELLOW. ⊞ GREEN.

Fig. 7 (*b*)

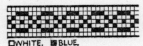

□ WHITE. ■ BLUE.

Fig. 7 (*c*)

244

a smaller pattern in two colours, blue and white, and something of this kind is usually arranged between the repetitions of the wider borders, as a kind of unifier.

Peasant patterns of the border type are always grouped in three because the Trinity is three, and all peasant design is strongly influenced by religious sentiment.

The practical result is also satisfactory, especially when the entire fabric is to be covered in pattern.

AS FOR TODAY

Modern symbols can be arranged on the same principle. Some peasant designs often show patterns comprised of cups and saucers, agricultural implements, horse-shoes, etc. The up-to-date young soldier or sailor will select aeroplanes, ships, guns, initials, footballs, etc. One sailor knitted his fiancée's initials sandwiched between hearts, arrows, and kisses all over a jumper!

Fig. 8

In creating a design, arrange only two different colours in any one line, as it is difficult to handle more than two colour yarns at the same time, since the colour not used is stranded along the back of the fabric, as in Fig. 8.

The same colours can be repeated or one colour changed on the next line. First effects should be simple, the whole design being confined to five or six different colours, though an expert Tartan knitter will use anything from ten to seventeen colours!

Keep the symbols compact, as a long stranded yarn passing behind many stitches will drag.

"ROUND" GOES QUICKLY

Colour knitting of this sort is more easily done round than flat, as only knit stitches and movements are used. In Flat knitting, one row is knit and one purl, and the latter is a little awkward.

The chart design is always read from right to left in Round Knitting, beginning the second line with the second round.

In Fig. 7a, the motif begins:

Line 1. K. 4 Green, K. 2 Orange, K. 4 Green, K. 4 Orange, etc.

In flat knitting, every *even* row must be read from left to right on the chart.

Fig. 9

Fig. 10

Fig. 11

Fig. 12

The correct technique is as in Fig. 9, each hand carrying a different coloured yarn, and using both right- and left-hand methods of yarn throwing. In practice, this is simpler, but the yarn can be dropped after knitting the green stitches and the orange yarn picked up, and this in turn dropped, and so on, if preferred. A more satisfactory result than stranding (Fig. 8) is obtained by weaving (Fig. 10). The second yarn is held first over the needle for one stitch (Fig. 11), and then under it for the next (Fig. 12).

THE CYLINDER BODY

Preference for circular knitting does not limit the work to socks. The peasant folk of all nations knit round, and, being of a practical mind, regard the body as a series of tubular shapes, which is exactly what it amounts to (Fig. 13). H. G. Wells prophesied this sort of man to appear in the next war, and here he is, ready to be clothed in knitting.

Now, if a body is this shape, and it certainly is, it is very obvious that it can be clothed from head to foot in a tubular elastic fabric, such as knitting, and so it was before the stylist came on the scene, and still is in two-thirds of the world.

The method is ingenious, but this is the charm.

In the Faroe Isles they clothe our H. G. W. man as follows. No other directions are necessary, as the patterned fabric is designed as just described.

Fig. 13

A TUBULAR SWEATER

Use 5 long steel needles, size 12.

A large tubular shape is knitted in gay colours for the body, casting on at the bottom and knitting upwards, straight, as for a sack. This body part can be increased in width where measurements demand. The extra stitches are " made " on the background of the pattern, where they will cause less disturbance to the design. They are rarely arranged vertically for pattern reasons, but added reasonably above each other and their position marked by a tied-in strand, so that the extra stitches can be adjusted in pattern on the next round.

When the necessary length is knitted, the " sack " is joined straight across the top, as shown, leaving a space in the middle for the head. To avoid a seam on the shoulders, the stitches are sewn and not cast off when joining. Fold the work flat and take a stitch from the front and then one from the back needle in a herringbone movement.

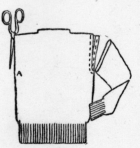

The neck stitches left in the middle are treated as another tube, knitting a length from 6 in. to 8 in. to form a polo neck, or shorter stand, as required.

The sleeves are also tubular, casting on at the cuffs and knitting upwards, increasing (K. into front and back of stitch) as necessary. They finish quite straight at the top and without any sleeve crown.

Fig. 14

The body tube is then cut straight down the sides, taking care to catch the bottom stitch, turned under, and sewn, as in Fig. 14. The sleeves are attached to this, stitch by stitch. The ribbing at the cuffs and the bottom gives the necessary grip.

BLACK-OUT KNITTING!

The method is exceedingly simple and comfortable in wear for children, boys, and men. What these garments lack in style they undoubtedly gain in charm of fabric, and women add them with pleasure to their sporting outfits.

Cutting at the armholes sounds monstrous, but if this is to be avoided, the top portion of the garment (which is also covered with pattern) would need to be done in flat knitting on 2 pins instead of circular. This is avoided, in the same way as the peasant always avoids what he considers unnecessary difficulties (see also *Note*, p. 248). Also these fabrics are generally knitted in the winter twilight, so here in war-time can be done in the " black-out "! Measurements should be known beforehand, and as the garment is always for some particular person, can be obtained.

MEASUREMENTS

Before beginning to knit, make a tension measurement with yarn and needles chosen. This gives the number of stitches to the inch. For example :
8 stitches to 1 in. width, 7 rounds to 1 in. depth.
Measurements :
Hips 36 in. Cast on $8 \times 36 = 288$ stitches.
Wrist 7 in. $8 \times 7 = 56$ stitches.
Upper arm width 12 in. $8 \times 12 = 96$ stitches.
The difference between 96 and 56 is 40 stitches, or 5 in. to be increased.
Sleeve length (under arm) 18 in. 7 rounds to 1 in.
$18 \times 7 = 126$ rounds.
Knit sleeve straight 6 in. Increase 1 in 6 rounds (3 times), 1 in 3 rounds (3 times), 1 in 2 rounds. Make 2 increases in last $2\frac{1}{2}$ in.

KNITTED COATS

Coats are made in the same way as described for the sweater. Knit the straight sack-like shape as before, no shaping. Where the centre opening will occur, the yarn must be wound round the needle some 10 or 12 times. In the next round these turns are dropped and another 12 turns made. When the garment is finished, these strands are cut down the front, cutting two at a time and then tying them. So the tubular fabric is opened.

The surrounding edges are finished with crochet and perhaps a few running stitches in gay colours, or beads threaded in matching wool, may be sewn all round. The coat can be sleeveless or finished with long or short sleeves as required. In the case of the former, the armholes are decorated to match the fronts, and the result is exceedingly coy (Fig. 15, especially the Bolero shapes)

Fig. 15

Note.—This method of stranding to form a central opening can also be used at armholes instead of cutting the fabric as in Fig. 14.

REGIMENTAL SCARVES

Regimental colours often run diagonally across the fabric, and these can be knitted tubular for scarves or men's silk knitted ties, using the correct colours, as follows :

SUGAR STICK RIBBING (Fig. 16)

Cast on stitches divisible by 12 and arrange on 3 needles.

The colours are cherry diagonal strip on black ground. Both colours are used in the same round, weaving the second colour as in Fig. 10.

Round 1 * (Black). S. 1, K. 1, P.S.S.O., K. 6, M. 1 into next stitch by knitting into the front and then into the back. For this back stitch, use the cherry wool, and then K. 3 (cherry). * Repeat from * to *. Round 2. Knit, using cherry for the cherry stitches and black for the black stitches. Repeat these 2 rounds.

If three colours are required, say a yellow, then increase the width of the cherry rib from 3 to 6 stitches. Knit 4 of these cherry and 2 yellow. The number of stitches to cast on will then be divisible by 15 (3 extra).

Fig. 16

If the black ground is too wide, or not wide enough, reduce the K. 6 to 4 (not less), or increase the number as required, and change the number to cast on accordingly. To finish, close the ends of scarf with a " knotted-in " fringe.

KNITTED VASE (Fig. 17)

This is a Victorian piece and the kind of work at which sailors excel. The shape just fits over a tumbler or a jam-jar.

Yarn 3-ply. Needles size 14.

The fabric must be very closely knit because of the decorative bead-work added afterwards. Hence the needle size. It is in two colours, scarlet and tangerine. Can be knitted to fit a flower-pot. Then take the measurements of pot to get the number to cast on. This specimen measures 8 in. round the base and 9 in. round the top. Depth 4½ in.

Tension 11 stitches to 1 in. 20 rounds to 1 in.

Cast on 88 stitches.

Rounds 1–12 (Tangerine). Knit.

Rounds 13–45 (Red). Knit.

Round 46. * K. 12, M. 1 by knitting into front and back of stitch. * Repeat.

Rounds 47–64 (Red). Knit.

Rounds 65–80 (Tangerine). Knit.

Cast off.

Fig. 17

248

The fabric is decorated with beads arranged between a double outline of Tambour Stitch, alternating the motifs in green and blue. Chalk-in the design on the fabric. Take a fine crochet hook. Hold the yarn at the back of the fabric. Insert the crochet hook from front to back through the middle of a stitch and draw through a loop. Insert the hook through this loop and the fabric as before (the stitch will now be diagonally left or right), and draw through another loop. Continue in this way to cover the whole of the outline. Thread white beads on red wool and lay them along between the lines. Thread a needle with red wool and sew in position, sewing over the wool between the beads. The edge at the base is finished with crochet (blue).

KNITTED BAGS

These are very simple to make in round knitting and make delightful presents, especially in Fair Isle patterns, when they should be lined. All bags should be knitted close and on fine needles as for a stocking.

Bags in round fabrics are knitted upside-down for convenience of beginning with a picot hem and joining when finished.

If initials, or a little house, pattern, etc., are being added for decoration, then these, too, must be knitted upside-down, so that they appear the right way up when the bag is finished.

SMALL KNITTED BAG

Bags of all sizes and shapes can be made—work bags, wool bags, knitting bags, etc. The latter should be lined with chamois leather to keep the steel needles bright. Effective in Fair Isle patterns. The method is as follows:

Bag measurements: 6 in. × 10 in.

Tension 8 stitches to 1 in.

8 × 6 = 48 stitches. Twice 48 = 96.

Cast on 96 stitches, divided on 2 needles. Knit with a third.

Begin with a picot hem as follows:

Rounds 1–7. Knit.

Round 8. * Over, K. 2 tog. * Repeat.

Rounds 9–15. Knit. Now take two extra

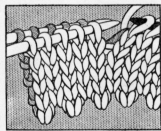

Fig. 18

needles and pick up all the stitches along the cast-on edge, the number of which should equal those already on the needles. Fold for hem and join as in Fig. 18, by inserting the needle through one front and one back stitch, and knitting them together.

Rounds 16 and 17. Knit.

Round 18. * Over, K. 2 tog. * Repeat. This will form a beading for the draw-string.

Round 19. Knit.

From here carry on in pattern, either Fair Isle or Stitch pattern.

To finish. Turn bag inside out, hold the needles together, and join by knitting a stitch from the front and the back as in Fig. 18 and casting off at the same time. Knit a draw-string.

Draw String
Cast on 2 stitches.
Row 1. Over, P. 2 tog.
Repeat until sufficient length and finish with tassels. Line bag.

MODERN KNITTED CUSHION

Presents for the home are always welcome.
This cushion is oblong in shape, and is in tubular knitting, made exactly like a sack. The depth of the tube is used to form the width of the cushion. Square shapes are made in the same way.

Fig. 19

The fabric is in Moss stitch and knitted with two yarns, each a different shade of the same colour. Oyster and pale fawn (4-ply). Both yarns are held together and knitted as one to give the modern "rough oatmeal" effect.

Can be done on 2 pins if preferred. Then halve the number to cast on (85) and seam at sides.

Quantity of yarn, 8 oz. of each shade.
Needles, size 10.
Cast on 171 stitches (odd number).
Round 1. * K. 1, P. 1. * Repeat all Rounds the same.
Knit a tube 19½ in. in depth.
To cast off, divide the stitches on 2 needles, hold these parallel, and knit the stitches off the 2 needles together (Fig. 18) and cast off at the same time. The other end is left open to receive the cushion pad.

KNITTED FRINGE

Use 4 balls of wool, 2 of each colour and knit with the yarn four-fold on 2 needles.
Cast on 6 stitches.
Row 1. * K. 1, Over, K. 2 tog. * Repeat.
Row 2 and each succeeding row the same.
Knit sufficient length for one end of the cushion, then cast off as follows:
Cast off first 3 stitches only, break yarn, and draw end through loop, and finish. Unravel the remaining 3 stitches from top to bottom, until one side of the strip presents a fringe of even loops and the other side a knitted braid. Overcast this to cushion, using matching wool. Knit second fringe for the other side.
Insert cushion pad and secure with overcast stitches in matching wool.

COLLIE KNOX

MR. COLLIE KNOX served for twelve years in the Regular Army and the Royal Flying Corps before becoming a journalist in 1927. He has told the full story of his life and adventures in a " best-seller" autobiography " It Might Have Been You." As a frank and sincere commentator and columnist on the modern scene he is exceedingly well known to readers of the newspapers.

THIS FLAG STILL FLIES OVER ALL MANKIND

TO us all come occasions when we pause in our stride and for a moment catch our breath. It may be the melody of some well-remembered song —the sight of a tiny white yacht swinging at anchor in the moonlight . . . the sudden meeting with someone with whom we are instantly in tune or the realisation of our own comparative unimportance.

For myself . . . and I believe in speaking personally—there are two " occasions " in particular when I feel a particularly un-British (so called) emotion welling up within me. To wit, when a massed band plays Land of Hope and Glory, and when I look up and see a white flag with a big Red Cross on it flying in the breeze.

Elgar's masterpiece may, and indeed does, bring that highly embarrassing lump to the throat. But the Red Cross flag . . . whether it flies from hospital or train . . . brings a sense of deep pride, a stable feeling that this is a symbol for all that is best in human nature.

To give succour when and where it is needed. To show the greatness of British generosity and kindness of heart. To care for the sick, to sustain the weak . . . to comfort the distressed.

What I should feel were I to hear Land of Hope and Glory played at the same moment as a Red Cross flag were unfurled I tremble to think. I might be compelled to raise a cheer and be told, inevitably, on arriving home that I ought to know better than to make a public exhibition of myself. At my age.

Under its Royal Charter the Red Cross is now dedicated to " the prevention of disease, the improvement of health and the mitigation of suffering throughout the world."

Here in sooth is a haven of humanitarianism.

Now once again the blast of war dins in our ears. A war in which there are no civilians . . . but all . . . men, women, and children may at any time be at the mercy of death or mutilation from a bomb loosed from the protesting skies. What of the war . which, so we who fought and suffered in it were

251

given to believe, was to end all wars ? But then human beings are given to believe many strange things.

There will always be suffering in the world. Shylock was being parochial when he said that " Suffering is the badge of all our tribe." Suffering visits no one race appreciably more than another. It comes alike to the just and the unjust. But how wonderful if the men and women who give such self-denying service to the British Red Cross and the Order of St. John of Jerusalem were to stamp out the ghastliness of man's inhumanity to man. The suffering which man needlessly, and viciously, imposes upon man . for greed . for lust . for Power—used for self-aggrandisement as an outlet of all that is vile.

The spirit of the Red Cross is the spirit of nobility and justice . of good will . and good deeds towards men. Its work in times of peace is untiring. In time of war it is all-comprehending, and beyond expression Christian.

Somebody, in a burst of platitudinous frenzy, once averred that the world knows nothing of its greatest men. Like all such truisms, wince at them how we may, it is painfully true.

Gather together any representative body of men, of average intelligence and means, and ask them to tell you the sad and tragic history of Henri Dunant, the Swiss banker. Do you not see already a blank look crowding over their worthy features ? They register every emotion . except awareness.

To read of the life of Dunant, the founder of the Red Cross, is to take part in a revealing experience. Fired by the dreadful sights he witnessed on the battlefield of Solferino eighty years ago he determined to "do something." But for him no Red Cross would be emblazoned on a thousand flags. He sacrificed money, everything . . . including his faith in his fellow beings. When everyone believed him dead he is discovered in the almshouse of a Swiss village. He was awarded the Nobel Prize. He died . . . still in the almshouse. Soon the Great War set the world on fire . . . dousing the lights of Europe one by one.

And now the lights have gone out again.

Martin Gumpert, in his enthralling book *Dunant*, writes that "The Red Cross is the first practical manifestation of international law, the first international agreement that mankind has ever—in the main—lived up to."

It will play its part in switching on the lights again.

But I am not much hand at history. Other and abler pens than mine have told, and will tell, of the saga of the Red Cross.

I can tell of its doings much more easily, and more convincingly, I trust, in the light of practical experience. Of personal experience . of one or two of the manifold errands of mercy which the Red Cross run so that all may read. Run only at the starting pistol of the generosity of the British public. Read how much that generosity was needed Then. Realise how much more it is needed Now.

For from October 1914 to June 20 . 1920 more than £2,000,000 was spent on the transport of the wounded, £5,000,000 on work and provision for prisoners of war, £5,000,000 on commissions abroad, and £1,500,000 on stores. There were more than 2,000 ambulances in all the fields of warfare . . . and these, including the vehicles at home, carried more than 10,000,000 sick and wounded people.

And here my personal experience comes in. For I was one of the noble 10,000,000. Not that there is, or ever was, anything noble about me. Least of all when I am sick—or wounded. For I am the least patient of all patients and am apt to bite the hand that feeds me with a spoon. Or through a tube in the neck.

Confessedly I do not recall much of the appointments of the ambulance which arrived, like all such ambulances, in the nick of time. To pluck a brand from the burning . . . from the wreckage of an aeroplane. For I was unconscious . having lapsed into a coma out of which my dearest enemies tell me I have never wholly emerged.

But awaking inside the friendly chariot I did not fail to feel grateful for its cosy springs . . . its soft blankets . . . at a time when I could not have stepped on a pebble without screaming.

For some months I was destined to lie in hospital . a " mending place " almost entirely staffed by members of the V.A.D., these three glorious initials standing then, and now, for patience, skill, and character. To say nothing of healing.

Though many years have passed by since I lay gazing up at the ceiling through a maze of bandages I have never forgotten my admiration for the women, the girls of that Service.

They came—as they still come—from every type of home. Some were girls who, until the outbreak of that Other War, had never done a day's work in their lives . . . until they took up training. They had always employed others to scrub floors and to carry in breakfast trays. And their eyes had been more accustomed to the sight of the latest Paris creation than to scars . and contusions . upon the faces and bodies of the male species.

At that period it could not be said even by those few who care for me most that my face was a thing of beauty. And by no stretch of the imagination could it have been called a joy for ever.

What there was left of it was round at the back of my neck. I must have appeared, when bandaged, as a cross between Himmler and Frankenstein. When not bandaged . . .

So thoughtful were these nurses that I was never allowed to have a looking-glass, lest I might do myself some violence following the shock. I did see my face in a spoon—dessert—one day, but that is another story.

But these girls " dressed " my peculiar face with no traces on their own comely countenances of horror, disgust, or aversion. Between me and the latest Paris creation there was a great gulf fixed.

All these things they did. All such sights they bore . . . as if they had been themselves nurtured on terrors. I used to watch two nurses " dressing " the face of an officer in the bed opposite me. He, like myself, had struck earth from a great height, but, unlike me, his face had been burned. Almost beyond recognition. The patience, the courage of the nurses equalled the patience and courage of the patient himself. I can think of no higher tribute.

Wearyingly long hours they worked. Sometimes they looked done to the world . and they would come and sit by my bedside and talk to me.

And I recall one girl . . . I wonder what has become of her ? . . . who found that her work . . . and the sufferings she had to witness . . . had entirely altered

253

her outlook on this business of living. It was a bitter outlook, I remember. Once.

Such an organisation, which deals in the humanities, gives all-embracing opportunities for Service. It has spread across the face of the earth and I have seen this Service at work in East Africa, India, and the Sudan. It knows no creeds nor colour.

Without being unduly visionary it seems to me, an ordinary man in an extra-ordinary world, that the material well-doing at the hands of the Red Cross workers is a trifle unduly stressed at the expense of the more spiritual side. One writes the word " spiritual " rather shyly . fearful lest the hasty reader may at this point ejaculate, " Oh, he's going to start That, is he ? " put down this book, and go to the pictures.

We are an inarticulate race. We are suspicious of those who talk to us about our souls. Have no fear. I know nothing about your souls. I have not yet entirely comprehended mine. Anyway, in some matters, I have a strong predilection for minding my own business.

But without preaching or a throb in the voice it is to my mind clearer than crystal that the qualities which show themselves in so great a Service of mercy, the qualities of forbearance and gentleness, are those which are so desperately needed throughout the world today.

Consider. The Red Cross lives up to its standards of work and rescue in times of peace just as in times of warfare. Its workers do not exclaim in peace-time, " Ah, well, we can slack off now," and only display their efficiency and unity when the shells begin to burst. They do not function only when the fields are strewn with dead and dying and horror, fire and destruction hold the day.

In this way do they teach a lesson. At least such is my opinion. Of course every individual reacts to signs and portents in different ways.

Why, I wonder, is it not possible in times when there are no sandbags in the streets and no threat from the skies, still to carry on the spirit of Service ? Why down tools when an Armistice is signed and, light-heartedly and without thought, go back once more to the selfish, cut our neighbour's throat manner of living ?

Dunant, that unhappy, disillusioned benefactor, saw his Red Cross campaign as a campaign primarily for Peace. He pictured the flag flying not only over the battlefield and the casualty clearing station, but over peaceful town, hamlet, and village. He dreamed of a mighty organisation dedicated to the service of humanity . . . to the care of the poor and needy. That it might alleviate the lot of the slum dweller and his children, and bring to them all the latest developments of medical aid . . . all the genius and skill of scientist, doctor, and nurse.

The cause of the Red Cross is the cause of every one of us. It touches the needs of mankind at every point. We do not realise all that it stands for . . . or all that the enormous body of voluntary workers do in their quiet fashion.

These are days of realisation. By the powers, but that is a true saying.

We have suddenly realised that any one of us might have need of succour . and not till that moment do we trouble to understand that the Red Cross is there for us. That it has been " there " for many, many years. But some of us saw little occasion . most of us . . . for it ever being of use to us. So we paid it scant attention. And gave it little material support.

Even an ambulance driving swiftly through the streets has now a new significance. It is no longer just a vehicle which point-duty policemen " let through " before our own car, but something vital to us.

" Looks pretty comfortable inside there," said a fellow to me one day as an ambulance drove by. He seemed reassured. Revealing.

The tentacles of mercy stretch far and wide. The treatment of prisoners of war . . . the tracing of missing combatants . . . the alleviation of those who might be starved, and ill-treated by merciless captors. Here are deeds of charity indeed.

Even books. Your books which you might have no further use for will help pass the dreary days for the captives of war. The monotony of a prison camp . . . the gnawing anxiety for those at home . . . the never-ceasing pain of separation . . . these may be lightened by books. By your books.

As we all so well know, when we are upset, and pestered by conditions which we cannot control, we turn to books. And in their pages we seek and find adventure . . . and travel afar in our minds to lands where the sun shines and where people are kind, amusing, and companionable.

Here lies surcease from present ills. From stark realities.

Have you, if a smoker, ever travelled in an empty railway carriage . . . on a non-stop journey and discovered that though your cigarette case is full to bursting you have left your matches on the hall table? The moment is awful. But nothing to the feelings of a sick or wounded man with no book to read.

Even as I write I hear of great efforts being made to add to the mobile X-ray units. They proved invaluable in the last war and are now recognised as essentials.

Private individuals are working for this section with inspiring results. And the Red Cross is fortunate in having as its organiser of mobile X-rays a man whose practical experience since 1914 is second to none. So it goes on . . . internationally, provincially . . . the work of healing . of alleviation of human ills. The workers are legion . . . Their enthusiasm is boundless. The cross of red on a white background. How bravely it unfurls . . . no longer, alas, free from danger. For can we be sure under modern war conditions that hospitals will be protected . . . that those who come to the aid of the wounded will be spared ?

Youth is flocking to the Red Cross service. And Youth, newly awakened and grown up in a night, will, to quote the words of Martin Gumpert, see to it that the Red Cross will be one of the few sources from which humanitarianism may once more water the parched and ruined earth.

It is a consummation most devoutly to be wished.